Nov. 1988

Jerry,

For all your kindness in assisting me with your liturgical gifts!

Fondly,
Angela Ann

LEAD ME, GUIDE ME

THE AFRICAN AMERICAN CATHOLIC HYMNAL

G.I.A. PUBLICATIONS, INC.
CHICAGO

DEDICATION

Renowned Liturgist and Musician

Father Clarence Jos. Rivers, Ph.D.

who paved the way for liturgical inculturation and inspired
Black Catholics to bring their artistic genius to Catholic worship

PREFACE

LEAD ME, GUIDE ME
The African American Catholic Hymnal

*We believe that liturgy of the Catholic Church can be an even more intense
expression of the spiritual vitality of those who are of African origin, just as
it has been for other ethnic and cultural groups.*[1]

LEAD ME, GUIDE ME is born of the needs and aspirations of Black Catholics for
music that reflects both our African American heritage and our Catholic faith. For a long
time, but particularly within the last two decades, Black Catholics and the pastoral staffs
who minister to our people have increasingly seen the need for liturgical and devotional
settings and hymnody that lend themselves to the unique and varied styles of song and
expression that are characteristic of our people. Similarly, Black Catholics, who embody
various religious and cultural traditions, wish to share our gifts with the wider ecclesial
community and draw from the great musical corpus of our own Roman Catholic tradition
and that of our Sister Churches. Thus, LEAD ME, GUIDE ME is both universal and
particular as well as ecumenical in composition. While the various national Black Catholic
organizations and leaders have voiced these concerns, and while in the past specific
individuals have initiated proposals for this Hymnal, the fact is that its origin comes from
Black Catholics themselves. With all this in mind, in April of 1983, the National Black
Catholic Clergy Caucus and then its president, Father Donald Clark, authorized the work
on this Hymnal. The Institute for Black Catholic Studies of Xavier University, New Orleans,
with the encouragement of its co-founder, Father Thaddeus Posey, O.F.M., Cap., also
aligned itself with this project.

There are so many individuals to whom we owe thanks. First, the members of the Black
Catholic Hymnal Committee, comprised of representatives of the national Black Catholic
organizations: Father Arthur Anderson, O.F.M., who served as coordinating assistant;
Mr. Edmund Broussard, Knights of Peter Claver and Ladies Auxiliary; Mrs. Marjorie
Gabriel-Burrow, National Association of Black Catholic Administrators; the Most Reverend
Wilton D. Gregory, the National Black Catholic Clergy Caucus; Mr. Avon Gillespie, one
who developed a proposal for a hymnal in 1978; Mr. Rawn Harbor and Mr. Leon Roberts,
the National Association of Black Catholic Musicians; Ronald Sharps, the National Office
for Black Catholics; Brother Robert Smith, O.F.M., Cap., the National Black Catholic
Seminarians Association; and Sister Laura Marie Kendrick, H.V.M., the National Black
Sisters Conference.

However, a special word of appreciation must be given to Marjorie Gabriel-Burrow
(chairperson) and Rawn Harbor and Leon Roberts, who as a Sub-Committee devoted untold
hours, including vacation times, and incalculable energies to the study, selection, and even
composition and arrangement of the hymns. In all this, Mrs. Burrow was a great collabo-
rator and organizer. To state it pointedly, without this gifted and dedicated trio, there would
be no African American Catholic Hymnal. Also, significant time and effort were given
by Ronald Sharps, who researched potential publishers, and by members of the National

Association of Black Catholic Administrators, the principal contact persons in archdioceses and dioceses across the country.

There are others to whom we are indebted. Father Edward Foley, O.F.M., Cap., took time from his doctoral studies and gave a written theological assessment of each proposed hymn and made observations on inclusive language and liturgical usage. This evaluation alone could serve as a textbook for musicians. Father John Ford, S.T., evaluated the hymns from a Black theological perspective and helped us examine the music from a historical and cultural perspective. Sister Thea Bowman, F.S.P.A., and Father J-Glenn Murray, S.J., wrote the two introductions, which provide a liturgical and catechetical foundation for our endeavors. Dr. Fred Moleck and Ms. Anne Flaherty examined the text of the hymns for inclusive language and literary composition and Father Robert H. Oldershaw compiled the indexes and organized and classified the contents according to the church year. Sister Angela Williams, O.S.F., enriched the Hymnal with artistic designs.

To our composers, many of whom offered original contributions, we offer our profound gratitude. Brother Booker Ashe, O.F.M., Cap., lent encouragement to the coordinator, without which he would not have undertaken this task. Mrs. Mary Brookie and Mrs. Jean M. Swetel, the coordinator's secretaries, exhibited unparalleled devotion and enthusiasm in personal support and after-hours work.

We are most grateful to the American Board of Catholic Missions, which provided the major grant for this project, and to the Congregation of the Holy Ghost and Mr. Richard F. Glennon, who also contributed to this endeavor.

We are grateful to our publishers, G.I.A., Inc. Mr. Edward Harris and Mr. Robert Batastini took a very personal interest in this project and felt honored to help bring the contributions of African American expression to the Catholic Church. Then, women and men, musicians, educators, parishioners, and pastoral staffs from our Black parishes and institutions participated in the consultation and offered us feedback. Thanks to them, too.

Finally, we thank the African American Bishops of the United States, especially Bishop Joseph Francis, board member of the American Board of Catholic Missions, and Bishop Wilton D. Gregory, our liturgist, who enthusiastically endorsed this project and encouraged the Committee to its completion. The Subcommittee on Black Liturgy of the Bishops' Committee on Liturgy, chaired by Bishop Gregory and staffed by Father John Gurrieri, gave priority attention to the Hymnal at its meetings and made many helpful suggestions.

These notable words from *What We Have Seen and Heard* are both a fitting conclusion and stirring challenge:

> There is a splendid opportunity for the vast richness of African American culture to be expressed in our liturgy. It is this opportunity, thanks to the norms established in the revised Roman liturgy, which enables our work of evangelization to be filled with such promise for the future.[2]

The Most Reverend James P. Lyke, O.F.M., Ph.D.
Auxiliary Bishop of Cleveland
Coordinator of the Hymnal Project

The Reverend William Norvel, S.S.J.
President, National Black Catholic Clergy Caucus

April 4, 1987
The Anniversary of the Deaths of Saint Benedict the Black
and Reverend Dr. Martin Luther King, Jr.

Footnotes:

[1] *What We Have Seen and Heard*, a Pastoral Letter from the Black Bishops of the United States, September 9, 1984. p. 30

[2] *What We Have Seen and Heard*, p. 31.

THE GIFT OF AFRICAN AMERICAN SACRED SONG[1]

Sister Thea Bowman, F.S.P.A., Ph.D.

From the African Mother Continent, African men and women, through the Middle Passage, throughout the Diaspora, to the Americas, carried the African gift and treasure of sacred song. To the Americas, African men and women brought sacred songs and chants that reminded them of their homelands and that sustained them in separation and in captivity, songs to respond to all life situations, and the ability to create new songs to answer new needs.

African Americans in sacred song preserved the memory of African religious rites and symbols, of a holistic African spirituality, of rhythms and tones and harmonies that communicated their deepest feelings across barriers of region and language.

African Americans in fields and quarters, at work, in secret meetings,[2] in slave festivals,[3] in churches, camp meets and revivals, wherever they met or congregated, consoled and strengthened themselves and one another with sacred song—moans, chants, shouts, psalms, hymns, and jubilees, first African songs, then African American songs. In the crucible of separation and suffering, African American sacred song was formed.

In *My Bondage and My Freedom,* Frederick Douglass wrote:

> Slaves are generally expected to sing as well as to work. A silent slave is not liked by masters or overseers. 'Make a noise,' 'make a noise,' and 'bear a hand,' are words usually addressed to the slaves when there is silence amongst them. This may account for the almost constant singing heard in the southern states. There was, generally, more or less singing among the teamsters, as it was one means of letting the overseer know where they were, and that they were moving on with the work. But, on allowance day, those who visited the great house farm were peculiarly excited and noisy. While on their way, they would make the dense old woods, for miles around, reverberate with their wild notes. These were not always merry because they were wild. On the contrary, they were mostly of a plaintive cast and told a tale of grief and sorrow. In the most boisterous outbursts of rapturous sentiment, there was ever a tinge of deep melancholy.[4]

As early as 1691, slaves in colonial homes, slave galleries or separate pews participated in worship services with white slave holders. They learned to sing the traditional European psalms and hymns from the *Cambridge Short Tune,* the *Dutch Tune* or the *Hymns and Psalms* of Dr. Watts, which they loved and adapted to their own style and use.[5] In 1755, Reverend Samuel Davies wrote:

> The Negroes . . . have an Ear for Musick, and a kind of ecstatic Delight in Psalmody and there are no Books they learn so soon or take so much pleasure in, as those used in that heavenly Part of divine Worship.[6]

Slave records dating back as far as 1723 show there were proficient slave musicians— singers and instrumentalists who played fiddle, violin, trumpet, drums, guitar, French horn or flute, slave musicians highly valued for their musicianship, slave musicians, some who were able to read and write.[7]

In 1801, Richard Allen, founder of the African Methodist Episcopal Church, published *A Collection of Hymns and Scriptural Songs from Various Authors*,[8] hymns and songs which were used by slaves and fugitive slaves in worship. In 1871, the Fisk Jubilee Singers began concert tours of America and Europe, which for the first time brought the original sacred song of Black America to white audiences and to the concert stage. Harry Burleigh, John Wesley Work, James Weldon and J. Rosamond Johnson scored and arranged Black American sacred songs for soloists and ensembles in concert performance. In 1921, Thomas A. Dorsey, the Father of Gospel Music, composed "If I Don't Get There", and initiated a new rhythm, a new harmony and a new style. Gospel singers like Kenneth Morris, Roberta Martin, Mahalia Jackson, James Cleveland and Edwin Hawkins enriched Black sacred song.

In the sixties, Father Clarence Joseph Rivers revitalized Catholic worship, inaugurated a revolution in liturgical music, stirred international interest in the indigenization of Catholic Liturgy, and brought new hope, joy, and spirit to millions of Black Americans when he introduced the melodies, rhythms, harmonies, symbols and rituals of African American Sacred Song into Roman Catholic worship. His *American Mass Program* and subsequent compositions and recordings popularized Black music for Catholic worship. His *Soulfull Worship* and *The Spirit in Worship*[9] analyzed the history, theology, theory and practice of Black sacred song and its appropriateness and effectiveness in Catholic liturgy and worship.[10] Rawn Harbor, Grayson Brown, Eddie Bonnemere, Leon Roberts, and others began to compose for Catholic worship.

Black sacred song is soulful song—

1. *holistic:* challenging the full engagement of mind, imagination, memory, feeling, emotion, voice, and body;

2. *participatory:* inviting the worshipping community to join in contemplation, in celebration and in prayer;

3. *real:* celebrating the immediate concrete reality of the worshipping community — grief or separation, struggle or oppression, determination or joy — bringing that reality to prayer within the community of believers;

4. *spirit-filled:* energetic, engrossing, intense;

5. *life-giving:* refreshing, encouraging, consoling, invigorating, sustaining.

Influenced by Africa, the Middle Passages, the Islands, Europe and the Americas; created, shaped, treasured, and shared by Black American Christians across time, geographic, socioeconomic and denominational lines, our heritage of sacred song encompasses a vast variety of kinds, styles, and forms.

Wyatt Tee Walker charts the development of five distinctive kinds of Black Sacred Music:

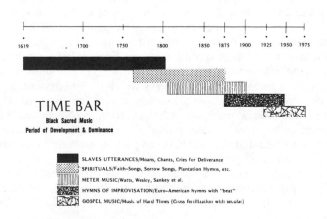

TIME BAR
Black Sacred Music
Period of Development & Dominance

SLAVES UTTERANCES/Moans, Chants, Cries for Deliverance
SPIRITUALS/Faith-Songs, Sorrow Songs, Plantation Hymns, etc.
METER MUSIC/Watts, Wesley, Sankey et al.
HYMNS OF IMPROVISATION/Euro–American hymns with "beat"
GOSPEL MUSIC/Music of Hard Times (Cross fertilization with secular)

Wendel Whalum shows how the various kinds of Black sacred song are related:

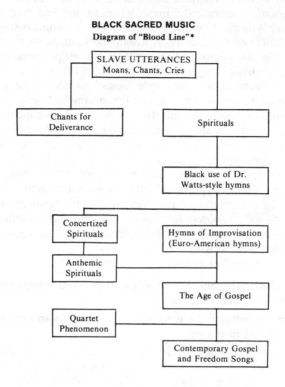

BLACK SACRED MUSIC
Diagram of "Blood Line"*

* Adapted from Wendel Whalum's diagram appearing in *Review and Expositor*,
Spring, 1972, p. 581.

Black sacred song celebrates our God, His goodness, His promise, our faith and hope, our journey toward the promise. Black sacred song carries melodies and tonalities, rhythms and harmonies; metaphors, symbols and stories of faith that speak to our hearts; words, phrases and images that touch and move us.[13]

Stephen Henderson says of Black speech:

> Certain words and construction seem to carry an inordinate charge of emotional and psychological weight, so whenever they are used they set all kinds of bells ringing, all kinds of synapses snapping, on all kinds of levels . . . I am speaking of words . . . which have levels of meaning that seem to go back to our earliest grappling with the English language in a strange and hostile land. These words, of course, are used in complex associations, and thus form meaningful wholes in ways which defy understanding by outsiders. I call such words "mascon" words, borrowing from (of all places!) the National Aeronautics and Space Administration. NASA invented the acronym to mean a "massive concentration" of matter below the lunar surface after it was observed that the gravitational pull on a satellite was stronger in some places than in others.
>
> I use it to mean a massive concentration of Black experimental energy which powerfully affects the meaning of Black speech, Black song, and Black poetry — if one, indeed, has to make distinctions.[14]

Black sacred music lifts up Biblical symbols which bear the accumulated meanings of four hundred years of experience of the Black community in America:

God is Father, Mother, Sister, Brother, Captain,
 King, Liberator, Friend;

God is a God of Peace, a God of War;

God is water to the thirsty, bread to the hungry,
 shelter to the homeless;

God is my rock, my sword, my shield;

God is rest in a weary land;

God is my all and all.

African people are diunital people, seeking richness of meaning in *apparent* contradiction. They are comfortable with bringing together realities which may appear contradictory or in opposition: for example, body/spirit, sacred/secular, individual/community. They reach toward unification or synthesis of opposites. God is like father and mother (Father - mother - sister - brother symbols are not sexist). God is like fire and balm. African people are comfortable with symbol. African Americans for 400 years have used symbol and song to express a faith and yearning too high, too low, too wide, too deep for words, too passionate to be confined by concepts. As Father Rivers writes:

Music is important for worship because in worship we have to express the unexpressable, the transcendent, human values that defy ordinary expression. Music, like its other self, poetry, seems capable of doing what plain rational words cannot do: namely, to express the unexpressable, to touch men's hearts, to penetrate their souls, create an experience of things that cannot be reasoned.[15]

Black sacred song—old or new, folk or composed, rural or urban, traditional or contemporary—is in a very real sense, the song *of the people.*

  • The music comes from a people who share and claim a common history, common experience, common oppression, common values, hopes, dreams and visions.

  • The singer, the singers, the instrumentalists voice the experience and faith of the community.

  • The leader (some would say soloist) leads the community in worship. The leader revives and inspirits.

  • The worshipping community is active, not passive. People participate — sing, pray, clap, sway, raise their hands, nod their heads. Eye contact, voiced response, the silent testimony of tears, a smile of relief or contemplation or ecstasy says, "This is my story; this is my song."

  • The singer is chosen from the people by the people to suit their immediate need.
    "Sometimes *I* feel like a motherless child."
    "*I* just came from the fountain."
    "*I* love the Lord."
    "*My* Heavenly Father watches over *me*."

  • The first person pronoun, the 'I' reference, is communal. The individual sings the soul of the community. In heart and voice and gesture the Church, the community responds.

  • The singer lifts the Church, the people, to a higher level of understanding, feeling, motivation, and participation.

Among African peoples, most art is designed for use, that is to express a feeling or insight, to have an impact in the real world.[16] Song is not an object to be admired so much as an instrument to teach, comfort, inspire, persuade, convince, and motivate. Music is chosen precisely for its effect upon the worshipping community. The aim is *effective* worship. Black sacred song is designed to move. It moves because depth of feeling gives it "spiritual power." Father Clarence Rivers explains:

> A singer who performs without feeling lacks soul. As in original biblical concept of the spiritual, the spirit or the soul is the life principal, the source of life and liveliness, of dynamism and movement, of motion and emotion. That which is unmoved and unmoving is not spiritual, it is dead! To be spiritual is to be alive, to be capable of moving and responding to movement . . . Since the Spirit moves, that which does not move would seem to lack the presence of the Spirit.[17]

Black sacred song has been at once a source and an expression of Black faith, spirituality and devotion. By song, our people have called the Spirit into our hearts, homes, churches, and communities. Seeking to enrich our liturgies and lives with the gift of sacred song, we pray:

"Spirit, Sweet Holy Spirit, fall afresh on me."

"Everytime I hear the Spirit
Moving in my heart
I will pray."

[1] Confer Pope Paul IV, "To the Heart of African," *The Pope Speaks* 14, (no. 3, 1969): 218-219. This citation concerning cultural pluralism within the Church gives the theological foundation for this essay. Similarly, Pope John Paul II has written numerous commentaries on the place of cultural expression in the Catholic Church.

[2] See Miles Mark Fisher *Negro Slave Songs in the United States* (New York: Citadel Press, 1969), 32-33, 66-79.

[3] Festivals in which slaves in large numbers sang in their own African languages survived in the English colonies. Africans gathered to share stories, dances, songs and customs of various nations in Africa. See Miles Fisher *Negro Slave Songs in the United States* (New York Citadel Press, 1969), 66-79.

[4] Frederick Douglass *My Bondage and My Freedom* (New York: 1855), 96, 97.

[5] See Eileen Southern, *The Music of Black Americans* (New York: Norton & Company, 1971), 30-45.

[6] Quoted in Southern, *The Music of Black Americans,* 59.

[7] See in Southern, *The Music of Black Americans,* 27-29.

[8] Early American Imprints, Nos. 38, 39, Series No. 2 (1801-1820).

[9] *Soulfull Worship* (Washington, D.C.: National Office for Black Catholics, 1974). *Spirit in Worship* (Cincinnati: Stimuli, Inc.), 1978.

[10] Confer "The Church at Prayer, A Holy Temple of the Lord," December 4, 1983, the National Conference of Catholic Bishops, page 23, #45; and Second Vatican Council, Constitution on the Sacred Liturgy, "Sacrosanctum Concilium," 4 December, 1983, 37-40.

[11] *"Somebody's Calling My Name" Black Sacred Music and Social Changes* (Valley Forge, Pa.: Judson Press, 1979), 38

[12] From Wyatt Tee Walker, *"Somebody's Calling My Name,* 146.

[13] The Bishops' Committee on Liturgy, "Music in Catholic Worship," Revised Edition, 1983, 3, 41.

[14] *Understanding the New Black Poetry: Black Speech and Black Music as Poetic References* (New York: William Morrow & Co., 1973) 44.

[15] Father Clarence Joseph Rivers, *Soulfull Worship,* p. 39. See also, *The Spirit in Worship,* 14, 15.

[16] "The Church at Prayer, A Holy Temple of the Lord," 14, 15.

[17] *The Spirit in Worship,* 22.

THE LITURGY OF THE ROMAN RITE AND
AFRICAN AMERICAN WORSHIP
Reverend J-Glenn Murray, S.J.

What marvels have already been wrought; what challenges we are still called to meet because of the Second Vatican Council! During this Council our Church leaders called us to reach out to serve and renew our world, to renew our Christian life and worship, a renewal to plumb the very depths of our hearts and spirits. Toward meeting this challenge in life and worship, there has been the on-going reform of the Roman Liturgy and the recovery of the principle of "full, conscious, and active participation in liturgical celebrations."[1] In addition, the Council urged us to wed the Liturgy and our varied cultures.[2] This marriage, which presupposes and demands in-depth knowledge of both a culture and the Roman Liturgy, is called "acculturation" (the process whereby cultural elements which are compatible with Roman Liturgy are incorporated into it either as substitutes for or illustrations of ritual elements of the Roman rite) and "inculturation" (the process whereby a pre-Christian rite is permanently given a Christian meaning).[3] This marriage is yet a further task to which we must continue to bring our intelligence, genius, artistry, and muscle.

This hymnal, prepared by Black Catholics in the United States of America, attempts both to meet the challenges of our faith and to incorporate the achievements of our centuries of vibrant life in the Spirit. What follows then in this introduction is several points of consideration for the development of Black Catholic worship and music's place in that unique celebration of God's love.

First, let us consider the Liturgy. "The celebration of the Sacred Mysteries is that moment when the Church is most fully actualized."[4] Its purpose is "to make people holy, to build up the Body of Christ, and finally, to give worship to God."[5] It is the "summit toward which the activity of the Church is directed; it is also the fount from which all her powers flow."[6] It is "like a parable [that] takes us by the hair of our heads, lifts us momentarily out of the cesspool of injustice we call home, puts us in the challenging reign of God, where we are treated like we have never been treated anywhere else . . ., where we are bowed to and sprinkled and censed and kissed and touched and where we share equally among all a holy food and drink."[7] It is and has been for us disenfranchised African Americans a sacred time which is both profound and central; a time of celebration and of wholeness; a time to "sing a new song unto the Lord." (Psalm 98.1)

Second, our celebration is Catholic. What makes our worship truly Catholic is that we all remember, give thanks, and carry out the mandate of Christ Jesus by eating and drinking together, and agree to join the Lord in being broken and poured out for the world as a *sacrificium laudis* - a living "sacrifice of praise." What makes our worship genuinely Catholic is that the community of believers gathers at the table of the Lord, which is both the table of God's Word (the Liturgy of the Word) and the table of Christ's Body and Blood (the Liturgy of the Eucharist), a table at which God's people are nourished by Holy Word and Sacred Meal.[8] What makes our worship uniquely Catholic is that everything that is done in our worship clearly serves (and does not interrupt) this ritual action of Word and Sacrament which has its own rhythm and movement, all built on the direction, rites, and forms of the Roman Catholic Liturgy as they are approved and promulgated. And, what makes our celebration fundamentally "catholic" (universal) is that it is open to welcome the spiritual contributions of all peoples which are consistent with our biblical faith and our historical continuity.

Third, our celebration is Black. While "a rose is a rose is a rose is a rose,"[9] a Louisiana Black Catholic is not a West Baltimore Black Catholic; neither is a New York Haitian Catholic a Los Angeles Black Catholic or a Chicago Black Catholic. What does reveal our worship as authentically Black is the interplay of some or all of the following: our indigenous music, dialogic preaching, effective and spontaneous prayer; a spirit of "fellowship"; hospitality; suspension of time; freedom of expression; body movement; conversion; the use of visual symbols; numerous poetic names for God; silence; clapping; personal testimony; vibrant color, and rich cloth.[10] What makes our worship fundamentally Black is our Black life which arises from and shares in a common history, a common experience, a common struggle, a common culture, and a common soul. What makes our worship uniquely Black is our indomitable and uncanny ability to "sing the Lord's song in a strange land!" (Psalm 137:4)

Fourth, music is integral to our worship. It is integral in that "from ancient times to the present, music has filled in the gaps made by humanity's attempt to express the inexpressible"[11]; integral in that "among the many signs and symbols used by the Church to celebrate its faith, music is of preeminent importantce"[12]; integral in that "among Afro-Americans, just as in African culture, religion permeates the whole of life, and so does music."[13]

Though integral, music is not an end in itself. It must serve the ritual action; it must assist and minister to the community of believers in our celebration of the mighty acts of God and in the renewal of our total commitment of faith. To that end, the value of any musical component must be judged by the following criteria as set forth by

1) our Catholic teaching:[14]

   a) musical — is there an aesthetic and technical quality in its rhythm, harmony, and melody? besides the quality of the rhythmic, harmonic, and melodic elements, is there a concern with the wedding of text to music?

   b) liturgical — is the music appropriate to the nature and importance of the liturgy? is its theological content sound? does it take into consideration what parts of the Mass should be sung and the relative festivity of the day (principle of progressive solemnity)?[15] is there a proper concern for the different roles of the assembly, cantor, choir, instrumentalists? are the soloists and choir effectively leading and supporting the assembly in its worship of the Lord or are they merely displaying their virtuosity and unduly delaying the particular rite (e.g. Preparation of the Altar-Table and the Gifts, the Sign of Peace)?

   c) pastoral — is the music appropriate to the ability of the assembly? does the music in the celebration enable the assembly to express the faith of the Church, in this place, in this age, in our culture, aware that the "United States of America is a nation of nations, a country in which people speak many tongues, live their lives in diverse ways, celebrate events in song and music in the folkways of their cultural, ethnic and racial roots"?[16] and

2) our Black heritage:[17]

   a) it (the musical component) must express the communal nature of the Black experience – we are not alone in our struggle for freedom;

   b) it must hold in tension the emphasis on this world and the expectations of the "new age";

c) it must balance a freedom of spirit and liturgical restriction, i.e., spontaneity must be tempered with a sense of order and meaningful content;

d) it must be celebratory.

At this juncture, we would be wise to examine our need to express the complete variety of our Black Catholic musical heritage. In order to express adequately this heritage, we need to be attentive not only to our Euro-American legacy (Latin chants, motets, polyphony, and hymns), but to the musical variety of our Afro-American culture as well. Modern Gospel music with its distinct sound, with its freedom of improvisation and its use of percussion: drums, piano, tambourines, and brass-winds, has already added a rich dimension to our liturgical celebrations (e.g., Margaret Douroux's "Give Me A Clean Heart," Andre Crouch's "Soon and Very Soon," and Robert Fryson's "God Is"), and yet Gospel music is not the only style of music our heritage has to offer. To be utterly faithful to our heritage, we must use:

a) spirituals — our forebears' Christocentric commentaries on the past (e.g., "Balm in Gilead") and wellsprings of hope for the future (e.g., "We Shall Overcome");[18]

b) hymns — those hymns and psalms which used the process of "lining out," i.e., the process wherein the worship leader spoke a line or so, which the congregation sang thereafter (a very effective tool in a time when illiteracy was widespread and the use of hymnals virtually non-existent: e.g., Charles Gabriel's "His Eye Is on the Sparrow" and William Bradbury's "Jesus Loves Me");[19]

c) contemporary compositions — music which has its feet firmly planted in the past and yet is attuned to the needs of the faith community today (Clarence Rivers' "God Is Love," Grayson Brown's "Jesus Died Upon the Cross," and Leon Roberts' "Responsorial Psalm: Let Us Go Rejoicing").

Fifth, in order to utilize the rich resources of our past, invite the composition of new music, and use this present volume to its best advantage, let us take the time to sketch the present structure of the Eucharistic Liturgy, "the source and summit" of our liturgical life. We do this because "the first place to look for guidance in the *use* and *choice* of music is the rite itself."[20] Other liturgical celebrations are well examined in the "rites" section of this present volume.

An outline of the Eucharistic Liturgy:[21]

I. Introductory Rites
    Entrance
    Greeting
    The Blessing and Sprinkling of Holy Water
    Penitential Rite
    Lord, Have Mercy
    Glory to God
    Opening Prayer

The purpose of these rites is to help the assembly come to an awareness of itself as a community in celebration. It should be noted that when the Third Form of the Penitential Rite is used, it should function as a "general confession made by the entire assembly and praise of Christ's compassionate love and mercy."[22]

II. Liturgy of the Word
   Reading I
      Responsorial Psalm
   Reading II
      Gospel Acclamation
   Gospel
   Homily
   Profession of Faith
   General Intercessions

The primary focus here is that the assembly *hear* God's message; *digest* it with the aid of psalms, silence (particularly after each of the Readings) and the homily; and *respond,* by involving themselves in the great covenant of love and redemption which immediately follows.

III. Liturgy of the Eucharist
   A. Preparation of the Altar-Table and the Gifts
      The purpose of this rite is to prepare the Table of the Eucharist for the sacrifice. Assembly singing is not always necessary or desirable at this time. Instrumental interludes or the skillful use of a choral repertoire can effectively accompany the procession and preparation of the Gifts and Table, and thus keep this part of the Mass in proper perspective relative to the Eucharistic Prayer which follows.

   B. Eucharistic Prayer
      This prayer of thanksgiving and blessing is the center of the entire celebration. This prayer is affirmed and ratified by all through acclamations of faith: the Holy, the Memorial Acclamation, and the Great Amen. Since this prayer is central, all these acclamations should be sung by all present. It is further recommended that, for these Acclamations, one musical style be employed for greater musical integrity and unity.[23]

   C. Communion Rite
      The eating and drinking of the Body and Blood of the Lord in the paschal meal is the climax of our Eucharistic celebration. The Lord's Prayer, when it is sung, should be in a musical setting that allows all to participate; the Sign of Peace, a time to share Christ's peace, should not interrupt and delay the Communion Rite; the Lamb of God is a litany-song to accompany completely the breaking of the Eucharistic Bread and pouring of the Eucharistic Wine; the distribution of Communion should be done with dignity and warmth; the Communion Song should express and foster a sense of unity. The Prayer after Communion closes this rite.

IV. Concluding Rite
   Greeting
   Blessing
   Dismissal

These send forth each member of the assembly to live what we have celebrated, praising God and blessing the Lord. The Recessional Song has never been an official part of the rite, hence musicians are free to plan music which provides an appropriate closing to the Liturgy.

V. In addition
   A selection from our diverse Black musical repertory may well be used as a prelude to the Liturgy or as the assembly's preparation to hear the Homily.

Sixth, if our celebration of the Eucharistic Liturgy (and by extension, all the other liturgical rites) is to be both Catholic and Black, then those whose responsibility it is to plan and execute worship must continue to *study* the Roman Liturgy in order to understand its inner dynamics, come to *appreciate* the significance and integrity of each of its parts, *learn* those places where improvisation may legitimately occur, *keep the assembly central, read* voraciously about inculturation, and *remain open* to the Spirit. It can and must be done!

These spirituals, hymns, anthems, songs, and contemporary compositions, many drawn from the rich heritage of sacred music of the Black community, are chosen with the aforementioned challenges in mind. It is our hope that, used with wisdom, sensitivity, and faith, they may prove appropriate, beautiful, and edifying, for the fitting praise of God and the enrichment of us, God's people.

Notes

1. Second Vatican Council, Constitution on the Sacred Liturgy: "Sacrosanctum Concilium" (=SC), 4 December 1963, #14.

2. SC, #37. Also, National Conference of Catholic Bishops, "The Church at Prayer - A Holy Temple of the Lord," December 4, 1983, p. 23, #45.

3. Anscar Chupungo, *Cultural Adaption of the Liturgy* (New York: Paulist Press, 1982) pp. 81-86.

4. Black Catholic Bishops of the United States, "What We Have Seen and Heard," September, 1984, p. 30.

5. SC, #59.

6. SC, #10.

7. Robert W. Hovda, "The Vesting of Liturgical Ministers," *Worship,* Volume 54, Number 2, March 1980, p. 105.

8. Bishops' Committee on the Liturgy, "Music in Catholic Worship" (−MCW), Revised Edition, 1983, #43.

9. Gertrude Stein, "Sacred Emily," in *Geography and Plays.* (New York: Something Else Press, 1922).

10. James P. Lyke, O.F.M., "Liturgical Expression in the Black Community," *Worship,* Volume 57, Number 1, January 1983, p. 17.

11. J. Wendell Mapson, Jr., *The Ministry of Music in the Black Church.* (Valley Forge: Judson Press, 1984), p.9.

12. MCW, #23.

13. Mapson, p. 16.

14. MCW, #s 26-41.

15. (BCL, "Liturgical Music Today," #13.) Bishops' Committee on the Liturgy, "Liturgical Music Today" (= LMT), 28 September 1982, #13.

16. LMT, #54.

17. Mapson, pp. 21-22.

18. Ibid., p. 45.

19. Ibid., p. 37.

20. LMT, #8.

21. MCW, #s 44-49, 61, 62, 65, 67, 68, 71, 73.

22. LMT, #21.

23. LMT, #14, 17.

Contents

The King Shall Come 1

1. The King shall come when morn - ing dawns And
2. Not as of old a lit - tle child, To
3. Oh, bright - er than the ris - ing morn When
4. Oh, bright - er than that glo - rious morn Shall
5. The King shall come when morn - ing dawns And

light tri - um - phant breaks, When beau - ty gilds the
bear and fight and die, But crowned with glo - ry
Christ, vic - to - rious, rose And left the lone - some
dawn up - on our race The day when Christ in
light and beau - ty brings. Hail, Christ the Lord! Your

east - ern hills And life to joy a - wakes.
like the sun That lights the morn - ing sky.
place of death De - spite the rage of foes.
splen - dor comes And we shall see his face.
peo - ple pray: Come quick - ly, King of kings.

Text: John Brownlie, 1859-1925, alt.
Tune: CONSOLATION, 86 86; John Wyeth, *Repository of Sacred Music,* Part II, 1813; Harm. from *Worship Supplement*

2   Prepare Ye the Way of the Lord

Pre-pare ye the way of the Lord.

Pre-pare ye the way of the Lord.

Text: Is. 40: 3-4, 9
Tune: James E. Moore, Jr.
© 1983, GIA Publications, Inc.

3 O Come, O Come, Emmanuel

1. O come, O come, Em - man - u - el, And ran - som
2. O come, O Wis - dom from on high, Who or - ders
3. O come, O come, great Lord of might, Who to your
4. O come, O Rod of Jes - se's stem, From ev - 'ry
5. O come, O Key of Dav - id, come, And o - pen

cap - tive Is - ra - el, That mourns in lone - ly
all things might - i - ly; To us the path of
tribes on Si - nai's height In an - cient times once
foe de - liv - er them That trust your might - y
wide our heav'n - ly home; Make safe the way that

*This alternate accompaniment may be used for some stanzas, as written or one octave lower.

ex - ile here Un - til the Son of God ap - pear.
knowl - edge show, And teach us in her ways to go.
gave the law, In cloud, and maj - es - ty, and awe.
pow'r to save, And give them vic - t'ry o'er the grave.
leads on high, And close the path to mis - er - y.

Re-joice! Re-joice! Em - man - u - el Shall come to you, O Is - ra - el.

6. O come, O Dayspring from on high
And cheer us by your drawing nigh;
Disperse the gloomy clouds of night,
And death's dark shadow put to flight.

7. O come, Desire of nations, bind
In one the hearts of humankind;
O bid our sad divisions cease,
And be for us our King of Peace.

Text: *Veni, veni, Emmanuel:* Latin 9th C.; Tr. by John M. Neale, 1818-1866, alt.
Tune: VENI, VENI EMMANUEL, LM with refrain; Mode I; Adapt. by Thomas Helmore, 1811-1890; Acc. by Richard Proulx, b.1937, © 1975, GIA Publications, Inc.

4 Soon and Very Soon

1. Soon and ver - y soon   we are goin' to see the King,
2. No more cry - in' there   we are goin' to see the King,
3. No more dy - in' there   we are goin' to see the King,
4. Soon and ver - y soon   we are goin' to see the King,

Soon and ver - y soon   we are goin' to see the King,
No more cry - in' there   we are goin' to see the King,
No more dy - in' there   we are goin' to see the King,
Soon and ver - y soon   we are goin' to see the King,

Soon and ver - y soon   we are goin' to see the King,
No more cry - in' there   we are goin' to see the King,
No more dy - in' there   we are goin' to see the King,
Soon and ver - y soon   we are goin' to see the King,

Hal - le - lu - jah, Hal - le - lu - jah, we're goin' to see the King!

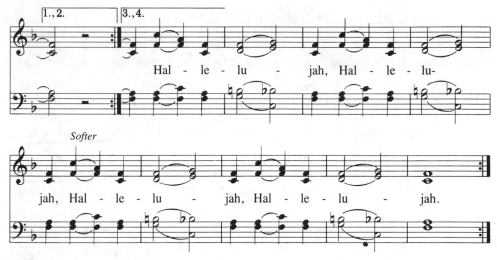

Hal - le - lu - jah, Hal - le - lu -

Softer

jah, Hal - le - lu - jah, Hal - le - lu - jah.

Text: Andraé Crouch
Tune: Andraé Crouch
© 1976, Lexicon Music Inc./Crouch Music
Used by permission. All rights reserved.

Come, O Long Expected Jesus 5

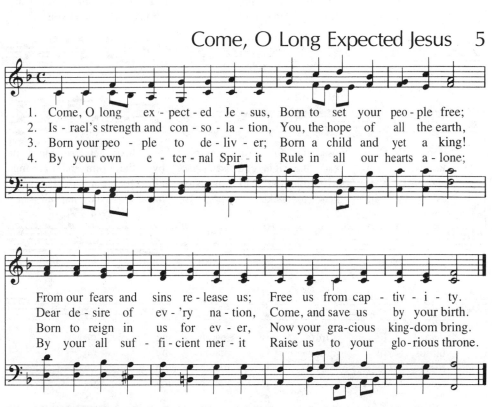

1. Come, O long ex - pect - ed Je - sus, Born to set your peo - ple free;
2. Is - rael's strength and con - so - la - tion, You, the hope of all the earth,
3. Born your peo - ple to de - liv - er; Born a child and yet a king!
4. By your own e - ter - nal Spir - it Rule in all our hearts a - lone;

From our fears and sins re - lease us; Free us from cap - tiv - i - ty.
Dear de - sire of ev - 'ry na - tion, Come, and save us by your birth.
Born to reign in us for ev - er, Now your gra - cious king - dom bring.
By your all suf - fi - cient mer - it Raise us to your glo - rious throne.

Text: Hag. 2:7; Charles Wesley, 1707-1788, alt.
Tune: STUTTGART, 8 7 8 7; Christian F. Witt, 1660-1716; Harm. by Kenneth D. Smith, b.1928; © National Christian Education Council

6 Mine Eyes Have Seen the Glory

1. Mine eyes have seen the glo - ry of the com - ing of the
2. I have seen him in the watch-fires of a hun - dred cir - cling
3. He has sound - ed forth the trum - pet that shall nev - er call re-
4. In the beau - ty of the lil - ies Christ was born a - cross the

Lord; He is tram-pling out the vin-tage where the grapes of wrath are
camps; They have build - ed him an al - tar in the eve - ning dews and
treat; He is sift - ing out all hu - man hearts be - fore his judg-ment
sea, With a glo - ry in his bos - om that trans - fig - ures you and

stored; He hath loosed the fate - ful light - ning of his ter - ri - ble swift
damps; I can read the right-eous sen - tence by the dim and flar - ing
seat; O be swift, my soul, to an - swer him; be ju - bi - lant, my
me; As he died to make us ho - ly, let us die that all be

sword; His truth is march - ing on.
lamps; His day is march - ing on.
feet! Our God is march - ing on.
free! While God is march - ing on.

Glo - ry! Glo - ry! Hal - le - lu - jah! Glo - ry!

Glo - ry! Hal - le - lu - jah! Glo - ry! Glo - ry! Hal - le-

lu - jah! His truth is march - ing on.

Text: Julia W. Howe, 1819-1910
Tune: BATTLE HYMN OF THE REPUBLIC, 15 15 15 6 with refrain; Attr. to William Steffe, d.1911

7 O Lord of Light, Who Made the Stars

1. O Lord of light, who made the stars, O Dawn, by whom we
2. In low - li - ness you came on earth To res - cue us from
3. To pay the debt we owed for sin, Your pain - ful cross was
4. But now you reign, the King of kings, A - dored in high - est

see the way, O Christ, re - deem - er of the world:
Sa - tan's snares; O won - drous love that healed our wounds
made the price; From bless - ed Mar - y's womb you came,
maj - es - ty; Your ver - y name is held in awe

Come now and lis - ten as we pray!
By tak - ing on our mor - tal cares!
A vic - tim pure for sac - ri - fice.
From pole to pole and sea to sea! A - men.

Text: Latin hymn. c.9th C.; Tr. by Melvin Farrell, b.1930, alt., © 1961-62, World Library Publications
Tune: CONDITOR ALME SIDERUM, Sarum plainsong; Mode IV; Harm. © 1978, *Lutheran Book of Worship*

5. Great judge of all, on earth's last day
   Have pity on your children's plight;
   Rise up to shield us with your grace;
   Deliver us from Satan's might.

6. To God the Father and the Son
   And Holy Spirit, Three in One,
   Praise, honor, might, and glory be
   From age to age eternally. Amen

On Jordan's Bank   8

1. On Jor-dan's bank the Bap-tist's cry An-
2. Then cleansed be ev-ery heart from sin; Make
3. For you are our sal - va-tion, Lord, Our
4. To heal the sick stretch out your hand, And
5. All praise the Son e - ter - nal - ly, Whose

noun-ces that the Lord is nigh; A - wake and heark - en,
straight the way of God with-in, And let each heart pre-
ref - uge, and our great re - ward; With - out your grace we
bid the fall - en sin - ner stand; Shine forth, and let your
ad - vent sets his peo - ple free; Whom with the Fa ther

for he brings Glad ti - dings of the King of kings.
pare a home Where such a might - y guest may come.
waste a - way Like flowers that with - er and de - cay.
light re - store Earth's own true love - li - ness once more.
we a - dore And Spir - it blest for ev - er - more.

Text: *Jordanis oras praevia;* Charles Coffin, 1676-1749; Tr. by John Chandler, 1806-1876
Tune: WINCHESTER NEW, LM; Adapt. from *Musikalisches Handbuch,* Hamburg, 1690

9 My Lord! What a Morning

Text: Afro-American Spiritual
Tune: Afro-American Spiritual

Christ is Coming: Prepare the Way 10

from *Advent Jazz Vespers II*
Music and Word Adaptation by Edward V. Bonnemère
Copyright © 1986 Amity Music Corporation

11 Come, Lord, and Tarry Not

1. Come, Lord, and tar - ry not! Bring the long-looked-for day!
2. Come, for your saints still wait; Dai - ly as - cends their sigh;
3. Come, for cre - a - tion groans, Im - pa - tient of your stay,
4. Come, and make all things new, Build up this ru - ined earth;
5. Come, and be - gin your reign Of ev - er - last - ing peace;

O why these years of wait - ing here, These a - ges of de - lay?
The Spir - it and the Bride say, "Come!" Do you not hear the cry?
Worn out with these long years of ill, These a - ges of de - lay?
Re - store our fad - ed par - a - dise, Cre - a - tion's sec - ond birth.
Come, take the king-dom to your - self, Great King of right-eous - ness!

Text: Rev. 22:17, Attr. to Horatius Bonar, 1808-1889
Tune: ST. BRIDE, SM, Samuel Howard, 1710-1782

12 Rise Up, Shepherd, and Follow

1. There's a star in the East on Christ - mas morn,
2. If you take good heed to the an - gel's words,

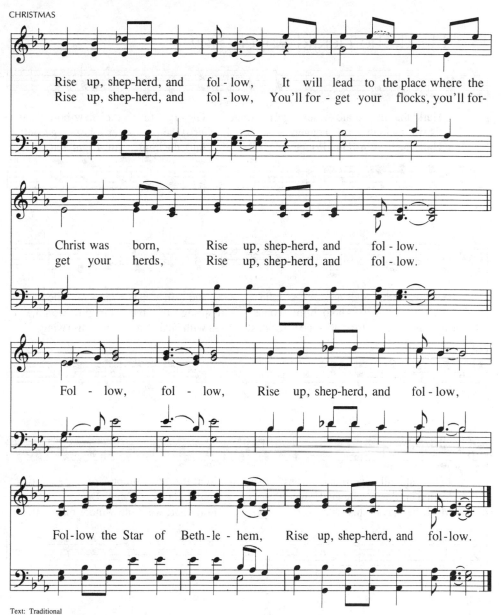

Rise up, shep-herd, and fol - low, It will lead to the place where the
Rise up, shep-herd, and fol - low, You'll for - get your flocks, you'll for-

Christ was born, Rise up, shep-herd, and fol - low.
get your herds, Rise up, shep-herd, and fol - low.

Fol - low, fol - low, Rise up, shep-herd, and fol - low,

Fol-low the Star of Beth-le - hem, Rise up, shep-herd, and fol-low.

Text: Traditional
Tune: Afro-American Spiritual

13 Hark! The Herald Angels Sing

1. Hark! the her - ald an - gels sing, "Glo-ry to the new-born King;
2. Christ, by high - est heaven a - dored, Christ the ev - er - last-ing Lord:
3. Hail the heav'n-born Prince of Peace! Hail the Sun of Right-eous-ness!

Peace on earth, and mer - cy mild God and sin - ners rec - on-ciled!"
Late in time be - hold him come, Off-spring of the Vir-gin's womb.
Light and life to all he brings, Risen with heal - ing in his wings.

Joy - ful, all you na - tions, rise, Join the tri - umph of the skies;
Veiled in flesh the God - head see: Hail the in-car - nate De - i - ty,
Mild he lays his glo - ry by, Born that we no more may die,

With the an-gel - ic host pro-claim, "Christ is born in Beth - le - hem!"
Pleased as man with us to dwell, Je - sus, our Em-man-u - el.
Born to raise us from the earth, Born to give us sec-ond birth.

Hark! the her-ald an-gels sing, "Glo-ry to the new-born King!"

Text: Charles Wesley, 1707-1788, alt.
Tune: MENDELSSOHN, 77 77 D with refrain; Felix Mendelssohn, 1809-1847

Gloria III 14

Glo - ri - a, glo - ri - a, in ex - cel - sis De - o!

Glo - ri - a, glo - ri - a, al - le - lu - ia, al - le - lu - ia!

Text: Luke 2:14; Taizé Community, 1978
Tune: Jacques Berthier, b.1923
© 1979, Les Presses de Taizé

15 Singing Glory Be to Jesus

Sing-ing glo - ry be to Je - sus

O come all ye faith - ful,

Joy to the world the Lord is come. Let

Son of God and Prince of Peace, He's might - y

Joy - ful and tri - um - phant, O

earth re - ceive her King.

Al - pha, and O - me - ga.

Come and be - hold him,

Glo - ry be to Je - sus

Born in our hearts on this Christ - mas morn.

Born in our hearts on this Christ - mas morn.

Born in our hearts on this Christ - mas morn.

Text: Adapted by Rawn Harbor
Tune: Rawn Harbor
© 1985, Rawn Harbor

Christmas Joy 16

1. In Ju - de - a shep - herds heard a won - drous
2. Since days long past proph - ets told of Da - vid's
3. Choirs of an - gels praised God for the birth of
4. Fear no long - er holds men in con - fin - ing
5. With the shep - herds and the hosts of heav'n - ly

sto - ry that the long - a - wait - ed Mes - si-
cit - y whence a ti - ny child would be called
Je - sus who would shine as light midst the dark-
bond - age. Je - sus Christ the Sav - ior has freed
an - gels let us ev - er - more sing his prais-

ah was born of a maid - en Mar - y.
forth, des - tined Prince of Peace for - ev - er.
ness, this child who brings peace to man - kind.
us; from guilt we are cleansed to serve him.
es, for he on - ly is the Sav - ior.

Text: Howard S. Olson
Tune: Nyaturu Tune; *Tumshangilie Mungu*, Makumira, Tanzania
© 1977, Augsburg Publishing House

17 Angels We Have Heard on High

1. An - gels we have heard on high Sweet-ly sing-ing o'er the plains,
2. Shep-herds, why this ju - bi-lee? Why your joy-ous strains pro-long?
3. Come to Beth - le - hem and see Him whose birth the an - gels sing;
4. See him in a man - ger laid, Whom the choirs of an - gels praise;

And the moun-tains in re-ply Ech - o back their joy - ous strains.
Say what may the ti - dings be, Which in-spire your heaven - ly song.
Come a - dore, on bend - ed knee, Christ, the Lord, the new - born King.
Mar - y, Jo - seph, lend your aid, While our hearts in love we raise.

Glo - - - - - - - - ri - a

in ex - cel - sis De - o, Glo - - - - -

- - - - - ri - a   in ex - cel - sis   De - - o.

Text: *Les anges dans nos campagnes;* French, c.18th C.; Tr. from *Crown of Jesus Music*, London, 1862
Tune: GLORIA, 7 7 7 7 with refrain; French Traditional

Angels, from the Realms of Glory   18

1. An - gels, from the   realms of glo - ry,   Wing your flight o'er   all   the earth;
2. Shep-herds, in the   fields a - bid - ing,   Watch-ing o'er your flocks by night,
3. Sag - es, leave your   con - tem-pla-tions,   Bright-er vi - sions beam a - far;
4. Though an in - fant   now we view him,   He shall fill his heav'n-ly throne,

You who sang cre - a - tion's sto - ry,   Now pro-claim Mes - si - ah's birth:
God on earth is   now re - sid - ing,   Yon-der shines the   in - fant light:
Seek the great De - sire of na - tions,   You have seen his morn-ing star:
Ga - ther all the   na - tions to him;   Ev - ery knee shall then bow down:

Come and wor - ship, come and wor-ship,   Wor-ship Christ, the   new-born King.

Text: Sts. 1-3, James Montgomery, 1771-1854; St. 4, *Christmas Box*, 1825
Tune: REGENT SQUARE, 8 7 8 7 8 7; Henry Smart, 1813-1879

19 Joy to the World

1. Joy to the world! the Lord is come:
2. Joy to the world! the Sav - ior reigns:
3. He rules the world with truth and grace,

Let earth re - ceive her King;
Let us, our songs em - ploy;
And makes the na - tions prove

Let ev - 'ry heart pre - pare him room,
While fields and floods, rocks, hills, and plains
The glo - ries of his right - eous - ness,

And heaven and na - ture sing, And
Re - peat the sound - ing joy, Re-
And won - ders of his love, And

And heaven and na - ture
Re - peat the sound - ing
And won - ders of his

heaven and na - ture sing, And
peat the sound - ing joy, Re-
won - ders of his love, And

sing, And heaven and na - ture
joy, Re - peat the sound - ing
love, And won - ders of his

heaven, and heaven and na - ture sing.
peat, re - peat the sound - ing joy.
won - ders, won - ders of his love.

sing,
joy,
love,

Text: Ps. 98; Isaac Watts, 1674-1748
Tune: ANTIOCH, CM; Arr. from George F. Handel, 1685-1759, in T. Hawkes' *Collection of Tunes,* 1833

20 O Come, All Ye Faithful/Adeste Fideles

1. O come, all ye faith - ful, joy - ful and tri - um - phant, O
2. Sing, choirs of an - gels, sing in ex - ul - ta - tion,
3. Yea, Lord, we greet thee, born this hap - py morn - ing,

1. Ad - és - te fi - dé - les, laé - ti, tri - um - phán - tes, Ve -
2. Can - tet nunc i - o, cho - rus an - ge - ló - rum,
3. Er - go qui na - tus Di - e ho - di - ér - na,

come ye, O come ye to Beth - le - hem;
Sing, all ye cit - i - zens of heav'n a - bove!
Je - sus, to thee be all glo - ry giv'n;

ní - te, ve - ní - te in Béth - le - hem.
Can - tet nunc au - la cae - lés - ti - um.
Je - su ti - bi sit gló - ri - a.

Come and be - hold him, born the King of an - gels;
Glo - ry to God, all glo - ry in the high - est;
Word of the Fa - ther, now in flesh ap - pear - ing;

Na - tum vi - dé - te, Re - gem an - ge - ló - rum.
Glo - ri - a, gló - ria, in ex - cél - sis De - o.
Pa - tris ae - ter - nae ver - bum ca - ro fa - ctum.

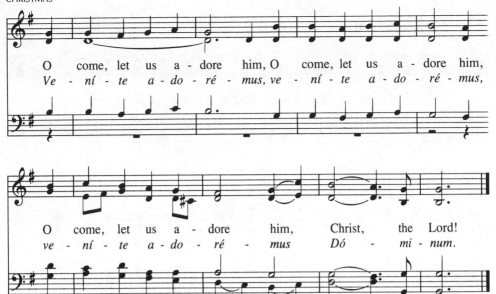

O come, let us a - dore him, O come, let us a - dore him,
Ve - ní - te a - do - ré - mus, ve - ní - te a - do - ré - mus,

O come, let us a - dore him, Christ, the Lord!
ve - ní - te a - do - ré - mus Dó - mi - num.

Text: *Adeste fideles;* John F. Wade, c.1711-1786; Tr. by Frederick Oakeley, 1802-1880, alt.
Tune: ADESTE FIDELES, Irr. with refrain; John F. Wade, c.1711-1786

21 Behold Your God

Oh thou that tell-est good ti-dings to Zi-on, oh thou that tell-est good ti-dings to Je-ru-sa-lem; Lift up your voice with strength, Lift it up don't be a-fraid, Be-hold your God. A-rise, and shine, for the light of the world is come. Be-hold your God!

Text: Is. 40:9
Tune: Kenneth W. Louis, © 1985, Kenneth W. Louis

Go Tell It on the Mountain 22

Go tell it on the moun-tain, O-ver the hills and ev-'ry-where;

Go tell it on the moun-tain That Je-sus Christ is born!

1. While shep-herds kept their watch-ing O'er si-lent flocks by night, Be-
2. The shep-herds feared and trem-bled When lo! a-bove the earth Rang
3. Down in a low-ly man-ger The hum-ble Christ was born, And

D.C.

hold through-out the heav-ens There shone a ho-ly light.
out the an-gel cho-rus That hailed our Sav-ior's birth.
God sent us sal-va-tion That bless-ed Christ-mas morn.

Text: Afro-American Spiritual; Adapt. by John W. Work, Jr., 1871-1925. © Mrs. John W. Work III
Tune: GO TELL IT ON THE MOUNTAIN. 7 6 7 6 with refrain; Afro-American Spiritual; Harm. by Paul Sjolund, b. 1935. © 1971. Walton Music Corp.

23 It Came upon the Midnight Clear

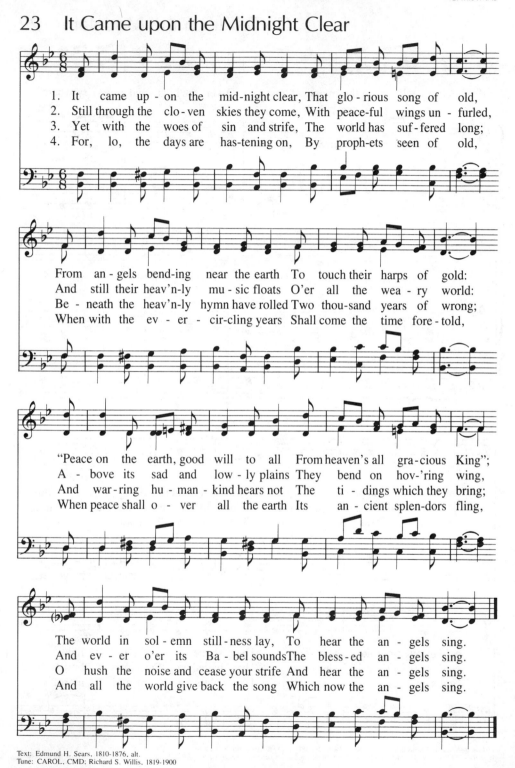

1. It came up-on the mid-night clear, That glo-rious song of old,
2. Still through the clo-ven skies they come, With peace-ful wings un-furled,
3. Yet with the woes of sin and strife, The world has suf-fered long;
4. For, lo, the days are has-tening on, By proph-ets seen of old,

From an-gels bend-ing near the earth To touch their harps of gold:
And still their heav'n-ly mu-sic floats O'er all the wea-ry world:
Be-neath the heav'n-ly hymn have rolled Two thou-sand years of wrong;
When with the ev-er-cir-cling years Shall come the time fore-told,

"Peace on the earth, good will to all From heaven's all gra-cious King";
A-bove its sad and low-ly plains They bend on hov-'ring wing,
And war-ring hu-man-kind hears not The ti-dings which they bring;
When peace shall o-ver all the earth Its an-cient splen-dors fling,

The world in sol-emn still-ness lay, To hear the an-gels sing.
And ev-er o'er its Ba-bel sounds The bless-ed an-gels sing.
O hush the noise and cease your strife And hear the an-gels sing.
And all the world give back the song Which now the an-gels sing.

Text: Edmund H. Sears, 1810-1876, alt.
Tune: CAROL, CMD: Richard S. Willis, 1819-1900

Lo, How a Rose E'er Blooming   24

1. Lo, how a Rose e'er bloom-ing From ten - der stem hath
2. I - sai - ah 'twas fore - told it, The Rose I have in
3. O Flower, whose fra-grance ten - der With sweet-ness fills the

sprung! Of Jes - se's lin-eage com - ing As seers of old have
mind, With Mar - y we be - hold it, The Vir-gin Moth - er
air, Dis - pel in glo-rious splen - dor The dark-ness ev - 'ry-

sung. It came, a blos-som bright, A - mid the cold of
kind. To show God's love a - right, She bore to us a
where; True man, yet ver - y God, From sin and death now

win - ter, When half spent was the night.
Sav - ior, When half spent was the night.
save us, And share our ev - 'ry load.

Text: Is. 11:1; *Es ist ein' Ros' entsprungen*; *Speier Gebetbuch*, 1599; Tr. Sts. 1-2 by Theodore Baker, 1851-1934; St. 3, *The Hymnal*, 1940
Text: ES IST EIN' ROS' ENTSPRUNGEN, 7 6 7 6 6 7 6; *Geistliche Kirchengesang*, Cologne, 1599; Harm. by Michael Praetorius, 1571-1621

25 O Little Town of Bethlehem

1. O lit - tle town of Beth - le - hem, How still we see thee lie!
2. For Christ is born of Mar - y, And gath - ered all a - bove,
3. How si - lent - ly, how si - lent - ly, The won - drous gift is giv'n!
4. O ho - ly Child of Beth - le - hem! De - scend to us we pray;

A - bove thy deep and dream-less sleep The si - lent stars go by;
While mor - tals sleep, the an - gels keep Their watch of won-d'ring love.
So God im-parts to hu - man hearts The bless - ings of his heav'n.
Cast out our sin and en - ter in, Be born in us to - day.

Yet in the dark streets shin - eth The ev - er - last - ing Light;
O morn-ing stars, to - geth - er Pro - claim the ho - ly birth!
No ear may hear his com - ing, But in this world of sin,
We hear the Christ-mas an - gels The great glad ti - dings tell;

The hopes and fears of all the years Are met in thee to - night.
And prais - es sing to God the King, And peace to all on earth.
Where meek souls will re - ceive him, still The dear Christ en - ters in.
O come to us, a - bide with us, Our Lord Em - man - u - el!

Text: Philips Brooks, 1835-1893
Tune: ST. LOUIS, 8 6 8 6 7 6 8 6; Lewis H. Redner, 1831-1908

Silent Night, Holy Night   26

1. Si - lent night, ho - ly night, All is calm, all is bright
2. Si - lent night, ho - ly night, Shep-herds quake at the sight;
3. Si - lent night, ho - ly night, Son of God, love's pure light

Round yon Vir - gin Moth-er and Child, Ho - ly In-fant, so ten-der and mild,
Glo - ries stream from heav-en a - far, Heav'n-ly hosts sing al - le - lu - ia;
Ra - diant beams from thy ho - ly face, With the dawn of re - deem - ing grace,

Sleep in heav-en - ly peace, Sleep in heav - en - ly peace.
Christ, the Sav-ior, is born! Christ, the Sav - ior, is born!
Je - sus, Lord, at thy birth, Je - sus, Lord, at thy birth.

Text: *Stille Nacht, heilige Nacht;* Joseph Mohr, 1792-1849; Tr. John F. Young, 1820-1885
Tune: STILLE NACHT, 66 89 66; Franz X. Gruber, 1787-1863

27 We Three Kings of Orient Are

1. We three kings of O - ri - ent are, Bear - ing
2. Born a babe on Beth - le - hem's plain, Gold we
3. Frank - in - cense to of - fer have I; In - cense
4. Myrrh is mine: its bit - ter per - fume Breathes a
5. Glo - rious now be - hold him rise, King and

gifts we trav - erse a - far   Field and foun - tain,
bring to crown him a - gain;   King for - ev - er,
owns a De - i - ty nigh,   Prayer and prais - ing
life of gath - 'ring gloom;   Sor - rowing, sigh - ing,
God and sac - ri - fice: Heav'n sing, "Hal - le-

Moor and moun - tain, Fol - low - ing yon - der star.
Ceas - ing nev - er, O - ver us all to reign.
Glad - ly rais - ing, Wor - ship - ing God on high.
Bleed - ing, dy - ing, Sealed in the stone cold tomb.
lu - jah!" "Hal - le - lu - jah!" earth re - plies.

O star of won - der, star of night, Star with roy - al beau - ty bright, West-ward lead-ing, still pro-ceed-ing, Guide us to the per-fect Light.

Text: Mt. 2:1-11; John H. Hopkins, Jr., 1820-1891
Tune: KINGS OF ORIENT, 88 44 6 with refrain; John H. Hopkins, Jr., 1820-1891

The First Nowell 28

Unison

1. The first Now-ell, the an-gel did say. Was to cer-tain poor shep-herds in fields as they lay; In fields where they lay keep-ing their sheep, On a cold win-ter's night that was so deep.

2. They look-ed up and saw a star Shin-ing in the east, be-yond them far, And to the earth it gave great light, And so it con-tin-ued both day and night.

3. And by the light of that same star Three wise men came from coun-try far; To seek for a king was their in-tent, And to fol-low the star where-ev-er it went.

4. This star drew nigh to the north-west. O'er Beth-le-hem it took its rest; And there it did both stop and stay, Right o-ver the place where Je-sus lay.

Harmony

Now-ell, Now-ell, Now-ell, Now-

ell,   Born   is   the   King   of   Is - ra - el.

5. Then entered in those wise men three,
   Full rev'rently upon their knee,
   And offered there, in his presence,
   Their gold and myrrh and frankincense.
   Nowell, Nowell, Nowell, Nowell,
   Born is the King of Israel.

6. Then let us all with one accord
   Sing praises to our heav'nly Lord;
   Who with the Father we adore
   And Spirit blest for evermore.
   Nowell, Nowell, Nowell, Nowell,
   Born is the King of Israel.

Text: English Carol, 17th C.
Tune: THE FIRST NOWELL, Irregular; English Melody; Harm. by David Willcocks, b.1919. © 1961, Oxford University Press

1. What child is this, who, laid to rest, On Mar-y's lap is sleep-ing?
2. Why lies he in such mean es - tate Where ox and ass are feed - ing?
3. So bring him in - cense, gold, and myrrh, Come, peas-ant, king to own him;

Whom an - gels greet with an-thems sweet, While shep-herds watch are keep - ing?
Good Chris-tian, fear; for sin-ners here The si - lent Word is plead-ing.
The King of kings sal - va - tion brings, Let lov - ing hearts en - throne him.

This, this is Christ the King, Whom shep-herds guard and an - gels sing;

Haste, haste to bring him laud, The babe, the son of Mar - y.

Text: William C. Dix, 1827-1898
Tune: GREENSLEEVES, 8 7 8 7 with refrain; English Melody, 16th C.; Harm. by John Stainer, 1840-1901

30 All Glory, Laud, and Honor

All glo-ry, laud, and hon - or To you, Re-deem-er, King!

To whom the lips of chil - dren Made sweet ho-san-nas ring.

1. You are the King of Is-ra-el, And Da-vid's roy-al Son,
2. The com-pa-ny of an - gels Are prais-ing you on high;
3. The peo-ple of the He - brews With palms be-fore you went:
4. To you be-fore your pas - sion They sang their hymns of praise:
5. Their prais-es you ac-cept - ed, Ac-cept the prayers we bring,

Now in the Lord's Name com - ing, Our King and Bless-ed One.
And mor-tals, joined with all things Cre - a - ted, make re - ply.
Our praise and prayers and an - thems Be - fore you we pre - sent.
To you, now high ex - alt - ed, Our mel - o - dy we raise.
Great source of love and good - ness, Our Sav - ior and our King.

Text: *Gloria, laus et honor;* Theodulph of Orleans, c.760-821; Tr. by John M. Neale, 1818-1866, alt.
Tune: ST. THEODULPH, 7 6 7 6 D; Melchior Teschner, 1584-1635

O How He Loves You and Me 31

1. O how He loves you and me.
2. Je - sus to Cal - vary did go,

O how He loves you and me;
His love for the world to show;

He gave His life, what more could He give:
What He did there brought hope from de - spair:

O how He loves you, O how He loves me,
O how He loves you, O how He loves me,

O how He loves you and me.
O how He loves you and me.

Text: Kurt Kaiser, b.1934
Tune: Kurt Kaiser, b.1934
© 1975, Word Music, Inc.

32 The Glory of These Forty Days

1. The glo - ry of these for - ty days We cel - e - brate with songs of praise; For Christ, by whom all things were made, Him - self has fast - ed and has prayed.

2. A - lone and fast - ing Mo - ses saw The lov - ing God who gave the law; And to E - li - jah, fast - ing, came The steeds and char - i - ots of flame.

3. So Dan - iel trained his mys - tic sight, De - liv - ered from the li - on's might; And John, the Bride-groom's friend, be - came The her - ald of Mes - si - ah's name.

4. Then grant that we like them be true, Con - sumed in fast and prayer with you; Our spir - its strength - en with your grace, And give us joy to see your face.

Text: *Clarum decus jejunii;* Gregory the Great, c.540-604; Tr. by Maurice F. Bell, 1862-1947
Tune: ERHALT UNS HERR, LM; Klug's *Geistliche Lieder,* 1543; Harm. by J. S. Bach, 1685-1750

Jesu, Jesu, Fill Us with Your Love   33

Je - su, Je - su, fill us with your love, show

us how to serve the neigh-bors we have from you.

1. Kneels at the feet of his friends,   Si - lent - ly wash - es their
2. Neigh-bors are rich and poor,   Neigh-bors are black and
3. These are the ones we should serve,   These are the ones we should
4. Kneel at the feet of our friends,   Si - lent - ly wash-ing their

D.C.

feet,   Mas-ter who pours out him - self for them.
white,   Neigh-bors are near and far a - way.
love.   All are neigh-bors to us and you.
feet,   This is the way we should live with you.

Text: John 13:3-5; Ghana Folk Song; Tr. by Tom Colvin, b.1925
Tune: CHEREPONI, Irregular; Ghana Folk song; Acc. by Jane M. Marshall, b.1924, © 1982, Hope Publishing Co.
© 1969, Hope Publishing Co.

34 Somebody's Knockin' at Your Door

Some-bod-y's knock-in' at your door; Some-bod-y's knock-in' at your door;

O sin - ner, why don't you an - swer? Some-bod-y's knock-in' at your door.

Solo: *All:*

door.
1. Knocks like Je - sus,
2. Can't you hear him? Some-bod-y's knock-in' at your door;
3. Je - sus calls you,
4. Can't you trust him?

Solo: *All:*

Knocks like Je - sus,
Can't you hear him? Some-bod-y's knock-in' at your door.   O
Je - sus calls you,
Can't you trust him?

sin - ner, why don't you an - swer? Some-bod-y's knock-in' at your door.

Text: Afro-American Spiritual
Tune: SOMEBODY'S KNOCKIN', Irregular; Afro-American Spiritual; Harm. by Richard Proulx, b.1937. © 1986, GIA Publications, Inc.

My Jesus, I Love Thee 35

1. My Jesus, I love Thee, I know Thou art mine—
2. I love Thee because Thou hast first lov-ed me
3. I'll love Thee in life, I will love Thee in death,
4. In man-sions of glo-ry and end-less de-light,

For Thee all the fol-lies of sin I re-sign;
And pur-chased my par-don on Cal-va-ry's tree;
And praise Thee as long as Thou lend-est me breath;
I'll ev-er a-dore Thee in heav-en so bright;

My gra-cious Re-deem-er, my Sav-ior art Thou:
I love Thee for wear-ing the thorns on Thy brow:
And say when the death-dew lies cold on my brow,
I'll sing with the glit-ter-ing crown on my brow,

If ev-er I loved Thee, my Je-sus, 'tis now.
If ev-er I loved Thee, my Je-sus, 'tis now.
"If ev-er I loved Thee, my Je-sus, 'tis now."
"If ev-er I loved Thee, my Je-sus, 'tis now."

Text: William R. Featherston, 1846-1873
Tune: GORDON, 11 11 11 11; Adoniram J. Gordon, 1836-1895

36 He Will Remember Me

1. When on the cross of Cal-v'ry The Lord was cru-ci-fied;
2. O what a shame to kill Him There on that rug-ged cross;
3. At His dear feet I'm kneel-ing, My sins I now con-fess;

The mob stood 'round a-bout Him And mocked un-til He died.
But such a death was need-ed To res-cue all the lost.
I bow in deep re-pent-ance, My soul He'll sure-ly bless.

Two thieves were nailed be-side Him To share the ag-o-ny,
His blood was made a ran-som To set the cap-tives free,
My blind-ed eyes He o-pens So that the light I see,

But one of them cried out to Him, "O Lord, re-mem-ber me."
I know that I'm in-clud-ed, and He will re-mem-ber me.
And when I reach the pearl-y gates, He will re-mem-ber me.

Refrain

Will the Lord re-mem-ber me, When I am called to
Will the Lord re-mem-ber me,

go? When I have crossed death's chill-y sea, Will
When I have crossed death's chill-y sea,

He His love there show? O yes, He heard my
yes, He heard my

fee-ble cries, From bond-age set me free. And
fee-ble cries,

when I reach the pearl-y gates He will re-mem-ber me.

Text: E. M. Bartlett, 1885-1941
Tune: E. M. Bartlett, 1885-1941
© Albert E. Brumley and Sons

37 The Old Rugged Cross

1. On a hill far a-way stood an old rug-ged cross,
2. O that old rug-ged cross, so de-spised by the world,
3. In the old rug-ged cross, stained with blood so di-vine,
4. To the old rug-ged cross I will ev-er be true,

The em-blem of suf-f'ring and shame;
Has a won-drous at-trac-tion for me;
A won-drous beau-ty I see;
Its shame and re-proach glad-ly bear;

And I love that old cross where the dear-est and best
For the dear Lamb of God left His glo-ry a-bove
For 'twas on that old cross Je-sus suf-fered and died
Then He'll call me some day to my home far a-way,

For a world of lost sin-ners was slain.
To bear it to dark Cal-va-ry.
To par-don and sanc-ti-fy me.
Where His glo-ry for-ev-er I'll share.

So I'll cher-ish the old rug-ged cross,
cross, the old rug-ged cross,

Till my tro-phies at last I lay down;

I will cling to the old rug-ged cross,
cross, the old rug-ged cross,

And ex-change it some day for a crown.

Text: George Bennard, 1873-1960
Tune: George Bennard, 1873-1960

38 Calvary

Very slowly

Cal - va - ry, Cal - va - ry, Cal - va-

ry, Cal - va - ry, Cal - va - ry, Cal - va-

Fine

ry, Sure - ly He died on Cal - va - ry.

1. Ev - 'ry time I think a-bout Je - sus, Ev - 'ry

time I think a-bout Je - sus, Ev - 'ry time I

D.C.

think a-bout Je - sus, Sure - ly He died on Cal - va - ry.

2. Sinner, do you love my Jesus?
   Surely He died on Calvary.
   Calvary, Calvary, etc.

3. We are climbing Jacob's ladder,
   Surely He died on Calvary.
   Calvary, Calvary, etc.

4. Ev'ry round goes higher and higher,
   Surely He died on Calvary.
   Calvary, Calvary, etc.

Text: Afro-American Spiritual
Tune: Afro-American Spiritual

39 Thy Way, O Lord

1. Thy way, O Lord, not mine, Thy will be done, not mine; Since Thou for me didst bleed, And now doth in-ter-cede, Each day I sim-ply plead, Thy will be done.
2. Thy way, O Lord, not mine, Let glo-ry all be Thine; Keep me, lest I may stray, Near Thee from day to day; Teach me to watch and pray, Thy will be done.
3. Hide me from self, O Lord, May I at-tend Thy word; Send pride be-yond re-call, Let each as-sail-er fall, Be Thou my all in all, Thy will be done.
4. Sub-mis-sive-ly I bow; With strength and grace en-dow This wea-ry, sin-ful heart; Shield from each cru-el dart; May I from Thee ne'er part, Thy will be done.

Refrain

Thy will, Thy will be done, Thy will, Thy will be done; In-
Thy will be done, Thy will be done;

cline my heart each day to say, "Thy will be done." A - men.

Text: Nina B. Jackson
Tune: E. C. Deas

Lord, Who throughout These Forty Days 40

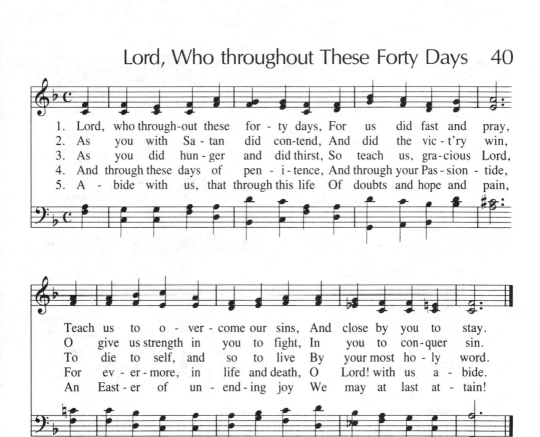

1. Lord, who through-out these for - ty days, For us did fast and pray,
2. As you with Sa - tan did con-tend, And did the vic - t'ry win,
3. As you did hun - ger and did thirst, So teach us, gra-cious Lord,
4. And through these days of pen - i - tence, And through your Pas - sion - tide,
5. A - bide with us, that through this life Of doubts and hope and pain,

Teach us to o - ver - come our sins, And close by you to stay.
O give us strength in you to fight, In you to con - quer sin.
To die to self, and so to live By your most ho - ly word.
For ev - er - more, in life and death, O Lord! with us a - bide.
An East - er of un - end - ing joy We may at last at - tain!

Text: Claudia F. Hernaman, 1838-1898, alt.
Tune: ST. FLAVIAN, CM; *John's Day Psalter*, 1562; Harm. based on the original *faux-bourdon* setting

41 I Heard the Voice of Jesus Say

1. I heard the voice of Je - sus say, "Come un - to Me and
2. I heard the voice of Je - sus say, "Be - hold, I free - ly
3. I heard the voice of Je - sus say, "I am this dark world's

rest, Lay down, thou wea - ry one, lay down Thy
give The liv - ing wa - ter; thirst - y one, Stoop
Light, Look un - to Me; thy morn shall rise, And

head up - on my breast!" I came to Je - sus
down, and drink, and live!" I came to Je - sus,
all thy day be bright!" I looked to Je - sus,

as I was, Wea - ry, and worn, and sad; I found in
and I drank Of that life - giv - ing stream; My thirst was
and I found In Him my Star, my Sun; And in that

Him a rest - ing place, And He has made me glad.
quenched, my soul re - vived, And now I live in Him.
light of life I'll walk Till trav - 'ling days are done.

Text: Horatius Bonar, 1808-1889
Tune: Old English Aire

Forty Days and Forty Nights 42

1. For - ty days and for - ty nights You were fast - ing in the wild;
2. Shall not we your sor - row share And from world - ly joys ab - stain,
3. Then if Sa - tan on us press, Flesh or spir - it to as - sail,
4. So shall we have peace di - vine: Ho - lier glad - ness ours shall be;
5. Keep, O keep us, Sav - ior dear, Ev - er con - stant by your side;

For - ty days and for - ty nights Tempt - ed and yet un - de - filed.
Fast - ing with un - ceas - ing prayer, Strong with you to suf - fer pain?
Vic - tor in the wil - der - ness, Grant we may not faint nor fail!
Round us, too, shall an - gels shine, Such as served you faith - ful - ly.
That with you we may ap - pear At the e - ter - nal East - er - tide.

Text: George H. Smyttan, 1822-1870, alt.
Tune: HEINLEIN, 7 7 7 7; Attr. to Martin Herbst, 1654-1681; Harm. attr. to J. S. Bach, 1685-1750

43 Were You There

1. Were you there when they cru - ci - fied my Lord? Were you
2. Were you there when they nailed him to the tree? Were you
3. Were you there when they pierced him in the side? Were you
4. Were you there when the sun re - fused to shine? Were you

there when they cru - ci - fied my Lord? O!
there when they nailed him to the tree? O!
there when they pierced him in the side? O!
there when the sun re - fused to shine? O!

Some-times it caus - es me to trem-ble, trem-ble, trem-ble,
Some-times it caus - es me to trem-ble, trem-ble, trem-ble,
Some-times it caus - es me to trem-ble, trem-ble, trem-ble,
Some-times it caus - es me to trem-ble, trem-ble, trem-ble,

Were you there when they cru - ci - fied my Lord?
Were you there when they nailed him to the tree?
Were you there when they pierced him in the side?
Were you there when the sun re - fused to shine?

5. Were you there when they laid him in the tomb?
Were you there when they laid him in the tomb?
O! Sometimes it causes me to tremble, tremble, tremble,
Were you there when they laid him in the tomb?

6. Were you there when they rolled the stone away?
Were you there when they rolled the stone away?
O! Sometimes it causes me to tremble, tremble, tremble,
Were you there when they rolled the stone away?

Text: Afro-American Spiritual
Tune: WERE YOU THERE, 10 10 with refrain; Afro-American Spiritual; Harm. by C. Winfred Douglas, 1867-1944, © 1940, 1943, 1961, Church Pension Fund

I Love Him 44

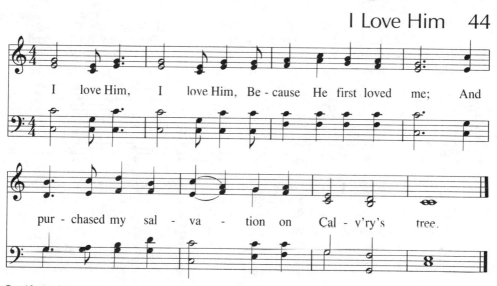

I love Him, I love Him, Be - cause He first loved me; And
pur - chased my sal - va - tion on Cal - v'ry's tree.

Text: Afro-American Folk song
Tune: American Folk song

45 Jesus, Keep Me Near the Cross

1. Je - sus, keep me near the cross—
2. Near the cross, a trem - bling soul,
3. Near the cross! O Lamb of God,
4. Near the cross I'll watch and wait,

There a pre - cious foun - tain, Free to all, a
Love and mer - cy found me; There the Bright and
Bring its scenes be - fore me; Help me walk from
Hop - ing, trust - ing ev - er, Till I reach the

heal - ing stream, Flows from Cal - v'ry's moun - tain.
Morn - ing Star Sheds its beams a - round me.
day to day With its shad - ows o'er me.
prom - ised Land Just be - yond the riv - er.

Chorus

In the cross, in the cross Be my glo - ry ev - er,

Till my rap - tured soul shall find Rest, be - yond the riv - er.

Text: Fanny J. Crosby, 1820-1915
Tune: William H. Doane, 1832-1915

Down at the Cross 46

1. Down at the cross where my Sav-ior died,
   Down where for cleans-ing from sin I cried,
   There to my heart was the blood ap-plied;
   Glo-ry to His name.

2. I am so won-drous-ly saved from sin,
   Je-sus so sweet-ly a-bides with-in;
   There at the cross where He took me in;
   Glo-ry to His name.

3. O pre-cious foun-tain that saves from sin,
   I am so glad I have en-tered in;
   There Je-sus saves me and keeps me clean;
   Glo-ry to His name.

4. Come to this foun-tain so rich and sweet;
   Cast your poor soul at the Sav-ior's feet;
   Plunge in to-day, and be made com-plete;
   Glo-ry to His name.

Glo-ry to His name, Glo-ry to His name! There to my heart was the blood ap-plied; Glo-ry to His name.

Text: Elisha A. Hoffman, 1839-1929
Tune: GLORY TO HIS NAME; John H. Stockton, 1813-1877

47 Savior, Like a Shepherd Lead Us

1. Sav - ior, like a shep - herd lead us,
2. We are Thine; do Thou be - friend us,
3. Thou hast prom - ised to re - ceive us,
4. Ear - ly let us seek Thy fa - vor;

Much we need Thy ten - der care; In Thy pleas - ant pas - tures
Be the Guard-ian of our way; Keep Thy flock, from sin de-
Poor and sin - ful tho' we be; Thou hast mer - cy to re-
Ear - ly let us do Thy will; Bless - ed Lord and on - ly

feed us, For our use Thy folds pre - pare.
fend us, Seek us when we go a - stray.
lieve us, Grace to cleanse, and power to free.
Sav - ior, With Thy love our bos - oms fill.

Bless-ed Je - sus, Bless-ed Je - sus, Thou hast
Bless-ed Je - sus, Bless-ed Je - sus, Hear Thy
Bless-ed Je - sus, Bless-ed Je - sus, Ear - ly
Bless-ed Je - sus, Bless-ed Je - sus, Thou hast

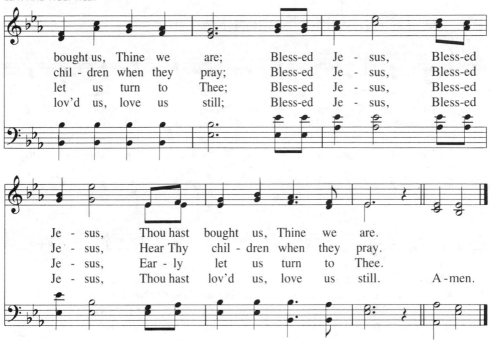

bought us, Thine we are; Bless-ed Je - sus, Bless-ed
chil - dren when they pray; Bless-ed Je - sus, Bless-ed
let us turn to Thee; Bless-ed Je - sus, Bless-ed
lov'd us, love us still; Bless-ed Je - sus, Bless-ed

Je - sus, Thou hast bought us, Thine we are.
Je - sus, Hear Thy chil - dren when they pray.
Je - sus, Ear - ly let us turn to Thee.
Je - sus, Thou hast lov'd us, love us still. A -men.

Text: Dorothy A. Thrupp, 1779-1847
Tune: William B. Bradbury, 1816-1868

Jesus, Remember Me   48

Je - sus, re - mem - ber me when you come in - to your King - dom.

Je - sus, re - mem - ber me when you come in - to your King - dom.

Text: Luke 23:42; Taizé Community, 1981
Tune: Jacques Berthier, b.1923
© 1981, Les Presses de Taizé

49 At the Cross Her Station Keeping

Not too slow

1. At the Cross her sta-tion keep-ing, Stood the mourn-ful
2. Through her heart, His sor-row shar-ing, All His bit-ter
3. O that bless-ed one, grief-lad-en, Bless-ed Moth-er,
4. How she stood in des-o-la-tion Up-ward gaz-ing

Moth-er, weep-ing, Close to Je-sus to the last.
an-guish bear-ing, Now at length the sword has passed.
Bless-ed Maid-en, Moth-er of the All-blest one.
on the pas-sion Of that death-less, dy-ing Son. A-men.

5. Who could see, from tears refraining,
   Christ's dear Mother uncomplaining
   In so great a sorrow bowed?

6. Who, unmoved, behold her languish
   Underneath His Cross of anguish,
   'Mid the fierce, unpitying crowd?

7. For His people's sins th' All-Holy
   She beheld, a Victim lowly,
   Bleed in torments, bleed and die.

8. Saw her well-beloved taken,
   Saw her Child in death forsaken,
   Heard His last expiring cry.

9. Fount of love and sacred sorrow,
   Mother! may my spirit borrow
   Sadness from thy holy woe.

10. May my spirit burn within me,
    Love my God, and great love win me
    Grace to please Him here below.

11. Those five Wounds on Jesus smitten,
    Mother, in my heart be written
    Deep as in thine own they be.

12. Thou, my Savior's Cross who bearest,
    Thou, Thy Son's rebuke who sharest,
    Let me share them both with thee.

13. In the Passion of my Maker
     Be my sinful soul partaker,
         Weep till death, and weep with thee.

14. Mine with thee be that sad station,
     There to watch the great Salvation,
         Wrought upon th' atoning Tree.

15. Virgin thou of Virgins fairest,
     May the bitter woe thou sharest
         Make on me impression deep.

16. Thus Christ's dying may I carry,
     With Him in His Passion tarry,
         And His Wounds in mem'ry keep.

17. May His Wounds transfix me wholly,
     May His Cross and Life Blood holy
         Mortify my heart and mind:

18. Thus inflamed with pure affection,
     In the Virgin's Son protection
         May I at the judgment find.

19. When in death my limbs are failing,
     Let Thy Mother's prayer prevailing
         Lift me, Jesus, to Thy throne;

20. To my parting soul be given
     Entrance through the gate of Heaven,
         There confess me for Thine own. Amen.

Text: *Stabat mater dolorosa*, Jacapone da Todi, 1230-1306; Tr. by Edward Caswall, 1814-1878, and others
Tune: STABAT MATER, 88 7; *Mainz Gesangbuch*, 1661; Harm. by Nicola M. Montani. © 1947, St. Gregory Guild, Inc.

50 Wherever He Leads, I'll Go

1. "Take up thy cross and fol - low Me," I heard my
2. He drew me clos - er to His side, I sought His
3. It may be through the shad - ows dim, Or o'er the
4. My heart, my life, my all I bring to Christ who

Mas - ter say; "I gave My life to ran - som thee,
will to know, And in that will I now a - bide,
storm - y sea, I take my cross and fol - low Him,
loves me so; He is my Mas - ter, Lord, and King,

Sur - ren - der your all to - day." Wher - ev - er He leads I'll go.
Wher - ev - er He leads I'll go. Wher - ev - er He
Wher - ev - er He lead - eth me.
Wher - ev - er He leads I'll go.

leads I'll go, Wher - ev - er He leads I'll go,

I'll fol - low my Christ who loves me so,

Wher - ev - er He leads I'll go.

Text: B. B. McKinney, 1886-1952
Tune: FALLS CREEK; B. B. McKinney, 1886-1952

51 Rock of Ages

1. Rock of a - ges, cleft for me, Let me
2. Could my tears for ev - er flow, Could my
3. While I draw this fleet - ing breath, When my

hide my - self in Thee; Let the wa - ter and the
zeal no lan - guor know, These for sin could not a -
eyes shall close in death, When I rise to worlds un -

blood, From Thy wound - ed side which flowed, Be of
tone— Thou must save, and Thou a - lone: In my
known And be - hold Thee on Thy throne, Rock of

sin the dou - ble cure, Save from wrath and make me pure.
hand no price I bring, Sim - ply to Thy cross I cling.
A - ges, cleft for me, Let me hide my - self in Thee.

Text: Augustus M. Toplady, 1740-1778
Tune: TOPLADY: Thomas Hastings, 1784-1872

O Sacred Head Surrounded   52

1. O Sa-cred Head sur-round-ed By crown of pierc-ing thorn!
2. I see your strength and vig-or All fad-ing in the strife,
3. In this, your bit-ter pas-sion, Good Shep-herd, think of me

O bleed-ing Head, so wound-ed, Re-viled and put to scorn!
And death with cru-el rig-or, Be-reav-ing you of life;
With your most sweet com-pas-sion, Un-worth-y though I be:

The pow'r of death comes o'er you, The glow of life de-cays,
O ag-o-ny and dy-ing! O love to sin-ner's free!
Be-neath your cross a-bid-ing For ev-er would I rest,

Yet an-gel hosts a-dore you, And trem-ble as they gaze.
Je-sus, all grace sup-ply-ing, O turn your face on me.
In your dear love con-fid-ing, And with your pres-ence blest.

Text: *Salve caput cruentatum;* Ascr. to Bernard of Clairvaux, 1091-1153; Tr. by Henry Baker, 1821-1877
Tune: PASSION CHORALE, 7 6 7 6 D; Hans Leo Hassler, 1564-1612; Harm. by J. S. Bach, 1685-1750

53 I've Been 'Buked

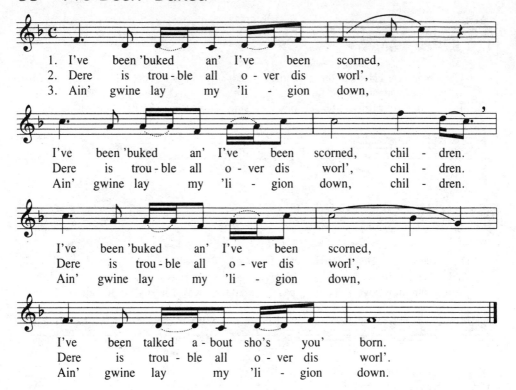

1. I've been 'buked an' I've been scorned,
2. Dere is trou-ble all o-ver dis worl',
3. Ain' gwine lay my 'li-gion down,

I've been 'buked an' I've been scorned, chil - dren.
Dere is trou-ble all o-ver dis worl', chil - dren.
Ain' gwine lay my 'li-gion down, chil - dren.

I've been 'buked an' I've been scorned,
Dere is trou-ble all o-ver dis worl',
Ain' gwine lay my 'li-gion down,

I've been talked a-bout sho's you' born.
Dere is trou-ble all o-ver dis worl'.
Ain' gwine lay my 'li-gion down.

Text: Afro-American Spiritual
Tune: Afro-American Spiritual

We Are Climbing Jacob's Ladder 54

1. We are climb-ing Ja-cob's lad-der, We are
2. Ev-'ry round goes high-er, high-er, Ev-'ry
3. Sin-ner, do you love my Je-sus? Sin-ner,
4. If you love Him, why not serve Him? If you
5. We are climb-ing high-er, high-er, We are

climb-ing Ja-cob's lad-der, We are climb-ing
round goes high-er, high-er, Ev-'ry round goes
do you love my Je-sus? Sin-ner, do you
love Him, why not serve Him? If you love Him,
climb-ing high-er, high-er, We are climb-ing

Ja-cob's lad-der, Sol-diers of the cross.
high-er, high-er, Sol-diers of the cross.
love my Je-sus? Sol-diers of the cross.
why not serve Him? Sol-diers of the cross.
high-er, high-er, Sol-diers of the cross. A-men.

Text: Afro-American Spiritual
Tune: Afro-American Spiritual

55 Rejoice!

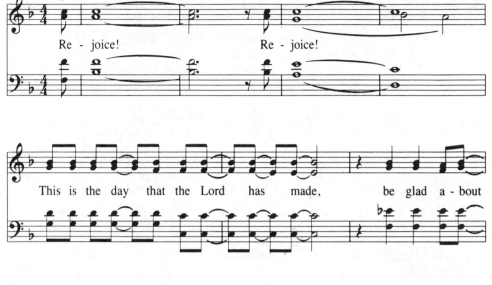

Fast four

Re - joice! Re - joice!

This is the day that the Lord has made, be glad a - bout

it. Ev - 'ry bod - y re - joice, re - joice!

This is the day that He's made be glad.

Text: Psalm (117) 118; Kenneth W. Louis
Tune: Kenneth W. Louis

He Is Lord 56

He is Lord, He is Lord, He is ris - en from the
dead and He is Lord; Ev - 'ry knee shall bow, ev - 'ry
tongue con - fess that Je - sus Christ is Lord.

Text: Anonymous
Tune: Anonymous

57 Christ the Lord Is Risen Today

1. Christ the Lord is ris'n to-day; Chris-tians, haste your vows to pay;
2. Christ, the vic-tim un-de-filed, God and sin-ners rec-on-ciled;
3. Hal-lowed, cho-sen dawn of praise, East-er, queen of all our days:
4. Christ, who once for sin-ners bled, Now the first-born from the dead,

Make your joy and prais-es known At the Pas-chal Vic-tim's throne;
When in fierce and blood-y strife Met to-geth-er death and life;
Zi-on's chil-dren now come forth; East to west and south to north.
Throned in end-less might and pow'r, Lives and reigns for ev-er-more.

For the sheep the Lamb has bled, Sin-less in the sin-ner's stead.
Chris-tians, on this hap-py day Raise your hearts with joy and say:
Let the peo-ple praise you, Lord, Be, by all that is, a-dored:
Hymns of glo-ry, songs of praise, Fa-ther, un-to you we raise:

Christ the Lord is ris'n on high; Now he lives, no more to die.
Christ the Lord is ris'n on high; Now he lives, no more to die.
Let the na-tions shout and sing; Glo-ry to their Pas-chal King.
Ris-en Lord, we now a-dore, With the Spir-it ev-er-more.

Text: *Victimae paschali laudes;* Ascr. to Wipo of Burgundy, d.1048; Tr. by Jane E. Leeson, 1809-1881, alt.
Tune: VICTIMAE PASCHALI, 77 77 D; Würth's *Katholisches Gesangbuch,* 1859; Revised in *Catholic Youth's Hymn Book,* 1871

Jesus Christ Is Risen Today 58

1. Je - sus Christ is ris'n to - day, Al - le - lu - ia!
2. Hymns of praise then let us sing, Al - le - lu - ia!
3. But the pains which he en - dured, Al - le - lu - ia!
4. Sing we to our God a - bove, Al - le - lu - ia!

Our tri - um - phant ho - ly day, Al - le - lu - ia!
Un - to Christ, our heav'n - ly King, Al - le - lu - ia!
Our sal - va - tion have pro - cured; Al - le - lu - ia!
Praise e - ter - nal as his love; Al - le - lu - ia!

Who did once up - on the cross, Al - le - lu - ia!
Who en - dured the cross and grave, Al - le - lu - ia!
Now a - bove the sky he's King, Al - le - lu - ia!
Praise him, now his might con - fess, Al - le - lu - ia!

Suf - fer to re - deem our loss. Al - le - lu - ia!
Sin - ners to re - deem and save. Al - le - lu - ia!
Where the an - gels ev - er sing. Al - le - lu - ia!
Fa - ther, Son, and Spir - it blest. Al - le - lu - ia!

Text: St. 1 *Surrexit Christus hodie*, Latin, 14th C.; Para. in *Lyra Davidica*, 1708, alt.; St. 2, 3, *The Compleat Psalmodist*, c.1750, alt.; St. 4, Charles Wesley, 1707-1788
Tune: EASTER HYMN, 77 77 with alleluias; *Lyra Davidica*, 1708

59 He Arose

1. They cru-ci-fied my Sav-ior and nailed Him to the
2. Jo-seph begged His bod-y and laid it in the
3. Mar-y, she came run-ning, a-look-ing for my
4. An an-gel came from heav-en and rolled the stone a-

cross, They cru-ci-fied my Sav-ior and nailed Him to the cross,
tomb, Jo-seph begged His bod-y and laid it in the tomb,
Lord, Mar-y, she came run-ning a-look-ing for my Lord,
way, An an-gel came from heav-en and rolled the stone a-way,

cross, And the Lord shall bear my spir-it home.
tomb, And the Lord will bear my spir-it home.
Lord, And the Lord will bear my spir-it home.
way, And the Lord will bear my spir-it home.

Refrain

He a - rose, He a - rose, He a - rose, He a - rose,

1.

He a - rose from the dead, He a - rose, He a - rose,

He a - rose, He a - rose, He a - rose from the dead;

2.

dead, And the Lord shall bear my spir - it home.

Text: Afro-American Spiritual
Tune: Afro-American Spiritual; Arr. by Willa A. Townsend

60 O Sons and Daughters

Al - le - lu - ia, al - le - lu - ia, al - le - lu - ia.

*

1. O sons and daugh - ters, let us sing!
2. That East - er morn, at break of day,
3. An an - gel clad in white they see,
4. That night the a - pos - tles met in fear;
5. When Thom - as, first the ti - dings heard,

This alternate accompaniment may be used for some stanzas, as written or one octave lower.

The King of heav'n, the glo - rious King,
The faith - ful wom - en went their way
Who sat, and spoke un - to the three,
A - midst them came their Lord most dear,
How they had seen the ris - en Lord,

D.C.

O'er death to - day rose tri - umph - ing. Al - le - lu - ia!
To seek the tomb where Je - sus lay. Al - le - lu - ia!
"Your Lord has gone to Gal - i - lee." Al - le - lu - ia!
And said, "My peace be on all here." Al - le - lu - ia!
He doubt - ed the dis - ci - ples' word. Al - le - lu - ia!

D.C.

D.C.

6. "My wounded side, O Thomas, see:
Behold my hands, my feet," said he,
"Not faithless, but believing be." Alleluia!

7. No longer Thomas then denied,
He saw the feet, the hands, the side;
"You are my Lord and God," he cried. Alleluia!

8. How blest are they who have not seen,
And yet whose faith has constant been,
For they eternal life shall win. Alleluia!

9. On this most holy day of days,
To God your hearts and voices raise,
In laud, and jubilee and praise. Alleluia!

Text: *O filii et filiae;* Jean Tisserand, d.1494; Tr. by John M. Neale, 1818-1866, alt.
Tune: O FILII ET FILIAE, 888 with alleluias; Mode II; Acc. by Richard Proulx, b.1937. © 1975, GIA Publications, Inc.

61 Christ Has Arisen

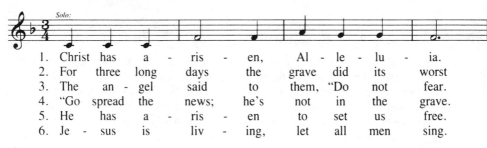

Solo:

1. Christ has a - ris - en, Al - le - lu - ia.
2. For three long days the grave did its worst
3. The an - gel said to them, "Do not fear.
4. "Go spread the news; he's not in the grave.
5. He has a - ris - en to set us free.
6. Je - sus is liv - ing, let all men sing.

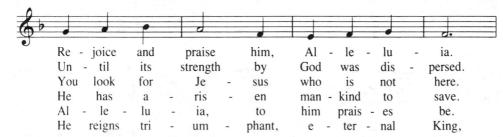

Re - joice and praise him, Al - le - lu - ia.
Un - til its strength by God was dis - persed.
You look for Je - sus who is not here.
He has a - ris - en man - kind to save.
Al - le - lu - ia, to him prais - es be.
He reigns tri - um - phant, e - ter - nal King,

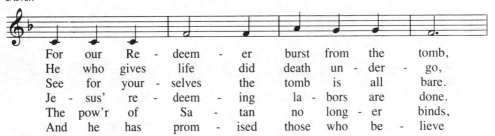

For our Re - deem - er burst from the tomb,
He who gives life did death un - der - go,
See for your - selves the tomb is all bare.
Je - sus' re - deem - ing la - bors are done.
The pow'r of Sa - tan no long - er binds,
And he has prom - ised those who be - lieve

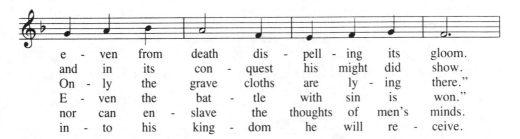

e - ven from death dis - pell - ing its gloom.
and in its con - quest his might did show.
On - ly the grave cloths are ly - ing there."
E - ven the bat - tle with sin is won."
nor can en - slave the thoughts of men's minds.
in - to his king - dom he will re - ceive.

Refrain

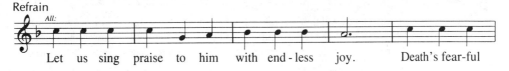

All:

Let us sing praise to him with end - less joy. Death's fear - ful

sting he has come to de - stroy, our sins for - giv - ing,

Al - le - lu - ia. Je - sus is liv - ing, Al - le - lu - ia.

Text: Swahili Text; Tr. by Howard S. Olson
Tune: Haya Tune; *Tumshangilie Mungu*, Makumira, Tanzania
© 1977, Augsburg Publishing House

62 Jesus Has Conquered Death

Refrain

Je-sus, Je-sus, he has con-quered death. Je-sus, Je-sus, he has con-quered death. He has done the Fa-ther's will com-plete-ly. He has con-quered death.

1. O broth-ers, let us fol-low him; he has con-quered death. O sis-ters, let us fol-low him; he has con-quered death. All peo-ple, let us fol-low him; he has con-quered death. Je-sus, Je-sus, you have con-quered death. Je-sus, Je-sus, you have con-quered death. Through your tri-umph you have freed your peo-ple, Sav-ior of us all.

2. Re-veal your-self to all man-kind, Sav-ior, Christ our Lord. Sal-va-tion grant us by your grace, Sav-ior, Christ our Lord. We trust and fol-low you a-lone, Sav-ior, Christ our Lord. Je-sus, Je-sus, you have con-quered death. Je-sus, Je-sus, you have con-quered death. We shall all be res-ur-rect-ed by you at the end of time.

3. Your com-ing we a-wait with joy, Je-sus, Lord and King. Your glo-ry may we all be-hold, Je-sus, Lord and King. Then we shall praise you cease-less-ly, Je-sus, Lord and King. Je-sus, Je-sus, he has con-quered death. Je-sus, Je-sus, he has con-quered death. He has done the Fa-ther's will com-plete-ly. He has con-quered death.

Text: Swahili Text; Tr. by Howard S. Olson
Tune: Nyaturu Tune; *Tumshangilie Mungu*, Makumira, Tanzania
© 1977, Augsburg Publishing House

I Know That My Redeemer Lives 63

1. I know that my Re - deem - er lives;
2. He lives, to bless me with his love;
3. He lives, and grants me dai - ly breath;
4. He lives, all glo - ry to his name;

What joy the blest as - sur - ance gives!
He lives, to plead for me a - bove;
He lives, and I shall con - quer death;
He lives, my Sav - ior, still the same;

He lives, he lives, who once was dead;
He lives, my hun - gry soul to feed;
He lives, my man - sion to pre - pare;
What joy the blest as - sur - ance gives;

He lives, my ev - er - last - ing Head!
He lives, to help in time of need.
He lives, to bring me safe - ly there.
I know that my Re - deem - er lives!

Text: Samuel Medley, 1738-1799
Tune: DUKE STREET, LM; John Hatton, c.1710-1793

64 The Strife Is O'er

Alle-lu - ia! Alle-lu - ia! Alle-lu - ia!

1. The strife is o'er the bat - tle done; Now is the Vic - tor's tri - umph won; Now be the song of praise be - gun: Alle-lu - ia!

2. Death's might - iest pow'rs have done their worst, And Je - sus has his foes dis - persed; Let shouts of praise and joy out - burst: Alle-lu - ia!

3. He closed the yawn - ing gates of hell; The bars from heav'n's high por - tals fell; Let hymns of praise his tri - umph tell: Alle-lu - ia!

4. On the third morn he rose a - gain Glo-rious in maj - es - ty to reign; O let us swell the joy - ful strain: Alle-lu - ia!

Text: *Finita iam sunt praelia;* Latin, 12th C.; Tr. by Francis Pott; 1832-1909, alt.
Tune: VICTORY, 888 with alleluias; Giovanni da Palestrina, 1525-1594; Adapt. by William H. Monk, 1823-1889

Christ Has Risen from the Dead 65

1. Christ has ris - en from the dead,
2. Sin - ners sing and dance for joy,
3. An - gels sing - ing, trum - pets sound, Al - le - lu - ia,
4. Lord of heav - en, glo - rious King,
5. Glo - ry be to God on high,
6. Fath - er, Son and Ho - ly Ghost,

al - le - lu.   Al - le - lu - ia, al - le - lu.

Al - le - lu - ia, al - le - lu.   He has done just
Pas - chal Lamb to
Prais - es be all

as he said,
thee we sing,   Al - le - lu - ia, al - le - lu.
Three in One,

Text: Anthony E. Jackson
Tune: Anthony E. Jackson
© 1983, Anthony E. Jackson

66 Go

1. Go ye there-fore and teach all na - tions,
2. If you love me, real - ly love me,

go, go, go.
feed my sheep.

Go ye there-fore and teach all na - tions,
If you love me, real - ly love me,

* with Pedal

67 Alleluia! Sing to Jesus

1. Al - le - lu - ia! sing to Je - sus! His the
2. Al - le - lu - ia! not as or - phans Are we
3. Al - le - lu - ia! Bread of An - gels, Here on
4. Al - le - lu - ia! King e - ter - nal, You the

scep - ter, his the throne; Al - le - lu - ia!
left in sor - row now; Al - le - lu - ia!
earth our food, our stay! Al - le - lu - ia!
Lord of lords we own; Al - le - lu - ia!

his the tri - umph, His the vic - to - ry a - lone;
he is near us, Faith be - lieves, nor ques - tions how:
here the sin - ful Flee to you from day to day:
born of Ma - ry, Earth your foot stool, heav'n your throne:

Hark! the songs of peace - ful Zi - on Thun - der
Though the cloud from sight re - ceived him, When the
In - ter - ces - sor, friend of sin - ners, Earth's re -
You, with - in the veil, have en - tered, Robed in

like   a   might - y   flood;   Je - sus   out   of
for - ty   days   were   o'er,   Shall   our   hearts for-
deem - er,   plead   for   me,   Where   the   songs   of
flesh,   our   great   high   priest;   Here   on   earth   both

ev - 'ry   na - tion   Has   re - deemed us   by   his   blood.
get   his   prom - ise,   "I   am   with   you   ev - er - more"?
all   the   sin - less   Sweep   a - cross   the   crys - tal   sea.
priest   and   vic - tim   In   the   eu - cha - ris - tic   feast.

Text: Rev. 5:9; William C. Dix, 1837-1898
Tune: HYFRYDOL, 8 7 8 7 D; Rowland H. Prichard, 1811-1887

68 Crown Him with Many Crowns

1. Crown him with man-y crowns, The Lamb up-on his throne;
2. Crown him the Lord of life, Who tri-umphed o'er the grave,
3. Crown him the Lord of love, Be-hold his hands and side,
4. Crown him the Lord of peace, Whose power a scep-ter sways
5. Crown him the Lord of years, The ris-en Lord sub-lime,

Hark! how the heaven-ly an-them drowns All mu-sic but its own.
And rose vic-to-rious in the strife For those he came to save.
Rich wounds yet vis-i-ble a-bove In beau-ty glo-ri-fied.
From pole to pole, that wars may cease, Ab-sorbed in prayer and praise.
Cre-a-tor of the roll-ing spheres, The Mas-ter of all time.

A-wake, my soul, and sing Of him who set us free,
His glo-ries now we sing, Who died and rose on high,
No an-gel in the sky Can full-y bear that sight,
His reign shall know no end, And round his pierc-ed feet
All hail, Re-deem-er, hail! For you have died for me;

And hail him as your heav'n-ly King Through all e-ter-ni-ty.
Who died, e-ter-nal life to bring, And lives that death may die.
But down-ward bends his burn-ing eye At mys-ter-ies so bright.
Fair flowers of Par-a-dise ex-tend Their fra-grance ev-er sweet.
Your praise and glo-ry shall not fail Through-out e-ter-ni-ty.

Text: Rev. 19:12; St. 1, 3-5, Matthew Bridges, 1800-1894; St. 2, Godfrey Thring, 1823-1903
Tune: DIADEMATA, SMD.; George J. Elvey, 1816-1893

Come, Holy Ghost 69

1. Come, Ho - ly Ghost, Cre - a - tor blest, And in our
2. O Com - fort - er, to thee we cry, Thou heav'n - ly
3. O Ho - ly Ghost, Through thee a - lone, Know we the
4. Praise we the Lord, Fa - ther and Son, And Ho - ly

hearts take up thy rest; Come with thy grace
gift of God most high; Thou fount of life,
Fa - ther and the Son; Be this our firm
Spir - it with them one; And may the Son

and heav'n - ly aid To fill the hearts which thou hast
and fire of love, And sweet a - noint - ing from a-
un - chang - ing creed, That thou dost from them both pro-
on us be - stow All gifts that from the Spir - it

made, To fill the hearts which thou hast made.
bove, And sweet a - noint - ing from a - bove.
ceed, That thou dost from them both pro - ceed.
flow, All gifts that from the Spir - it flow.

Text: *Veni, Creator Spiritus;* Attr. to Rabanus Maurus, 776-856; Tr. by Edward Caswall, 1814-1878, alt.
Tune: LAMBILLOTTE, LM; with repeat; Louis Lambillotte, SJ, 1796-1855; Harm. by Richard Proulx, b.1937. © 1986, GIA Publications, Inc.

70 Veni Creator Spiritus

1. Ve - ni Cre - á - tor Spí - ri - tus,
2. Qui dí - ce - ris Pa - rá - cli - tus,
3. Tu se - pti - fór - mis mú - ne - re,
4. Ac - cén - de lu - men sén - si - bus,
5. Hó - stem re - pél - las lón - gi - us,
6. Per te sci - á - mus da Pa - trem,
7. De - o Pa - tri sit gló - ri - a,

Men - tes tu - ó - rum ví - si - ta:
Al - tís - si - mi dó - num De - i,
Di - gi - tus pa - tér - nae déx - te - rae,
In - fun - de a - mó - rem cór - di - bus,
Pa - cém - que do - nes pró - ti - nus:
No - scá - mus at - que Fí - li - um
Et Fí - li - o, qui a mór - tu - is

*This alternate accompaniment may be used for some stanzas, as written or one octave lower.

Im - ple - su - pér - na - grá - ti - a
Fons vi - vus, i - gnis, cá - ri - tas,
Tu ri - te pro - mís - sum Pa - tris,
In - fír - ma no - stri cór - po - ris
Du - ctó - re sic te práe - vi - o,
Te - que u - tri - ús - que Spí - ri - tum
Sur - ré - xit, ac Pa - rá - cli - to,

Quae tu cre - á - sti pé - cto - ra.
Et spi - ri - tá - lis ún - cti - o.
Ser - mó - ne di - tans gút - tu - ra.
Vir - tú - te fír - mans pér - pe - ti.
Vi - té - mus oṁ - ne nó - xi - um.
Cre - dá - mus om - ni tém - po - re.
In sae - cu - ló - rum sáe - cu - la. A - men.

Text: Attr. to Rabanus Maurus, 776-856
Tune: VENI CREATOR SPIRITUS, LM; Mode VIII; Acc. by Richard Proulx, b.1937, © 1975, GIA Publications, Inc.

71 Let It Breathe on Me

Slow with feeling

Let it breathe on me, Let it breathe on me, Let the

breath of the Lord, now, breathe on me,

Let it breathe on me, Let it breathe on me,

Let the breath of the Lord, now, breathe on me.

Verses

1. While I'm work - ing Lord in your vine - yard here,
2. When the path - way Lord, I can not see,

I can do naught if Thou aren't near,
When the way is dark, Lord, breathe on me,

Oh, come, bless-ed Lord, just so close to me
Give me grace to know when Thou art near

That I may feel you breathe on me.
Oh, I pray Thee, Lord, please breathe on me.

Text: Magnolia Lewis-Butts
Tune: Magnolia Lewis-Butts; Harm. by W. O. Hoyle
© 1941, Bowles Music House

72 Blessed Quietness

1. Joys are flow - ing like a riv - er Since the
2. Bring-ing life and health and glad - ness All a-
3. Like the rain that falls from heav - en, Like the
4. See, a fruit - ful field is grow - ing, Bless - ed
5. What a won - der - ful sal - va - tion, Where we

Com - fort - er has come; He a - bides with us for-
round, this heav'n - ly Guest Ban-ished un - be - lief and
sun - light from the sky, So the Ho - ly Ghost is
fruit of right-eous - ness; And the streams of life are
al - ways see His face! What a per - fect hab - i-

ev - er, Makes the trust - ing heart His home.
sad - ness, Chang'd our wea - ri - ness to rest.
giv - en, Com - ing on us from on high.
flow - ing In the lone - ly wil - der - ness.
ta - tion, What a qui - et rest - ing place!

Chorus

Bless-ed qui - et - ness, ho - ly qui - et - ness— What as-
sur - ance in my soul! On the storm - y sea He speaks
peace to me— How the bil - lows cease to roll!

Text: Manie P. Ferguson
Tune: W. S. Marshall; Adapt. by James M. Kirk

73 Holy Spirit, Flow through Me

1. Ho - ly Spir - it, flow through me,
2. Ho - ly Spir - it, rest on me,
3. Ho - ly Spir - it, flow out from me,

Ho - ly Spir - it, flow through me, And
Ho - ly Spir - it, rest on me, And
Ho - ly Spir - it, flow out through me, That

make my life what it ought to be,
use me, Lord, win the lost to Thee,
oth - ers, Lord, may see You in me,

Ho - ly Spir - it, flow through me.
Ho - ly Spir - it, rest on me.
Ho - ly Spir - it, flow out through me.

Text: Walt Mills
Tune: Walt Mills

Spirit of God, Descend upon My Heart 74

1. Spir - it of God, de - scend up - on my heart;
2. I ask no dream, no proph - et ec - sta - sies,
3. Teach me to feel that thou art al - ways nigh;
4. Teach me to love thee as thine an - gels love,

Draw it from earth; through all its puls - es move;
No sud - den rend - ing of the veil of clay,
Teach me the strug - gles of the soul to bear,
One ho - ly pas - sion fill - ing all my frame;

Stoop to my weak - ness, might - y as thou art,
No an - gel vis - i - tant, no o - p'ning skies;
To check the ris - ing doubt, the reb - el sigh;
The kin - dling of the heav'n - de - scend - ed Dove,

And make me love thee as I ought to love.
But take the dim - ness of my soul a - way.
Teach me the pa - tience of un - an - swered prayer.
My heart an al - tar, and thy love the flame. A - men.

Text: George Croly, 1780-1860
Tune: MORECAMBE; Frederick C. Atkinson, 1841-1897

75 Sweet, Sweet Spirit

1. There's a sweet, sweet Spir - it in this place,
2. (There are) bless - ings you can - not re - ceive
3. (If you) say He saved you from your sin,

and I know that it's the Spir - it of the
till you know Him in His full - ness, and be-
now you're weak, you're bound, and can - not en - ter

Lord. There are sweet ex-press-ions on each
lieve. You're the one to pro-fit when you
in, you can make it right if you will

face, and I know they feel the
say, "I am going to walk with
yield; you'll en-joy the Ho-ly

pres - ence of the Lord.
Je - sus all the way."
Spir - it that we feel.

Sweet Ho-ly Spir-it, Sweet Heav-en-ly Dove, stay right here with us, fill-ing us with your love. And for these bless-ings we lift our hearts in praise; with-out a

doubt we'll know that we have been re - vived when

we shall leave this place. 2. There are
3. If you place.

rit.

Ped.

Text. Doris Akers, b.1922
Tune: Doris Akers, b.1922

76 Come, Now Almighty King

1. Come, now al - might - y King, Help us your
2. Come, now In - car - nate Son, Your life in
3. Come, ho - ly Com - fort - er, Your sa - cred
4. To the great One in Three E - ter - nal

name to sing, Help us to praise.
us be - gun, Our prayer at - tend.
wit - ness bear In this glad hour.
prais - es be For ev - er - more!

Fa - ther all glo - ri - ous, Ev - er vic - to - ri - ous,
Come and your peo - ple bless And give your Word suc-cess;
Your grace to us im - part, Now rule in ev - 'ry heart
Your sov - 'reign maj - es - ty May we in glo - ry see

Come and reign o - ver us, An - cient of Days.
Strength-en your right - eous-ness, Sav - ior and Friend!
Nev - er from us de - part, Spir - it of Pow'r!
And to e - ter - ni - ty Love and a - dore!

Text: Anon. c.1757
Tune: ITALIAN HYMN, 66 4 666 4; Felice de Giardini, 1716-1796

God the Father, Son and Spirit 77

1. God the Fa - ther, God the Son, and God the Spir - it,
2. God our Fa - ther, this whole world you have cre - a - ted,
3. God the Son, in whom a - lone we have sal - va - tion,
4. God the Spir - it, from whose pres - ence none can sev - er,

We ex - tol you and de - light to sing your prais - es.
heav'n and earth your might and love are man - i - fest - ing.
in the form of man you gave man - kind new mean - ing.
lead us in - to truth, en - light - en our be - hav - ior.

In your word you are re - vealed and thus we hear it
Birds and beasts, all liv - ing things to you re - lat - ed,
On the cross you bore the guilt of ev - 'ry na - tion,
You have prom - ised to re - main our guide for - ev - er,

com - ing to us with a grace that e'er a - maz - es.
e - ven sun and moon and stars your pow'r at - test - ing.
free - ing us from ev - 'ry - thing that is de - mean - ing.
make us bold to wit - ness to our Lord and Sav - ior.

Solo: All:
This lov - ing God wants us all to be his child - ren,

Solo: All:
blots out our sin, and de - clares we are for - giv - en.

Text: Swahili Text; Tr. by Howard S. Olson
Tune: Haya Tune; *Tumshangilie Mungu*, Makumira, Tanzania
© 1977, Augsburg Publishing House

78 Holy, Holy, Holy! Lord God Almighty

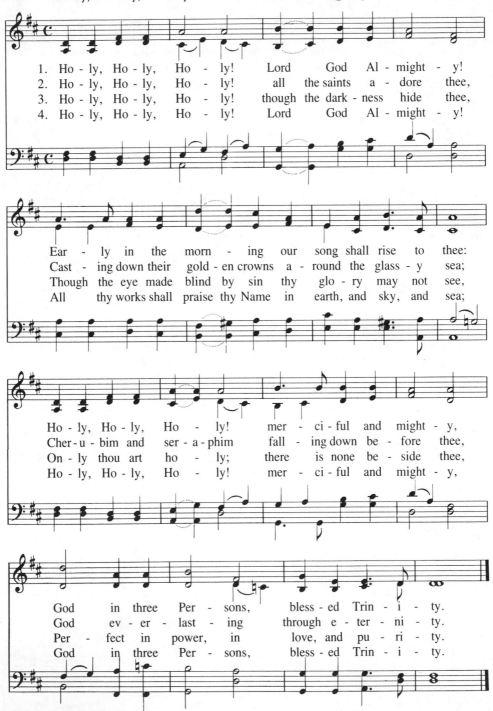

1. Ho - ly, Ho - ly, Ho - ly! Lord God Al - might - y!
2. Ho - ly, Ho - ly, Ho - ly! all the saints a - dore thee,
3. Ho - ly, Ho - ly, Ho - ly! though the dark - ness hide thee,
4. Ho - ly, Ho - ly, Ho - ly! Lord God Al - might - y!

Ear - ly in the morn - ing our song shall rise to thee:
Cast - ing down their gold - en crowns a - round the glass - y sea;
Though the eye made blind by sin thy glo - ry may not see,
All thy works shall praise thy Name in earth, and sky, and sea;

Ho - ly, Ho - ly, Ho - ly! mer - ci - ful and might - y,
Cher - u - bim and ser - a - phim fall - ing down be - fore thee,
On - ly thou art ho - ly; there is none be - side thee,
Ho - ly, Ho - ly, Ho - ly! mer - ci - ful and might - y,

God in three Per - sons, bless - ed Trin - i - ty.
God ev - er - last - ing through e - ter - ni - ty.
Per - fect in power, in love, and pu - ri - ty.
God in three Per - sons, bless - ed Trin - i - ty.

Text: Reginald Heber, 1783-1826, alt.
Tune: NICAEA, 11 12 12 10; John B. Dykes, 1823-1876

O God, Almighty Father   79

1. O God, al-might-y Fa-ther, Cre-a-tor of all things, The
2. O Je-sus, Word in-car-nate, Re-deem-er most a-dored, All
3. O God, the Ho-ly Spir-it, Who lives with-in our soul, Send

heav-ens stand in won-der, While earth your glo-ry sings.
glo-ry, praise, and hon-or Be yours, O sov-'reign Lord.
forth your light and lead us To our e-ter-nal goal.

O most ho-ly Trin-i-ty, Un-di-vid-ed u-ni-ty,

Ho-ly God, might-y God, God im-mor-tal be a-dored!

Text: *Gott Vater sei gepriesen;* Anon; Tr. by Irvin Udulutsch, OFM Cap., fl.1959, alt. © 1959, The Liturgical Press
Tune: GOTT VATER SEI GEPRIESEN, 76 76 with refrain; *Limburg Gesangbuch,* 1838; Harm. by Healey Willan, 1880-1968. © 1958, Ralph Jusko Publications, Inc.

80 This Is My Body

This is my bod - y giv-en up for you, this is my blood poured out for you. This is my bod - y giv-en up for you, this is my blood poured out for you.

from *Mary, Cause Of Our Joy*
Music by Edward V. Bonnenère
Copyright © 1985, 1987 Amity Music Corporation

81 O Saving Victim/O Salutaris

1. O Sav-ing Vic-tim, o-p'ning wide The gate of
2. To your great name be end-less praise, Im-mor-tal
1. O sa-lu-tá-ris hó-sti-a, Quae cae-li
2. U-ni tri-nó-que Dó-mi-no Sit sem-pi-

heav'n to us be-low! Our foes press on from
God-head, One in Three; O grant us end-less
pan-dis ó-sti-um: Bel-la pre-munt ho-
tér-na gló-ri-a: Qui vi tam si-ne

ev-'ry side: Your aid sup-ply, your strength be-stow.
length of days When our true na-tive land we see.
stí-li-a, Da ro-bur fer au-xí-li-um.
tér-mi-no No-bis do-net in pá-tri-a.

Text: Thomas Aquinas, 1227-1275; Tr. by Edward Caswall, 1814-1878, alt.
Tune: DUGUET, LM; Dieu donne Duguet, d.1767

Come Adore/Tantum Ergo 82

1. Come a-dore this won-drous pres-ence, Bow to Christ the
2. Glo-ry be to God the Fa-ther, Praise to his co-
1. Tan-tum er-go Sa-cra-mén-tum Ve-ne-ré-mur
2. Ge-ni-tó-ri, Ge-ni-tó-que Laus et ju-bi-

source of grace. Here is kept the an-cient prom-ise
e-qual Son, Ad-o-ra-tion to the Spir-it,
cér-nu-i: Et an-tí-quum do-cu-mén-tum
lá-ti-o, Sa-lus, ho-nor, vir-tus quo-que

Of God's earth-ly dwell-ing-place. Sight is blind be-
Bond of love, in God-head one. Blest be God by
No-vo ce-dat rí-tu-i: Prae-stet fi-des
Sit et be-ne-dí-cti-o: Pro-ce-dén-ti

fore God's glo-ry, Faith a-lone may see his face.
all cre-a-tion Joy-ous-ly while a-ges run.
sup-ple-mén-tum Sén-su-um de-fé-ctu-i.
ab u-tró-que Com-par sit lau-dá-ti-o.

Text: Thomas Aquinas, 1227-1274; Tr. by James Quinn, SJ, b.1919
Tune: ST. THOMAS, 8 7 8 7 8 7; John F. Wade, 1711-1786
Trans: © 1969, James Quinn, SJ. By permission of Geoffrey Chapman, a division of Cassell Ltd.

83 Let All the People Praise Thee

1. O mag - ni - fy the Lord with me, Ye peo - ple of His choice,
2. O praise Him for His ho - li - ness, His wis - dom and his grace;
3. Had I a thou-sand tongues to sing, The half could n'er be told

Let all to whom He lend - eth breath Now in His name re - joice;
Sing prais - es for the pre - cious blood Which ran - somed all our race;
Of love so rich, so full and free, Of bless-ings man - i - fold;

For love's blest rev - e - la - tion, For rest from con-dem - na - tion,
In ten - der - ness He sought us, From depths of Sin He brought us,
Of grace that fail - eth nev - er, Peace flow - ing like a riv - er,

For ut - ter - most sal - va - tion To Him give thanks.
The way of life then taught us, To Him give thanks.
From God the glo - rious Giv - er, To Him give thanks.
To Him give thanks.

BODY AND BLOOD OF CHRIST

Chorus

Let all (let all) the peo-ple praise Thee, Let all (let all) the peo-ple praise Thee! Let all (let all) the peo-ple praise Thy name For-ev-er and for-ev-er-more, for-ev-er-more, O Lord! Let more. A-men.

Text: Mrs. C. H. Morris
Tune: Mrs. C. H. Morris

84 I Know Jesus

With a steady beat

Chorus: I know Je - sus, He's my guid - ing light. I know
1. I need Je - sus, each and ev - 'ry day. I need
2. Share with oth - ers as you share with Him, Let Him
3. I found Je - sus in my broth - er's eye, I found

Je - sus, He's the light that shines. I know
Je - sus to show me the way. I need
en - ter your heart with - in. Share with
Je - sus in my sis - ter's eye. I found

Je - sus, He's my guid - ing light, let it
Je - sus, each and ev' - ry day, I need
oth - ers as you share with Him, Share with
Je - sus, he is by my side, I found

shine, let it shine, let it shine.
Je - sus, each and ev' - ry day.
oth - ers as you share with Him.
Je - sus, he is by my side.

Music and Word Adaptation by Edward V. Bonnemère

85   O How I Love Jesus

1. There is a name I love to hear, I love to sing its worth;
2. It tells me of a Sav-ior's love, Who died to set me free;
3. It tells me what my Fa-ther hath In store for ev-'ry day,
4. It tells of One whose lov-ing heart Can feel my deep-est woe,

It sounds like mu-sic in mine ear, The sweet-est name on earth.
It tells me of His pre-cious blood, The sin-ner's per-fect plea.
And tho' I tread a dark-some path, Yields sun-shine all the way.
Who in each sor-row bears a part, That none can bear be-low.

O how I love Je-sus, O how I love Je-sus,

O how I love Je-sus, Be-cause He first loved me!

Text: Frederick Whitfield, 1829-1904
Tune: American Melody

He Is King of Kings   86

He is King of kings, he is Lord of lords.

Je - sus Christ the first and last, no one works like him.

Solo:
1. He built his throne up in the air,
2. He pitched his tents on Ca - naan's ground,

All:
No one works like him.
No one works like him.

Solo:
And called his saints from
And broke the Ro - man

ev - 'ry - where,
king - dom down,

All:
No one works like him.
No one works like him.

D.C.

Text: Afro-American Spiritual; Ed. by John W. Work, III, 1901-1967
Tune: HE IS KING, Irregular; Afro-American Spiritual; Ed. by John W. Work, III, 1901-1967

87 His Name Is Wonderful

1. His name is Won-der-ful, His name is Won-der-ful,
2. He is the might-y King, Mas-ter of ev-'ry-thing,

His name is Won-der-ful, Je - sus, my Lord;

Je - sus, my Lord. He's the great Shep-herd, the Rock of all

a - ges, Al-might-y God is He;

Bow down be - fore Him, Love and a - dore Him,

His name is Won-der-ful, Je-sus my Lord.

Text: Audrey Mieir, b.1916
Tune: Audrey Mieir, b.1916
© Copyright 1919 by Manna Music, Inc. 25510 Ave. Stanford, Valencia, CA 91355. International Copyright Secured. All Rights Reserved. Used by Permission.

All Hail the Power of Jesus' Name 88

1. All hail the power of Je-sus' name! Let an-gels pros-trate fall;
2. Crown him, ye mar-tyrs of our God, Who from his al-tar call;
3. Ye cho-sen seed of Is-rael's race, A rem-nant weak and small,
4. O that, with yon-der sa-cred throng, We at his feet may fall,

Bring forth the roy-al di-a-dem And crown him Lord of all;
Ex-tol the stem of Jes-se's rod, And crown him Lord of all;
Hail him who saved you by his grace, And crown him Lord of all;
Join in the ev-er-last-ing song, And crown him Lord of all;

Bring forth the roy-al di-a-dem And crown him Lord of all.
Ex-tol the stem of Jes-se's rod, And crown him Lord of all.
Hail him who saved you by his grace, And crown him Lord of all.
Join in the ev-er-last-ing song, And crown him Lord of all.

Text: Edward Perronet, 1726-1792; Alt. by John Rippon, 1751-1836, alt.
Tune: CORONATION, CM with repeat; Oliver Holden, 1765-1844

89　All Hail the Power

1. All hail the pow'r of Je - sus' name!
2. Ye cho - sen seed of Is - rael's race,
3. Let ev - 'ry kin - dred, ev - 'ry tribe,
4. Oh, that with yon - der sa - cred throng

Let an - gels pros - trate fall, Let an - gels pros - trate
Ye ran - somed from the Fall, Ye ran - somed from the
On this ter - res - trial ball, On this ter - res - trial
We at His feet may fall, We at His feet may

fall. Bring forth the roy - al di - a - dem,
Fall, Hail Him who saves you by His grace,
ball, To Him all maj - es - ty as - cribe,
fall! We'll join the ev - er - last - ing song,

Text: Edward Perronet, 1726-1792
Tune: DIADEM; James Ellor, 1819-1899

90 Hallelujah Song

2. Hallelujah! Hallelujah!
   He is King, he is King.
   Hallelujah, Jesus is King!
   (repeat)

   Hallelujah, Jesus is King!

Text: Frank Hernandez
Tune: Frank Hernandez; Harm. by Betty Pulkingham, b. 1929

91 Jesus Is Our King

Al - le - lu - ia! Al - le - lu - ia! O - pen - ing our

hearts to him, Sing - ing al - le - lu - ia!

Al - le - lu - ia! Je - sus is our King!

Cre - ate in us, O God, A
We bear the name of Christ.
Let kin - dred voic - es join,
Pour out your Spir - it on us, Em-

hum - ble heart that sets us free To pro - claim the won-drous
Jus - ti - fied, we meet with him. His words and pres - ence
Hon - or - ing the Lamb of God Who teach - es us by
power - ing us to live as one, To car - ry your re-

maj - es - ty Of our Fa - ther in heav - en.
calm our fear, Re - veal - ing God, our Fa - ther, here.
bread and wine The mys - tery of his bod - y.
deem - ing love To a world en - slaved by sin.

Text: Sherrell Prebble and Howard Clark
Tune: POST GREEN; Sherrell Prebble
© 1978, Celebration/Admin. by Marantha Music

92 To Jesus Christ, Our Sovereign King

1. To Jesus Christ, our sov - 'reign King, Who
2. Your reign ex - tend, O King be - nign, To
3. To you, and to your church, great King, We

is the world's sal - va - tion, All praise and hom -age
ev - 'ry land and na - tion; For in your King-dom,
pledge our heart's ob - la - tion; Un - til be - fore your

do we bring And thanks and ad - o - ra - tion.
Lord di - vine, A - lone we find sal - va - tion.
throne we sing In end - less ju - bi - la - tion.

Christ Je - sus, Vic - tor! Christ Je - sus, Ru - ler!

Christ Je - sus, Lord and Re - deem - er!

Text: Martin B. Hellrigel, 1891-1981, alt., © 1941, Irene C. Mueller
Tune: ICH GLAUB AN GOTT, 8 7 8 7 with refrain; *Mainz Gesangbuch*, 1870; Harm. by Richard Proulx, b.1937, © 1986, GIA Publications, Inc.

93   Rejoice, the Lord Is King

1. Re - joice, the Lord is King! Your Lord and King a-
2. The Lord, our Sav - ior, reigns, The God of truth and
3. His king - dom can - not fail, He rules o'er earth and
4. Re - joice in glo - rious hope! Our Lord the judge shall

dore! Re - joice, give thanks, and sing, And tri - umph
love; When he had purged our sins, He took his
heav'n; The keys of death and hell Are to our
come And take his ser - vants up To their e-

ev - er - more: Lift up your heart, lift
seat a - bove:
Je - sus giv'n:
ter - nal home:

up your voice! Re - joice, a - gain I say, re - joice!

Text: Charles Wesley, 1707-1788
Tune: DARWALL'S 148TH, 6 6 6 6 88; John Darwall, 1731-1789; Harm. from *The Hymnal 1940*

Rejoice, O Pure in Heart 94

1. Re - joice, O pure in heart, Re - joice, give thanks and sing; Your fes - tal ban - ner wave on high, The cross of Christ your King.
2. Bright youth and snow-crowned age, All those for truth do seek; Raise high your free, ex - ult - ing song, God's won - drous prais - es speak.
3. With all the an - gel choirs, With all the saints on earth, Pour out the strains of joy and bliss, True rap - ture, no - blest mirth.
4. Yes, on thro' life's long path, Still chant - ing as ye go; From youth to age, by night and day, In glad - ness and in woe.
5. Then on, O pure in heart, Re - joice, give thanks and sing; Your glo - rious ban - ner wave on high, The cross of Christ your King.

Re - joice, re - joice, Re - joice, give thanks and sing.

Text: Edward H. Plumptre, 1821-1891
Tune: Arthur H. Messiter, 1834-1916

95 Ave Maria

A - ve Ma - rí - a, grá - ti - a ple - na,

Dó - mi - nus te - cum, be - ne - dí - cta tu in mu - li - é -

ri - bus, et be - ne - dí - ctus fru - ctus ven - tris tu-

i, Je - sus. San-cta Ma - rí - a, Ma-ter De - i,

o - ra pro no - bis pec - ca - tó - ri - bus,

nunc et in ho - ra mor - tis no - strae. A - men.

Text: Lk. 1:29; Latin, 13th C.
Tune: AVE MARIA, Irregular; Mode I; Acc. by Robert LeBlanc, b.1948, © 1986, GIA Publications, Inc.

96 Hail, Queen of Heaven/Salve, Regina

Hail, Queen of Heav - en, hail, our Moth - er com - pas - sion - ate,
Sal - ve, Re - gí - na, ma - ter mi - se - ri - cór - di - ae:

True life and com - fort and our hope, we greet you!
Vi - ta, dul - cé - do et spes no - stra sal - ve.

To you we ex - iles, chil - dren of Eve, raise our voic - es.
Ad te cla - má - mus, éx - su - les fí - li - i He - vae.

love and ten - der - ness, so full of pit - y.
cór - des ó - cu - los ad nos con - vér - te.

And grant us af - ter these, our days of lone - ly
Et Je - sum, be - ne - dí - ctum fru - ctum ven - tris

ex - ile, the sight of your blest Son and Lord, Christ
tu - i, no - bis post hoc ex - sí - li - um o-

Je - sus. O gen - tle, O lov - ing,
stén - de. O cle - mens, O pi - a,

O ho - ly sweet Vir - gin Ma - ry.
O dul - cis Vir - go Ma - rí - a.

Text: Latin, c.1080; Tr. by John C. Selner, SS, b.1904. © 1954, GIA Publications, Inc.
Tune: SALVE REGINA, Irregular; Mode V; Acc. by Gerard Farrell, OSB, b.1919. © 1986, GIA Publications, Inc.

97 Hail, Holy Queen Enthroned Above

1. Hail, ho - ly Queen en - throned a - bove, O Ma-
2. The cause of joy to all be - low, O Ma-
3. O gen - tle, lov - ing, ho - ly one, O Ma-

ri - a. Hail, Queen of mer - cy and of love,
ri - a. The spring through which all grac - es flow,
ri - a. The God of light be - came your Son,

O Ma - ri - a. Tri - umph, all ye Cher - u - bim,
O Ma - ri - a. An - gels, all your prais - es bring,
O Ma - ri - a. Tri - umph, all ye Cher - u - bim,

Sing with us, ye Ser - a - phim, Heav'n and earth re - sound the
Earth and heav - en, with us sing, All cre - a - tion ech - o-
Sing with us, ye Ser - a - phim, Heav'n and earth re - sound the

hymn: Sal - ve, Sal - ve, Sal - ve, Re - gi - na.
ing: Sal - ve, Sal - ve, Sal - ve, Re - gi - na.
hymn: Sal - ve, Sal - ve, Sal - ve, Re - gi - na.

Text: *Salve, Regina, mater misericordia;* c.1080; Tr. *Roman Hymnal*, 1884; St. 2-3, adapt. by M. Owen Lee, CSB, b.1930
Tune: SALVE REGINA COELITUM, 8 4 8 4 777 4 5; *Choralmelodien zum Heiligen Gesänge*, 1808; Harm. by Healey Willan, 1880-1968, © Willis Music Co.

Salamu Maria 98

1. Sa - la - mu Ma - ri - a, ee ma - ma, Sa - la - mu, sa-
2. *Hail Mar - y, oh moth - er, Hail, hail*
3. U - me - ja - a nee - ma, ee ma - ma.
4. *Full of grace oh moth - er*

la - mu Ma - ri - a, Ma - ri - a; ri - a.
Mar - y, Mar - y, y.

2. Bwana yu nawe: *The Lord is with you*
   umebarikiwa: *blessed are you*

3. Yesu, mzao wako: *Jesus your Son*
   amebarikiwa: *is blessed*

4. U mama wa Mungu: *You are the Mother of God*
   mtakatifu sana: *most holy*

5. Sisi wakosefu: *We are sinners*
   U mwombezi wetu: *You're our intercessor*

6. Utuombee sasa: *Pray for us now*
   na tunapokufa: *and when we die*

Text: African Folk Hymn
Tune: African Melody

99 Immaculate Mary

1. Im - ma - cu - late Mar - y, your prais - es we sing;
2. Pre - des - tined for Christ by e - ter - nal de - cree,
3. To you by an an - gel, the Lord God made known
4. Most blest of all wom - en, you heard and be - lieved,
5. The an - gels re - joiced when you brought forth God's Son;

You reign now in splen - dor with Je - sus our King.
God willed you both vir - gin and moth - er to be.
The grace of the Spir - it, the gift of the Son.
Most blest in the fruit of your womb then con - ceived.
Your joy is the joy of all a - ges to come.

A - ve, A - ve, A - ve, Ma - ri - a.

A - ve, A - ve, Ma - ri - a.

6. Your child is the Savior, all hope lies in him:
He gives us new life and redeems us from sin.

7. In glory for ever now close to your Son,
All ages will praise you for all God has done.

Text: St. 1 Jeremiah Cummings, 1814-1866, alt.; St. 2-7, Brian Foley, b.1919, © 1971, Faber Music Ltd.
Tune: LOURDES HYMN, 11 11 with refrain; Grenoble, 1882

Sing of Mary, Pure and Lowly   100

1. Sing of Mar-y,   pure and low-ly,   Vir-gin-moth-er   un-de-filed,
2. Sing of Je-sus, son of Mar-y,   In the home at   Naz-a-reth.
3. Glo-ry be to God the Fa-ther; Glo-ry be to God the Son;

Sing of God's own Son most ho-ly,   Who be-came her   lit-tle child.
Toil and la-bor can-not wea-ry Love en-dur-ing un-to death.
Glo-ry be to God the Spir-it; Glo-ry to the Three in One.

Fair-est child of fair-est moth-er, God   the Lord who came to earth,
Con-stant was the love he gave her, Though he went forth from her side,
From the heart of bless-ed Mar-y, From all saints the song as-cends,

Word made flesh, our ver-y broth-er, Takes our na-ture by his birth.
Forth to preach, and heal, and suf-fer, Till on Cal-va-ry he died.
And the church the strain re-ech-oes Un-to earth's re-mot-est ends.

Text: Roland F. Palmer, b.1891
Tune: PLEADING SAVIOR, 8 7 8 7 D; *Christian Lyre*, 1830; Harm. by Richard Proulx, b.1937. © 1986, GIA Publications, Inc.

101 O Sanctissima

1. O Sanc - tis - si - ma, O pi - is - si - ma, Dul - cis
2. Tu so - la - ti - um Et re - fu - gi - um, Vir - go

Vir - go Ma - ri - a! Ma - ter a - ma - ta,
Ma - ter Ma - ri - a! Quid - quid o - pta - mus,

In - te - me - ra - ta, O - ra, O - ra pro no - bis.
Per te spe - ra - mus; O - ra, O - ra pro no - bis.

3. Ecce debiles,
   Perquam flebiles,
   Salva nos, Maria!
   Tolle languores,
   Sana dolores,
   Ora, ora pro nobis.

4. Virgo respice,
   Mater, adspice,
   Audi nos, Maria!
   Tu medicinam,
   Portas divinam;
   Ora, ora pro nobis.

Text: St. 1, *Stimmen der Völker in Liedern*, 1807; St. 2, *Arundel Hymnal*, 1902.
Tune: O DU FRÖLICHE, 55 7 55 7; Tattesall's *Improved Psalmody*, 1794; Harm. by Nicola A. Montani, © 1947, St. Gregory Guild, Inc.

How Firm a Foundation 102

1. How firm a foun - da - tion, you saints of the Lord,
2. "Fear not, I am with you, O be not dis - mayed,
3. "When through the deep wa - ters I call you to go,
4. "The soul that on Je - sus still leans for re - pose,

Is laid for your faith in his ex - cel - lent Word!
For I am your God, and will still give you aid;
The riv - ers of woe shall not you o - ver - flow;
I will not, I will not de - sert to its foes;

What more can he say than to you he has said,
I'll strength - en you, help you, and cause you to stand,
For I will be with you, your trou - bles to bless,
That soul, though all hell should en - deav - or to shake,

To you who for ref - uge to Je - sus have fled?
Up - held by my right - eous, om - nip - o - tent hand.
And sanc - ti - fy to you, your deep - est dis - tress.
I'll nev - er, no nev - er, no nev - er for - sake!"

Text: 2 Peter 1:4; "K" in Rippon's *A Selection of Hymns*, 1787
Tune: FOUNDATION, 11 11 11 11; Funk's *Compilation of Genuine Church Music*, 1832; Harm. by Richard Proulx, b.1937, © 1975, GIA Publications, Inc.

103 Shall We Gather at the River

1. Shall we gath - er at the riv - er, Where bright
2. On the mar - gin of the riv - er, Wash - ing
3. Ere we reach the shin - ing riv - er, Lay we
4. Soon we'll reach the shin - ing riv - er, Soon our

an - gel feet have trod; With its crys - tal tide for-
up its sil - ver spray, We will walk and wor - ship
ev - 'ry bur - den down; Grace our spir - its will de-
pil - grim-age will cease, Soon our hap - py hearts will

ev - er Flow-ing by the throne of God?
ev - er, All the hap - py gold - en day.
liv - er, And pro - vide a robe and crown.
quiv - er With the mel - o - dy of peace.

Yes, we'll gath - er at the riv - er, The beau - ti - ful, the

beau-ti-ful riv – er; Gath - er with the saints at the

riv – er That flows by the throne of God.

Text: Robert Lowry, 1826-1899
Tune: Robert Lowry, 1826-1899

104 Ye Watchers and Ye Holy Ones

1. Ye watch-ers and ye ho-ly ones, Bright ser-aphs, cher-u-bim, and thrones, Raise the glad strain, Al-le-lu-ia! Cry out, do-min-
2. O high-er than the cher-u-bim, More glo-rious than the ser-a-phim, Lead their prais-es, Al-le-lu-ia! O bear-er of
3. Re-spond, ye souls in end-less rest, Ye pa-tri-archs and proph-ets blest, Al-le-lu-ia, Al-le-lu-ia! Ye ho-ly Twelve,
4. O friends, in glad-ness let us sing, Su-per-nal an-thems ech-o-ing, Al-le-lu-ia, Al-le-lu-ia! To God the Fa-

ions, prince-doms, powers, Vir - tues, arch - an - gels, an - gels'
the e -ter - nal Word, Most gra - cious, mag - ni - fy the
ye mar - tyrs strong, All saints tri - um-phant, raise in
ther, God the Son, And God the Spir - it, Three in

choirs,
Lord, Al - le - lu - ia, Al - le - lu - ia,
song,
One,

Al - le - lu - ia, Al - le - lu - ia, Al - le - lu - ia!

Text: John A. Riley, 1858-1945, © Oxford University Press
Tune: LASST UNS ERFREUDEN, LM with alleluias; *Geistliche Kirchengesänge*, Cologne, 1623; Harm. by Ralph Vaughan Williams, 1872-1958,
© Oxford University Press

105　For All the Saints

1. For all the saints who from their la-bors rest, All
2. You were their rock, their for-tress and their might;
3. O may your sol - diers, faith-ful, true and bold,
7. But then there breaks a yet more glo-rious day: The
8. From earth's wide bounds, from o-cean's far-thest coast, Through

who by faith be - fore the world con - fessed, Your
You, Lord, their Cap - tain in their well-fought fight;
Fight as the saints who no - bly fought of old, And
saints tri - umph - ant rise in bright ar - ray; The
gates of pearl streams in the count-less host,

name, O Je - sus, be for ev - er blest.
You in the dark - ness drear, their one true light.
win with them, the vic - tor's crown of gold.
King of glo - ry pass - es on his way.
Sing - ing to Fa - ther, Son, and Ho - ly Ghost:

Al - le - lu - ia! Al - le - lu - ia!
Al - le - lu - ia! Al - le - lu - ia!
Al - le - lu - ia! Al - le - lu - ia!
Al. - le - lu - ia! Al - le - lu - ia!
Al - le - lu - ia! Al - le - lu - ia!

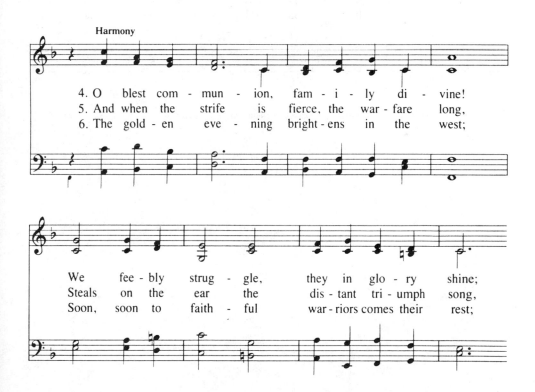

Harmony

4. O blest com - mun - ion, fam - i - ly di - vine!
5. And when the strife is fierce, the war - fare long,
6. The gold - en eve - ning bright - ens in the west;

We fee - bly strug - gle, they in glo - ry shine;
Steals on the ear the dis - tant tri - umph song,
Soon, soon to faith - ful war - riors comes their rest;

Yet all are one with-in your great de - sign.
And hearts are brave a - gain, and arms are strong.
Sweet is the calm of par - a - dise the blest.

Al - le - lu - ia! Al - le - lu - ia!
Al - le - lu - ia! Al - le - lu - ia!
Al - le - lu - ia! Al - le - lu - ia!

Text: William W. How, 1823-1897
Tune: SINE NOMINE, 10 10 10 with alleluias; Ralph Vaughan Williams, 1872-1958, © Oxford University Press

Jesus Loves Me 106

1. Je - sus loves me! this I know, For the Bi - ble tells me so;
2. Je - sus loves me! He who died Heav-en's gates to o - pen wide!
3. Je - sus loves me! loves me still, Tho' I'm ver - y weak and ill;
4. Je - sus loves me! He will stay Close be-side me all the way;

Lit - tle ones to Him be-long, They are weak, but He is strong.
He will wash a - way my sin, Let His lit - tle child come in.
From His shin - ing throne on high, Comes to watch me where I lie.
If I love Him when I die, He will take me home on high.

Yes, Je - sus loves me, Yes, Je - sus loves me,

Yes, Je - sus loves me, the Bi - ble tells me so.

Text: Traditional
Tune: William B. Bradbury, 1816-1868

107 Wade in the Water

Wade in the wa-ter, (chil-dren,) Wade in the
wa-ter, chil-dren, Wade in the wa-ter,

God's a-going to trou-ble the wa-ter. O wa-ter.

1. See that host all dressed in white,
2. See that band all dressed in red,
3. Look o-ver yon-der, what do I see?
4. If you don't be-lieve I've been re-deemed,

God's a-going to trou-ble the wa-ter; The Lead-er looks like the
God's a-going to trou-ble the wa-ter; Looks like the band that
God's a-going to trou-ble the wa-ter; The Ho-ly Ghost a-com-
God's a-going to trou-ble the wa-ter; Just fol-low me down to

(Hum)

D.C.

Is - ra - el - ite,	God's a - going to trou-ble the wa - ter.
Mo - ses led,	God's a - going to trou-ble the wa - ter.
ing on me,	God's a - going to trou-ble the wa - ter.
Jor - dan's stream,	God's a - going to trou-ble the wa - ter.

Text: Afro-American Spiritual
Tune: Afro-American Spiritual; Harm. by Willa A. Townsend

Take Me to the Water 108

1. Take me to the wa - ter, take me to the wa-
2. None but the right - eous, none but the right-
3. I love Je - sus, I love Je-
4. He's my Sav - ior, He's my Sav-

ter, Take me to the wa - ter to be bap - tized.
eous, None but the right - eous shall see God.
sus, I love Je - sus, yes, I do.
ior, He's my Sav - ior, yes, He is.

Text: Afro-American Spiritual
Tune: Afro-American Spiritual

109 Jesus Loves the Little Children

Je - sus loves the lit - tle chil - dren,

All the chil - dren of the world; Red and

yel - low, black and white, They are pre - cious in His sight; Je - sus

loves the lit - tle chil - dren of the world.

Text: Anonymous
Tune: George F. Root, 1820-1895

I've Just Come from the Fountain 110

Text: Afro-American Spiritual
Tune: Afro-American Spiritual

111 Sign Me Up

Sign me up for the Chris-tian ju - bi - lee,

Sign me up for the Chris-tian ju - bi - lee,

Write my name on heav-en's

Write my name on the roll.

roll, For I've been changed since the Lord has lift - ed

I've been changed since the Lord has lift - ed

me, I want to be read - y when Je - sus

me, I want to be read - y when Je - sus

that He's com-ing back a - gain, My
hearts, that He's com-ing back a - gain, Ooo,

heart is fix'd and my mind's made up.
Ah, Ooo, I

I want to be read - y when Je-sus comes. Sign me
want to be read - y when Je-sus comes.

Text: Kevin Yancy and Jerome Metcalfe
Tune: Kevin Yancy and Jerome Metcalfe; Harm. by Kenneth Morris © 1979, Kevin Yancy with permission of Martin and Morris Music, Inc.

112 I've Decided to Make Jesus My Choice

1. Some folk would rath-er have hous-es and land.
2. These clothes may be rag-ged that I'm wear - ing.

Some folk choose sil - ver and gold.
Heav - y is the load that I'm bear - ing.

These things they treas - ure and for - get a - bout their souls;
These old bur - dens that I'm car - rying

I've de - cid - ed to make Je - sus my choice.

The road is rough; the go - ing gets tough, and the

hills are hard to climb. I've start-ed out a
long time a-go, there's no doubt in my mind; I've de-
cid - ed to make Je - sus my choice.

Text: Harris Johnson
Tune: Harris Johnson

113   I'll Be Somewhere Listening for My Name

1. When He calls me I will an-swer, When He calls me
2. With a glad heart I will an-swer, With a glad heart
3. When He calls you, will you an-swer? When He calls you,

I will an-swer, When He calls me I will an-swer;
I will an-swer, With a glad heart I will an-swer;
will you an-swer? When He calls you, will you an-swer?

I'll be some-where list-'ning for my name.
I'll be some-where list-'ning for my name.
Some-where list-'ning, list-'ning for your name.

1.2. I'll be some-where list-'ning, I'll be some-where list-'ning,
3. You'll be some-where list-'ning, You'll be some-where list-'ning,

I'll be some-where list-'ning for my name. (for my name.)
You'll be some-where list-'ning for your name. (for your name.)

I'll be some-where list-'ning, I'll be some-where list-'ning,
You'll be some-where list-'ning, You'll be some-where list-'ning,

I'll be some-where list-'ning for my name.
Some-where list-'ning, list-'ning for your name.

Text: Eduardo J. Lango
Tune: Eduardo J. Lango

114 Close to Thee

1. Thou my ev - er - last - ing por - tion, More than friend or
2. Not for ease or world - ly pleas - ure, Nor for fame my
3. Lead me thro' the vale of shad - ows, Bear me o'er life's

life to me, All a - long my pil - grim jour - ney,
prayer shall be; Glad - ly will I toil and suf - fer,
fit - ful sea; Then the gate of life e - ter - nal

Sav - ior, let me walk with Thee. Close to Thee, Close to
On - ly let me walk with Thee. Close to Thee, Close to
May I en - ter, Lord, with Thee. Close to Thee, Close to

Thee, Close to Thee, Close to Thee; All a - long my
Thee, Close to Thee, Close to Thee; Glad - ly will I
Thee, Close to Thee, Close to Thee; Then the gate of

pil - grim jour - ney, Sav - ior, let me walk with Thee.
toil and suf - fer, On - ly let me walk with Thee.
life e - ter - nal May I en - ter, Lord, with Thee. A - men.

Text: Fanny J. Crosby, 1820-1915
Tune: Silas J. Vail, 1818-1884

The Way Is Jesus 115

Solo:

1. To go to heav - en my heart is long - ing.
2. The peace of heav - en all else ex - cel - ling;
3. The Fa - ther loves us as no one oth - er.
4. Why de - lay long - er? This is the best day

How shall I get there with - out pro - long - ing?
The place ce - les - tial where God is dwell - ing.
He sent us Je - sus to be our broth - er.
to choose to fol - low Je - sus, the true way.

All:

The way is Je - us. He chang - es nev - er.

The Sav - ior wants you with him for - ev - er.

Text: Swahili Text; Tr. by Howard S. Olson
Tune: Kinga Tune; *Tumshangilie Mungu,* Makumira, Tanzania
© 1977, Augsburg Publishing House

116 Lord, When You Came / Pescador de Hombres

1. Lord, when you came to the sea - shore
   Tú has ve - ni - do a la o - ri - lla,
2. Lord, you knew what my boat car - ried:
   Tú sa - bes bien lo que ten - go,
3. Lord, have you need of my la - bor,
   Tú ne - ce - si - tas mis ma - nos,
4. Lord, send me where you would have me,
   Tú pes - ca - dor de o - tros, ma - res,

You weren't seek - ing the wise or the wealth - y,
no has bus - ca - do ni a sa - bios, ni a ri - cos,
Nei - ther mon - ey nor weap - ons for fight - ing,
en mi bar - ca no hay o - ro ni es - pa - das,
Hands for ser - vice, a heart made for lov - ing,
mi can - san - cio que a o - tros des - can - se,
To a vil - lage, or heart of the cit - y;
an - sia e - ter - na, al - mas que es - per - an.

But on - ly ask - ing that I might fol - low.
tan só - lo quie - res que yo te si - ga.
But nets for fish - ing, my dai - ly la - bor.
tan só - lo re - des y mi tra - ba - jo.
My arms for lift - ing the poor and bro - ken?
a - mor que quie - ra se - guir a - man - do.
I will re - mem - ber that you are with me.
A - mi - go bue - no, que a - sí me lla - mas.

O Lord, in my eyes you were gaz - ing,
Se - ñor me has mi - ra - do a los o - jos,

Kind - ly smil - ing, my name you were say - ing;
son - ri - en - do has di - cho mi nom - bre,

All I trea - sured, I have left on the sand there;
en la_a - re - na he de - ja - do mi bar - ca,

Close to you, I will find oth - er seas.
jun-to_a tí bus - ca - ré o - tro mar.

Text: *Pescador de Hombres*, César Gabaráin; Tr. by Willard Francis Jabusch, b.1930
Tune: César Gabaráin, © 1979, Ediciones Paulinas. All rights reserved. Sole U.S. agent: OCP Publications.

117 A Follower of Christ

1. I want to be a fol-low-er of Christ, I
   want to be a fish-er, now for Christ. I

want to be one of His Dis-ci-ples, I
want to bring oth-er souls to Him, I

want to live in the new-ness of life, Just
want to help rid this world of its strife, Just

let me be a fol-low-er of Christ.

What do I have to do? What do I have to say?

How do I have to walk each and ev - 'ry day?

Tell me what does it cost if I car-ry the cross? Just

let me be a fol - low - er of Christ. I

Christ. Yes I want to be a fol - low-er of Christ.

Text: J. W. Harris, alt.
Tune: J. W. Harris; Harm. by Kenneth Morris, © 1980, Martin and Morris, Inc.

I Have Decided to Follow Jesus 118

1. I have de - cid - ed to fol - low Je - sus,
2. Tho' no one join me, still I will fol - low,
3. The world be - hind me, the cross be - fore me,

I have de - cid - ed to fol - low Je - sus,
Tho' no one join me, still I will fol - low,
The world be - hind me, the cross be - fore me,

I have de - cid - ed to fol - low Je - sus—
Tho' no one join me, still I will fol - low—
The world be - hind me, the cross be - fore me—

No turn - ing back, (no turn - ing back,) no turn - ing back!

Text: Ascribed to an Indian prince; as sung in Garo, Assam
Tune: Indian Folk Melody, Paul B. Smith, © 1949, Zondervan Music Publishers; Harm. by Norma Johnson, © 1963, Zondervan Music Publishers

119 Lord, I Want to Be a Christian

1. Lord, I want to be a Chris-tian In my heart, in my heart;
2. Lord, I want to be more lov-ing In my heart, in my heart;
3. Lord, I want to be more ho-ly In my heart, in my heart;
4. I don't want to be like Ju-das In my heart, in my heart;
5. Lord, I want to be like Je-sus in my heart, in my heart;

Lord, I want to be a Chris-tian In my heart,
Lord, I want to be more lov-ing In my heart,
Lord, I want to be more ho-ly In my heart,
I don't want to be like Ju-das In my heart,
Lord, I want to be like Je-sus In my heart,

In my heart, In my heart,
In my heart, In my heart,

Lord, I want to be a Chris-tian In my heart.
Lord, I want to be more lov-ing In my heart.
Lord, I want to be more ho-ly In my heart.
I don't want to be like Ju-das In my heart.
Lord, I want to be like Je-sus In my heart.

Text: Afro-American Spiritual
Tune: Afro-American Spiritual

Where He Leads Me 120

1. I can hear my Sav - ior call - ing, I can
2. I'll go with Him thru the gar - den, I'll go
3. I'll go with Him thru the judg - ment, I'll go
4. He will give me grace and glo - ry, He will

Chorus: Where He leads me I will fol - low, Where He

hear my Sav - ior call - ing, I can hear my Sav - ior
with Him thru the gar - den, I'll go with Him thru the
with Him thru the judg - ment, I'll go with Him thru the
give me grace and glo - ry, He will give me grace and

leads me I will fol - low, Where He leads me I will

call - ing, "Take thy cross and fol - low, fol - low Me."
gar - den, I'll go with Him, with Him all the way.
judg - ment, I'll go with Him, with Him all the way.
glo - ry, And go with me, with me all the way.

fol - low, I'll go with Him, with Him all the way.

Text: E. W. Blandy, c.1890
Tune: John S. Norris, 1844-1907

121 Certainly, Lord

Joyfully

Have you got good re-li-gion? Cer-t'nly, Lord! Have you got good re-li-gion? Cer-t'nly, Lord! Have you got good re-li-gion? Cer-t'nly, Lord! Cer-t'nly, Cer-t'nly, Cer-t'nly, Lord!

Leader:	**Response:**
2. Have you been redeemed?	Cert'nly, Lord!
3. Have you been to the water?	Cert'nly, Lord!
4. Have you been baptized?	Cert'nly, Lord!

Text: Afro-American Spiritual
Tune: Afro-American Spiritual

122 Just As I Am

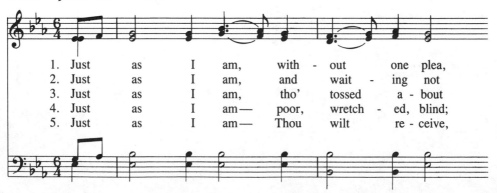

1. Just as I am, with-out one plea,
2. Just as I am, and wait-ing not
3. Just as I am, tho' tossed a-bout
4. Just as I am— poor, wretch-ed, blind;
5. Just as I am— Thou wilt re-ceive,

But that Thy blood was shed for me,
To rid my soul of one dark blot,
With man-y a con-flict, many a doubt,
Sight, rich-es, heal-ing of the mind,
Wilt wel-come, par-don, cleanse, re-lieve,

And that Thou bidd'st me come to Thee,
To Thee whose blood can cleanse each spot,
Fight-ings and fears with-in, with-out,
Yea, all I need in Thee to find,
Be-cause Thy prom-ise I be-lieve,

O Lamb of God, I come! I come!
O Lamb of God, I come! I come!
O Lamb of God, I come! I come!
O Lamb of God, I come! I come!
O Lamb of God, I come! I come!

Text: Charlotte Elliott, 1789-1871
Tune: William B. Bradbury, 1816-1868

123 Be Not Afraid

1. You shall cross the bar-ren des-ert, but you shall not die of thirst. You shall wan-der far in safe-ty though you do not know the way. You shall speak your words in

for-eign lands and all will un - der - stand.

You shall see the face of God and live.

Refrain
Be not a - fraid. I go be-fore you al - ways. Come fol-low Me, and

you shall not be harmed. If you stand be-fore the

pow'r of hell and death is at your side,

know that I am with you through it all.

3. Bless-ed are your poor, for the King-dom shall be

Keep Me, Every Day 124

1. Lord, I want to live for Thee, Ev - 'ry day and hour;
2. In my weak-ness be my strength; In my tri - als all,
3. Leave me not to walk a - lone, Lest I droop and die;

Let Thy Spir - it be with me, In its sav - ing pow'r!
Be Thou near me all the day, Hear my ev - 'ry call!
Let Thy Spir - it go with me, And at - tend my cry!

Keep my heart, and keep my hand, Keep my soul, I pray!

Keep my tongue to speak Thy praise, Keep me all the way!

Text: F. L. Eiland
Tune: Emmet S. Dean

125　God Sends Us His Spirit

1. God sends us his Spir - it　to be - friend and help us.
2. Dark-ened roads are clear - er,　heav - y bur - dens light - er,
3. Now we are God's peo - ple,　bond - ed by God's pres - ence,

Re - cre - ate and guide us,　Spir - it - Friend.
When we're walk - ing with our　Spir - it - Friend.
A - gents of God's pur - pose,　Spir - it - Friend.

Spir - it who en - liv - ens,　sanc - ti - fies, en - light - ens,
Now we need not fear the　pow - ers of the dark - ness.
Lead us for - ward ev - er,　slip - ping back-ward nev - er,

Sets us free, is now our　Spir - it - Friend.
None can o - ver - come our　Spir - it - Friend.
To your re - made world, our　Spir - it - Friend.

Spir - it of our Mak - er, Spir - it - Friend.
Spir - it of our Je - su, Spir - it - Friend.

Spir - it of God's peo - ple, Spir - it - Friend.

*Hand claps

Text: Tom Colvin, b.1925
Tune: NATOMAH, 12 9 12 9 with refrain; Gonja Folk Song; Adapt. by Tom Colvin, b.1925
Copyright © 1969 by Hope Publishing Company, Carol Stream, IL 60188.
All Rights Reserved. Used by Permission.

126 Spirit of the Living God

Spir - it of the Liv - ing God, Fall fresh on me,

Spir - it of the Liv - ing God, Fall fresh on me.

Melt me, mold me, Fill me, use me.

Spir - it of the Liv - ing God, Fall fresh on me.

Text: Daniel Iverson, 1890-1977
Tune: Daniel Iverson, 1890-1977
© 1935, 1963, Moody Press, Moody Bible Institute of Chicago

Veni Sancte Spiritus 127

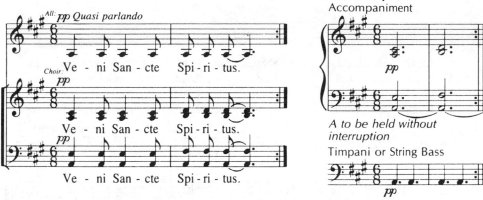

Verses

As the ostinato continues, vocal and instrumental verses are sung or played as desired with some space always left between the verses (after the cantor's "Veni Sancte Spiritus").

1. Come, Ho - ly Spir - it, from heav - en shine forth with your glo - rious light. Ve - ni San - cte Spi - ri - tus.

2. Come, Fa - ther of the poor, come, gen - er - ous Spir - it, come, light of our hearts. Ve - ni San - cte Spi - ri - tus.

Text: *Come Holy Spirit;* Verses drawn from the Pentecost Sequence; Taizé Community, 1978
Tune: Jacques Berthier, b.1923
© 1979, Les Presses de Taizé

128 Mold Me, Lord

Descant:

1. Mold me, Lord. Shape me, Lord. Make me ac-
2. Save us, Lord. Keep us, Lord. Guide us ac-
3. Cleanse us, Lord. Purge us, Lord. Heal us ac-
4. Use us, Lord. Lead us, Lord. Send us ac-

Melody:

cord - ing to your will all a - new.
cord - ing to your will with your hand.
cord - ing to your will by your grace.
cord - ing to your will in your strength.

My thoughts ac - cord - ing to your will all a - new.
In time of tri - al, guide us, Lord, with your hand.
From sin and e - vil, heal us, Lord, by your grace.
To those in suf - f'ring, send us, Lord, in your strength.

My words ac - cord - ing to your will all a - new.
In joy and sor - row, guide us, Lord, with your hand.
From pride and en - vy, heal us, Lord, by your grace.
To those in dark - ness, send us, Lord, in your strength.

My deeds ac - cord - ing to your will all a - new.
Lest we for - get you, guide us, Lord, with your hand.
From guilt and ter - ror, heal us, Lord, by your grace.
To those un - heed - ing, send us, Lord, in your strength.

Text: Howard S. Olson
Tune: Nyaturu Tune
© 1977, Augsburg Publishing House

Taste and See 129

Taste and see. Taste and see the good - ness
of the Lord. O Taste and see. Taste and
see the good - ness of the Lord, of the Lord.

glo - ry   in   the   Lord;   for
Lord   and He   an - swered me;   from
see   that God   is   good;   in

He   has been   so good to   me.
all   my trou - bles he set me   free.
Him   we need   put all our   trust.

Text: Ps. 34
Tune: James E. Moore, Jr., © 1983, GIA Publications, Inc.

130 Eat This Bread

Ostinato Response

Mixed Voices

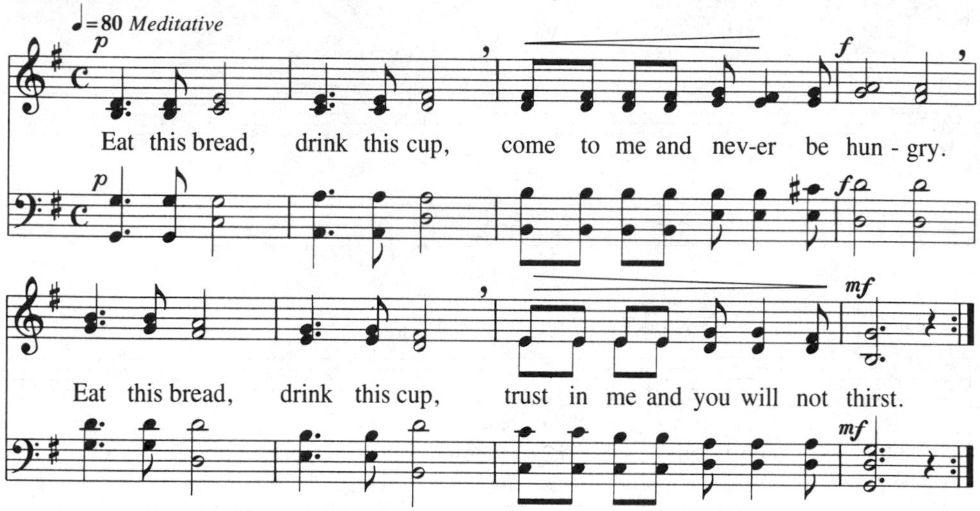
♩=80 Meditative
Eat this bread, drink this cup, come to me and nev-er be hun - gry.
Eat this bread, drink this cup, trust in me and you will not thirst.

Accompaniment

Keyboard or Guitar

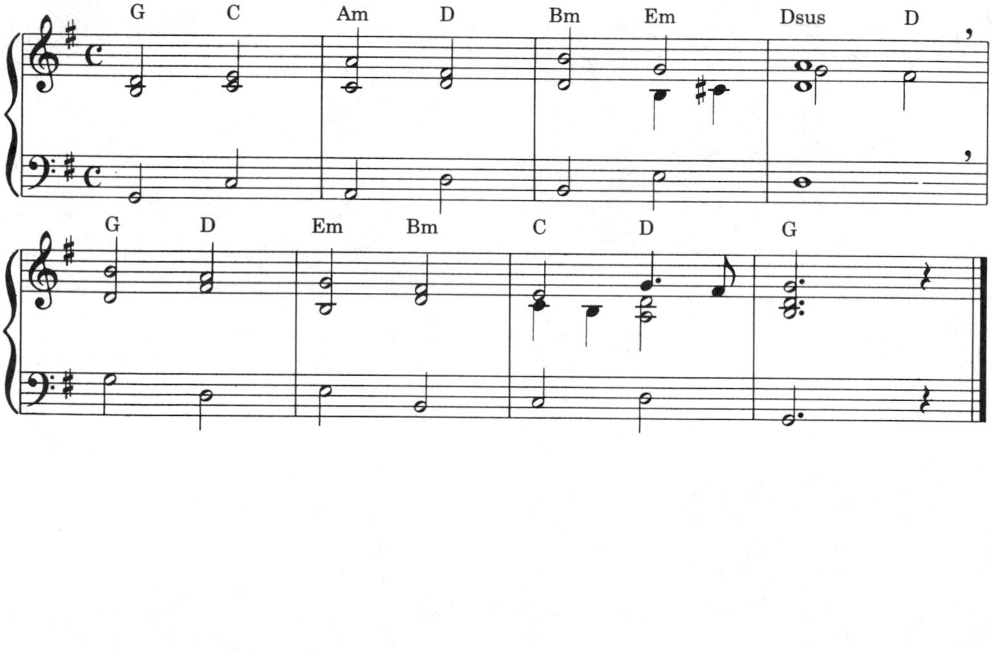
G C Am D Bm Em Dsus D
G D Em Bm C D G

Verses (*in this case, the response is not repeated as an ostinato, both the response and verses are sung one after the other*)

Choir (humming) or Keyboard

1. I am the bread of life, the
2. Your an - ces - tors ate man - na in the des - ert, but
3. Eat my flesh and drink my blood, and
4. A - ny one who eats this bread, will
5. If you be - lieve and eat this bread,

Choose either part

Text: John 6; Adapt. by Robert J. Batastini, b.1942, and the Taizé Community, 1984
Tune: Jacques Berthier, b.1923
© 1984, Les Presses de Taizé

Jesus in the Morning   131

1. Je - sus, Je - sus, Je - sus in the morn - ing,
2. Praise Him, Praise Him, Praise Him in the morn - ing,
3. Love Him, Love Him, Love Him in the morn - ing,
4. Serve Him, Serve Him, Serve Him in the morn - ing,
5. Je - sus, Je - sus, Je - sus in the morn - ing,

Je - sus in the noon time; Je - sus,
Praise Him in the noon time; Praise Him,
Love Him in the noon time; Love Him,
Serve Him in the noon time; Serve Him,
Je - sus in the noon - time; Je - sus

Je - sus, Je - sus when the sun goes down!
Praise Him, Praise Him when the sun goes down!
Love Him, Love Him when the sun goes down!
Serve Him, Serve Him when the sun goes down!
Je - sus, Je - sus when the sun goes down!

Text: Afro-American Folk song
Tune: American Folk song

132 The Lord Is My Light

strength-en thine heart. Whom shall I fear, whom shall I fear? The Lord is the strength of my life; whom shall I fear?

Text: Lillian Bouknight
Tune: Lillian Bouknight; Arr. by Paul Gainer
© 1980, Savgos Music, Inc.

133   I Am the Bread of Life

1. ___ I am the Bread of life. You who
2. The bread that ___ I will give is my
3. Un - less ___ you ___ eat of the
4. ___ I am the Res - ur - rec - tion, ___
5. Yes, Lord, ___ I be - lieve ___ that ___

come to me shall not hun - ger; and who be-
flesh for the life of the world, ___ and if you
flesh of the Son of Man ___ and ___
I ___ am the life. ___ If you be-
you ___ are the Christ, ___ the ___

lieve in me shall not thirst. No one can come to
eat ___ of this bread, you shall live for-
drink ___ of his blood, and drink ___ of his
lieve ___ in ___ me, e - ven though you
Son ___ of ___ God, Who ___ have ___

me un - less the Fa - ther beck - ons.
ev - er, you shall live for - ev - er.
blood, you shall not have life with - in you.
die, you shall live for ev - er.
come in - to the world.

Harmony

And I will raise you up, and I will raise you

up, and I will raise you up on the last day.

Text: John 6; Suzanne Toolan, SM, b.1927
Tune: BREAD OF LIFE, Irregular with refrain; Suzanne Toolan, SM, b.1927
© 1966, GIA Publications, Inc.

134 At That First Eucharist

1. At that first Eu - cha - rist be - fore you died,
   O Lord, you prayed that all be one in you;
   At this our Eu - cha - rist a - gain pre - side,
   And in our hearts your law of love re - new.

2. For all your church, O Lord, we in - ter - cede;
   O make our lack of char - i - ty to cease;
   Draw us the near - er each to each we plead,
   By draw - ing all to you, O Prince of Peace.

3. We pray for those who wan - der from the fold;
   O bring them back, Good Shep - herd of the sheep,
   Back to the faith which saints be - lieved of old,
   Back to the Church which still that faith does keep.

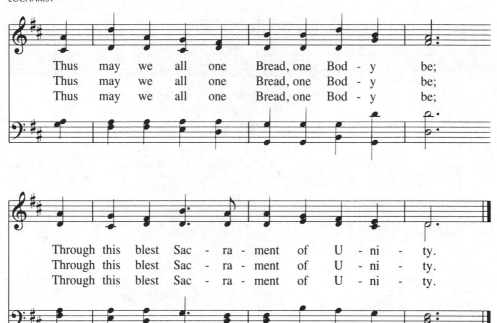

Thus may we all one Bread, one Bod - y be;
Thus may we all one Bread, one Bod - y be;
Thus may we all one Bread, one Bod - y be;

Through this blest Sac - ra - ment of U - ni - ty.
Through this blest Sac - ra - ment of U - ni - ty.
Through this blest Sac - ra - ment of U - ni - ty.

Text: William H. Turton, 1859-1938, alt.
Tune: UNDE ET MEMORES, 10 10 10 10 with refrain; William H. Monk, 1823-1889, alt.

135 Let Us Break Bread Together

1. Let us break bread to-geth-er on our knees;
2. Let us drink wine to-geth-er on our knees;
3. Let us praise God to-geth-er on our knees;

Let us break bread to-geth-er on our knees;
Let us drink wine to-geth-er on our knees;
Let us praise God to-geth-er on our knees;

When I fall on my knees, With my

face to the ris - ing sun, O Lord, have

mer - cy on me.

Text: Afro-American Spiritual
Tune: Afro-American Spiritual; Harm. by David Hurd, b.1950. © 1986, GIA Publications, Inc.

136   Gift of Finest Wheat

You sat - is - fy the hun - gry heart With
gift of fin - est wheat; Come give to us, O
sav - ing Lord, The bread of life to eat.

1. As when the shep - herd calls his sheep, They
2. With joy - ful lips we sing to you Our
3. Is not the cup we bless and share The
4. The mys - t'ry of your pres - ence, Lord, No
5. You give your - self to us, O Lord; Then

know and heed his voice; So when you call your
praise and grat - i - tude, That you should count us
blood of Christ out - poured? Do not one cup, one
mor - tal tongue can tell: Whom all the world can-
self - less let us be, To serve each oth - er

fam - 'ly, Lord, We fol - low and re - joice.
wor - thy, Lord, To share this heav'n - ly food.
loaf, de - clare Our one - ness in the Lord?
not con - tain Comes in our hearts to dwell.
in your name In truth and char - i - ty.

Text: Omer Westendorf, b.1916
Tune: BICENTENNIAL, CM, with refrain: Robert E. Kreutz, b.1922, © 1977, Archdiocese of Philadelphia

137 I Received the Living God

Unison

I re - ceived the liv - ing God, and my heart is full of joy. I re - ceived the liv - ing God, and my heart is full of joy.

Harmony

1. He has said: I am the Bread Knead - ed
2. He has said: I am the Way, And my
3. He has said: I am the Truth; If you
4. He has said: I am the Life Far from

long   to   give   you   life;   You who   will   par-
Fa - ther longs   for   you;   So I   come   to
fol - low close   to   me,   You will know   me
whom no thing   can   grow,   But re - ceive   this

D.C.

take of   me   Need not ev - er fear to   die.
bring you home   To be one with him a - new.
in your heart,   And my word shall make you   free.
liv - ing bread,   And my Spir - it you shall   know.

Text: Anonymous
Tune: LIVING GOD, 7 7 7 7 with refrain; Anonymous; Harm. by Richard Proulx, b.1937. © 1986, GIA Publications, Inc.

138 Even Me

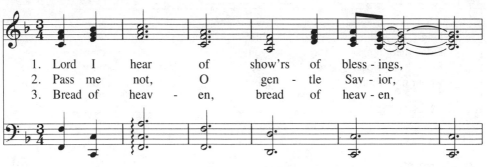

1. Lord I hear of show'rs of bless - ings,
2. Pass me not, O gen - tle Sav - ior,
3. Bread of heav - en, bread of heav - en,

Thou art scat - t'ring full and free;
Sin - ful though my heart may be;
Ev - er let me feed on Thee;

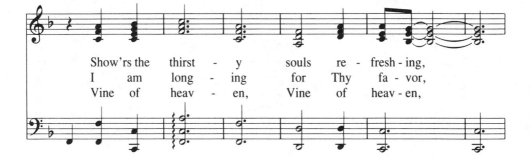

Show'rs the thirst - y souls re - fresh - ing,
I am long - ing for Thy fa - vor,
Vine of heav - en, Vine of heav - en,

Let some drops now fall on me!
Whilst Thou'rt bless - ing, Oh bless me!
Let Thy blood a - tone for me!

E - ven me, yes! E - ven me!

E - ven me, Lord! E - ven me!

Let some drops now fall on me!
Whilst Thou'rt bless - ing, Lord, bless me!
Let Thy blood a - tone for me!

Text: Traditional
Tune: Traditional; Harm. by Roberta Martin, ©

139 One Bread, One Body

Tranquil and slow (♩=69)

One bread, one bod-y, one Lord of all, one cup of bless-ing which we bless. And we, though

man-y, through-out the earth, we are one

Last time ⊕ *a tempo*

bod - y in this one Lord.

Last time ⊕

a tempo

Slightly faster, with excitement (♩=72)

Verses

Melody: **f** *marcato*

Harmony:

1. Gen - tile or Jew, ser - vant or
2. Man - y the gifts, man - y the
3. Grain for the fields, scat-tered and

Sw.

f

free,
works,
grown,

wom-an or man,
one in the Lord
gath-ered to one,

no more.
of all.
for all.

One
One
One

CODA

Lord.

Text: 1 Cor. 10: 16, 17; 12:4; Gal. 3:28; The Didache 9
Tune: John Foley, SJ
© 1978, John B. Foley, SJ and North American Liturgy Resources

We Give You Thanks   140

We give you thanks for all our bless-ings: Lord, we give you thanks.

We sing your praise to all the na-tions; Lord, we give you thanks.

1. Je - sus, you come to your peo - ple un - der the
2. Sing, O my soul, of this un - ion, heav - en on
3. Your peace is our con - so - la - tion, Your Word our

form of bread and wine; Word of God, our sal -
earth be - gun; By this most sa - cred com -
lan - tern of life, We fol - low You in con -

va - tion. Christ, our King di - vine.
mun - ion, we with You are one.
tent - ment, de - spite all trou - ble and strife.

Text: Evelyn Haettenschwiller, © 1980
Tune: Evelyn Haettenschwiller, © 1980; Harm. by Glenn R. Hufnagel

141 Jesus, the Bread of Life

Steady (♩=50) *largo*

Je - sus, the Bread of life, Je-
sus, the Bread of life. All who eat and
drink of Him will nev - er die,

will nev - er die. **Fine**

1. I am the Bread that came down from heav - en.
2. All who come to Me will not hun - ger,
3. All who love and keep My com - mand-ments

I will be your food.
nor will they ev - er thirst.
will be loved by My Fa - ther.

All who put their trust in Me will
If you turn to Me in faith I'll
And we shall both com - fort them and

nev - er die.
nev - er turn a - way.
make our home in them.

Text: John 6; Grayson Warren Brown
Tune: Grayson Warren Brown; Harm. by Michael B. Lynch
© 1979, North American Liturgy Resources

Jesus Is Here Right Now   142

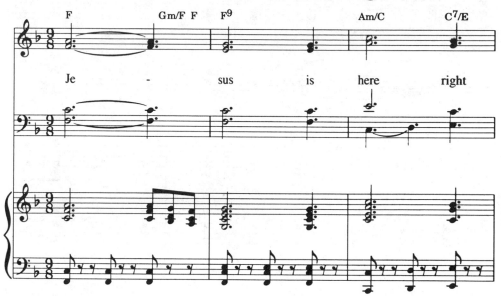

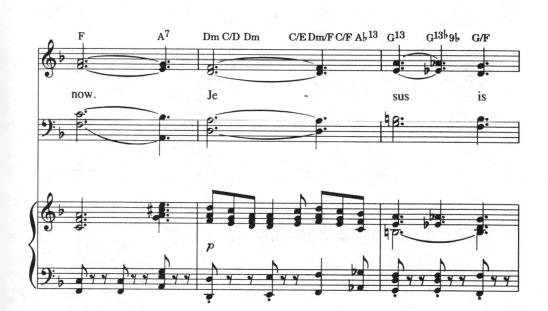

here. With this bread and

wine his peace you'll find, Christ

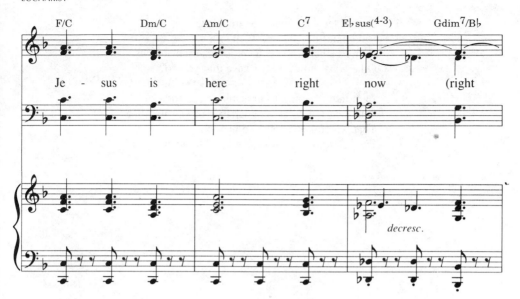

Je - sus is here right now (right

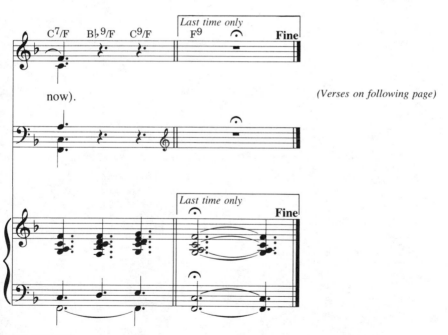

now).

(Verses on following page)

Text: Leon Roberts
Tune: Leon Roberts
© 1986, Leon Roberts

1. Do not let your hearts be troubled.
   Have faith in God and faith in me.
   In my Father's house there are many mansions;
   Otherwise, how could I have told you so?

2. I am indeed going to prepare a place for you
   And then I shall come back to take you with me
   That where I am you also may be.
   For you know the way that leads to where I go.

Text: Leon C. Roberts; verses, John 14:1-4
Tune: Leon C. Roberts
© 1986, Leon C. Roberts and Associates

Nearer, My God, to Thee 143

1. Near - er, my God, to Thee, Near - er to Thee!
2. Tho like the wan - der - er, The sun gone down,
3. There let the way ap - pear, Steps un - to heav'n;
4. Then with my wak - ing thoughts, Bright with Thy praise,
5. Or if on joy - ful wing, Cleav - ing the sky,

E'en tho' it be a cross That rais - eth me;
Dark - ness be o - ver me, My rest a stone,
All that Thou send - est me, In mer - cy giv'n—
Out of my ston - y griefs, Beth - el I raise;
Sun, moon, and stars for - got, Up - ward I fly,

Still all my song shall be,
Yet in my dreams I'd be
An - gels to beck - on me Near - er, my God, to Thee,
So by my woes to be
Still all my song shall be,

Near - er, my God, to Thee, Near - er to Thee!

Text: Sarah F. Adams, 1805-1848
Tune: BETHANY, Lowell Mason, 1792-1872

144 He Understands; He'll Say, "Well Done"

1. If when you give the best of your serv - ice,
2. Mis - un - der - stood, the Sav - ior of sin - ners,
3. If when this life of la - bor is end - ed,
4. But if you try and fail in your try - ing,

Tell - ing the world that the Sav - ior is come;
Hung on the cross; He was God's on - ly Son;
And the re - ward of the race you have run;
Hands sore and scarred from the work you've be - gun;

Be not dis - mayed when friends don't be - lieve you;
Oh! hear Him call - ing His Fa - ther in Heav'n,
Oh! the sweet rest pre - pared for the faith - ful,
Take up your cross, run quick - ly to meet Him;

He un - der - stands; He'll say, "Well done."
Not my will, but Thine be done."
Will be His blest and fi - nal "Well done."
He'll un - der - stand; He'll say, "Well done."

Oh, when I come to the end of my jour-ney,
Wea-ry of life and the bat-tle is won;
Car-r'ing the staff and cross of re-demp-tion,
He'll un-der-stand, and say, "Well done."

Text: Lucie E. Campbell
Tune: Lucie E. Campbell

145 Where We'll Never Grow Old

1. I have heard of a land on the far a-way strand,
2. In that beau-ti-ful home where we'll nev-er-more roam,
3. When our work here is done and the life crown is won,

'Tis a beau-ti-ful home of the soul;
We shall be in the sweet by and by;
And our trou-bles and tri-als are o'er,

Built by Je-sus on high, there we nev-er shall die,
Hap-py praise to the King through e-ter-ni-ty sing,
All our sor-rows will end, and our voic-es will blend

'Tis a land where we nev-er grow old.
'Tis a land where we nev-er shall die.
With the loved ones who've gone on be-fore.

Never grow old, never grow old,
Where we'll
In a land where we'll never grow old;
Never grow old, never grow old,
Where we'll
In a land where we'll never grow old.

Text: James C. Moore
Tune: James C. Moore

146 Just A Little While

1. Soon this life will all be o - ver And our pil - grim-
2. Soon we'll see the light of morn - ing Then the new day
3. Soon we'll meet a - gain our loved ones And we'll take them

age will end, Soon we'll take our heav'n - ly jour - ney,
will be - gin, Soon we'll hear the Fa - ther call - ing,
by the hand, Soon we'll press them to our bos - om

Be at home a - gain with friends; Heav-en's gates are stand - ing
"Come, my chil - dren, en - ter in"; Then we'll hear a choir of
O - ver in the prom - ised land; Then we'll be at home for-

o - pen, Wait - ing for our en - trance there, Some sweet
an - gels, Sing - ing out the vic - t'ry song, All our
ev - er, Through-out all e - ter - ni - ty, What a

day we're go - ing   o - ver, All the beau - ties there to   share.
trou - bles will be   end - ed   And we'll live in heav - en's   throng.
bless - ed, bless - ed   morn - ing That e - ter - nal morn will   be!

Just a lit - tle while   to   stay   here,   Just a lit - tle
stay here, stay here,

while   to   wait,   Just a lit - tle while   to
to   wait,

la - bor   in   the   path that's al - ways
la - bor, la - bor,

straight,   Just   a   lit - tle more   of
that's al - ways straight and nar - row,

trou - bles, In this low and sin - ful
trou - bles, trou - bles,

state, Then we'll en - ter Heav - en's por-
sin - ful state, por - tals,

tals, Sweep-ing through the pearl - y gates.
por - tals, pearl - y gates.

Text: Eugene M. Bartlett, 1885-1941
Tune: Eugene M. Bartlett, 1885-1941; Harm. by Albert E. Brumley
© 1949, Albert E. Brumley and Sons

147 Swing Low, Sweet Chariot

Slowly

Swing low, sweet char - i - ot, Com-ing for to car - ry me

Fine

home, Swing low, sweet char - i - ot, Com-ing for to car - ry me home.

1. I looked o - ver Jor - dan, and what did I see,
2. If you get there be - fore I do,
3. I'm some - times up, I'm some - times down,

Com-ing for to car - ry me home? A band of an - gels
Com-ing for to car - ry me home? Tell all my friends I'm
Com-ing for to car - ry me home? But still my soul feels

D.C.

com - ing af - ter me, Com-ing for to car - ry me home.
com - ing too, Com-ing for to car - ry me home.
heav-en - ly bound, Com-ing for to car - ry me home.

Text: Afro-American Spiritual
Tune: Afro-American Spiritual

148 I'll Be Singing Up There

I'll be sing-ing up there,
sing-ing up there,
I'll be sing-ing up there,
yes, sing-ing up there,
Oh!
come on up to bright glo - ry, I'll be sing-ing up there.

1. If you miss me sing - ing down here, If you miss me
2. If you miss me pray - ing down here, If you miss me
3. If you miss me walk - ing down here, If you miss me
4. If you miss me shout - ing down here, If you miss me

FUNERAL

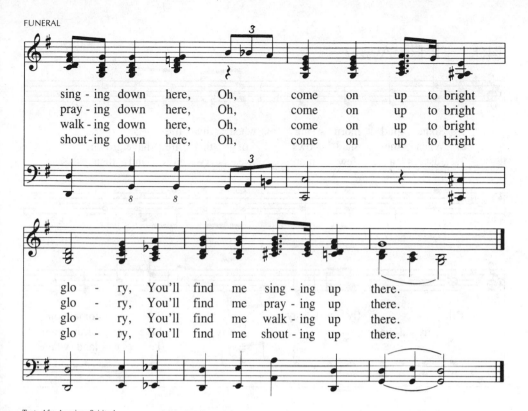

sing - ing down here, Oh, come on up to bright
pray - ing down here, Oh, come on up to bright
walk - ing down here, Oh, come on up to bright
shout - ing down here, Oh, come on up to bright

glo - ry, You'll find me sing - ing up there.
glo - ry, You'll find me pray - ing up there.
glo - ry, You'll find me walk - ing up there.
glo - ry, You'll find me shout - ing up there.

Text: Afro-American Spiritual
Tune: Afro-American Spiritual; Harm. by W. O. Hoyle, Lillian Bowles, and W. Webb, © 1938, Lillian M. Bowles Music House

149 I'll Fly Away

1. Some glad morn - ing when this life is o'er,
2. When the shad - ows of this life have grown,
3. Just a few more wea - ry days and then,

I'll   fly a - way;   fly a - way;   To a home on
fly a-way,   fly a-way;   Like a bird from
                                         To a land where

God's ce - les - tial shore,   I'll   fly a-
pris - on bars has flown,   fly a-way,
joys shall nev - er end,

way.   I'll   fly a - way, O glo - ry,
fly a-way.   fly a-way,

FUNERAL

I'll fly a - way;
fly a-way, in the morn-ing;
When I die, hal - le-
lu - jah by and by, I'll fly a - way.
fly a-way, fly a-way.

Text: Albert E. Brumley
Tune: Albert E. Brumley
© 1932, 1960, Albert E. Brumley

150 Deep River

Deep river, my home is o-ver Jor-dan,
Deep, deep

Deep river, Lord, I want to cross o-ver in-to camp-ground.
Deep, deep

O don't you want to go to that gos-pel feast, That

prom-ised land where all is peace, O don't you want to

D.C.

go to that prom-ised land, that land where all is peace?

Text: Afro-American Spiritual
Tune: Afro-American Spiritual

Near to the Heart of God 151

1. There is a place of qui - et rest, Near to the heart of God;
2. There is a place of com-fort sweet, Near to the heart of God;
3. There is a place of full re-lease, Near to the heart of God;

A place where sin can - not mo-lest, Near to the heart of God.
A place where we our Sav - ior meet. Near to the heart of God.
A place where all is joy and peace, Near to the heart of God.

O Je - sus, blest Re - deem - er, Sent from the heart of God,

Hold us, who wait be - fore Thee, Near to the heart of God.

Text: Cleland B. McAfee, 1866-1944
Tune: Cleland B. McAfee, 1866-1944

152 The Lord Is My Shepherd

1. The Lord is my Shep-herd, no want shall I know;
2. Thro' the val-ley and shad-ow of death tho' I stray,
3. In the midst of af-flic-tion my ta-ble is spread;
4. Let good-ness and mer-cy, my boun-ti-ful God,

I feed in green pas-tures, safe-fold-ed I rest;
Since Thou art my Guard-ian, no e-vil I fear;
With bless-ings un-meas-ured my cup run-neth o'er;
Still fol-low my steps till I meet Thee a-bove:

He lead-eth my soul where the still wa-ters flow,
Thy rod shall de-fend me, Thy staff be my stay;
With per-fume and oil Thou a-noint-est my head;
I seek by the path which my an-ces-tors trod,

Re-stores me when wan-d'ring, re-deems when op-pressed;
No harm can be-fall, with my Com-fort-er near;
O what shall I ask of Thy prov-i-dence more?
Thro' the land of their so-journ, Thy king-dom of love;

Re - stores me when wan-d'ring, re - deems when op - pressed.
No harm can be - fall, with my Com - fort - er near.
O what shall I ask of Thy prov - i - dence more?
Thro' the land of their so - journ, Thy king - dom of love.

Text: James Montgomery, 1771-1854
Tune: Thomas Koschat

153   A Wedding Prayer

1. Draw near this cou - ple, Lord, grant to them your bless - ing.
2. We come to wit - ness, Lord, grant to us your bless - ing.
3. Our homes en - light - en, Lord, grant to all your bless - ing.

To wed is your will, Lord, grant to them your bless - ing.
Their joy is our joy, Lord, grant to us your bless - ing.
A place of ref - uge, Lord, grant to all your bless - ing.

They need you near them, Lord, grant to them your bless - ing.
Their pain is our pain, Lord, grant to us your bless - ing.
A light to strang - ers, Lord, grant to all your bless - ing.

Help them to trust you, Lord, grant to them your bless - ing.
We pledge as - sis - tance, Lord, grant to us your bless - ing.
Where par - ents love you, Lord, grant to all your bless - ing.

In - crease de - vo - tion, Lord, grant to them your bless - ing.
An arm to lean on, Lord, grant to us your bless - ing.
Where chil - dren love you, Lord, grant to all your bless - ing.

In peace a - bid - ing, Lord, grant to them your bless - ing.
An ear for lis - t'ning, Lord, grant to us your bless - ing.
Where each one serves you, Lord, grant to all your bless - ing.

As friends to neigh - bors, Lord, grant to them your bless - ing.
To pray and coun - sel, Lord, grant to us your bless - ing.
A taste of heav - en, Lord, grant to all your bless - ing.

Text: Howard S. Olson
Tune: Meru Tune
© 1977, Augsburg Publishing House

O Perfect Love   154

1. O   per - fect   Love,   all   hu - man thought tran - scend - ing,
2. O   per - fect   Life,   be   now their full   as - sur - ance
3. Grant them the   joy   which   bright-ens earth - ly   sor - row;

Low - ly   we   kneel   in   prayer be - fore your   throne
Of   ten - der   char - i - ty   and stead - fast   faith,
Grant them the   peace which   calms all   earth - ly   strife,

That   theirs may   be   the   love which knows   no   end - ing,
Of   pa - tient   hope   and   qui - et, brave   en - dur - ance,
And   to   life's   day   the   glo - rious   un - known   mor - row

Whom you   for - ev - er - more   u - nite   in   one.
With   child - like   trust that   fears   no   pain   or   death.
That   dawns up - on   e - ter - nal   love   and   life.

Text: Dorothy F. Gurney, 1858-1932, © Oxford University Press
Tune: O PERFECT LOVE, 11 10 11 10, Joesph Barnby, 1838-1896, adapt.

155 Bwana Awabariki

1. Bwa - na a - wa - ba - ri - ki, Bwa - na a - wa - ba - ri - ki,
2. May the Lord bless you, May the Lord bless you,

Bwa - na a - wa - ba - ri - ki mi - le - le.
May the Lord bless you for - ev - er.

U - ki - mcha Bwa - na, Bwa - na a - wa - ba - ri - ki.
Re - vere the Lord, May the Lord bless you.

Text: African Folk Hymn
Tune: African Melody

Just a Closer Walk with Thee 156

1. I am weak but Thou art strong; Je - sus,
2. Through this world of toil and snares, If I
3. When my fee - ble life is o'er, Time for
Refrain: Just a clos - er walk with Thee, Grant it,

keep me from all wrong; I'll be sat - is - fied as
fal - ter, Lord, who cares? Who with me my bur - den
me will be no more; Guide me gent - ly, safe - ly
Je - sus, is my plea, Dai - ly walk - ing close to

D.C. for refrain

long As I walk, let me walk close to Thee.
shares? None but Thee, dear Lord, none but Thee.
o'er To Thy king - dom shore, to Thy shore.
Thee, Let it be, dear Lord, let it be.

Text: Afro-American Spiritual
Tune: Afro-American Spiritual

157 There Is a Balm In Gilead

There is a balm in Gil - e - ad To make the wound - ed whole, There is a balm in Gil - e - ad to heal the sin - sick soul.

1. Some - times I feel dis - cour - aged And
2. If you can - not preach like Pe - ter, If you
3. Don't ev - er feel dis - cour - aged, For

think my work's in vain, But then the Ho - ly
can - not pray like Paul, You can tell the love of
Je - sus is your friend; And if you lack for

Spir - it Re - vives my soul a - gain.
Je - sus, And say, "He died for all!"
knowl-edge He'll ne'er re - fuse to lend.

D.C.

Text: Jer. 8:22, Afro-American Spiritual
Tune: BALM IN GILEAD, Irregular; Afro-American Spiritual; Harm. by David Hurd, b.1950. © 1985, GIA Publications, Inc.

158 Lord, Touch Me

let good-ness touch me, Thy touch will cleanse me from

sin.

1. Some folks want trea-sures of sil - ver and
2. Teach me to love and teach me to

gold, Some want to reign with pow - ers un - told;
pray, Grant me a light to shine day by day;

But in my life, all that I can say,
Just to a - bide where joys nev - er cease

D.C.

Lord, be my guide and have thine own way.
Will be great joy, such com - fort and ease.

Text: Martha Eason Banks
Tune: Martha Eason Banks; Harm. by James A. Jones; Special harm. by Clara Ward, 1924-1973, © 1955, Clara Ward

159 I Don't Feel No Ways Tired

I don't feel no ways tired, I come too far from where I start - ed from, No-bod - y told me that the road would be eas - y, I

1. don't be-lieve He brought me this far to leave me.

2. brought me this far, *Repeated continuously while soloist sings verses:* I don't be-lieve He brought me this far, I
(would bring)

Solo Verses

1. I've been sick but God brought me. I've been in trou - ble, but God brought me.

2. I've been friendless, but God brought me.
   I've been lonely, but God brought me.
3. Please don't leave me, don't leave me, Jesus.
   Don't leave me, don't leave me, Lord.
4. I don't believe that God would bring me,
   I don't believe that God would bring me,
5. I don't believe that God would . . . *(to final ending)*

Final ending

bring me this far just to leave me.

bring me this far, leave me.

bring me this far, leave me.

Text: Curtis Burrell
Tune: Curtis Burrell, © 1978, Savgos Music, Inc.; Harm. by Kenneth Morris, b.1916, Martin and Morris, Inc.

160 Shine on Me

light - house, (Lord,) Shine on me. O, Shine on me. Shine on

me, Let the light from the light - house Shine on me.

Text: Afro-American Spiritual
Tune: Afro-American Spiritual; Harm. by Jefferson Cleveland, b.1927, and Verolga Nix, b.1933, from *Songs of Zion,* © 1981 by Abingdon

161 Leave It There

1. If the world from you with-hold of its sil - ver and its
2. If your bod - y suf - fers pain and your health you can't re-
3. When your en - e - mies as - sail and your heart be - gins to
4. When your youth - ful days are gone and old age is steal - ing

gold, And you have to get a - long with mea - ger fare,
gain, And your soul is al - most sink - ing in de - spair,
fail, Don't for - get that God in heav - en an - swers prayer;
on, And your bod - y bends be - neath the weight of care,

Just re - mem - ber, in His Word, how He feeds the lit - tle
Je - sus knows the pain you feel, He can save and He can
He will make a way for you and will lead you safe - ly
He will nev - er leave you then, He'll go with you to the

bird— Take your bur - den to the Lord and leave it there.
heal— Take your bur - den to the Lord and leave it there.
through-Take your bur - den to the Lord and leave it there.
end— Take your bur - den to the Lord and leave it there.

Leave it there, leave it there, Take your

Leave it there, leave it there,

bur - den to the Lord and leave it there; If you

leave it there;

trust and nev - er doubt, He will sure - ly bring you out—

Take your bur - den to the Lord and leave it there.

Words and Music: C. Albert Tindley

162 Precious Lord, Take My Hand

Slowly, with spirit

Pre-cious Lord, take my hand, Lead me on, let me stand,

I am tired, I am weak, I am worn; Thru the

storm, thru the night, Lead me on to the light,

Take my hand, pre-cious Lord, Lead me home.

1. When my way grows drear, pre-cious Lord, lin - ger
2. When the dark - ness ap - pears and the night draws

near,   When my   life   is   al - most   gone,
near,   And the   day   is   past and   gone,

Hear my   cry,   hear my call,   Hold my   hand   lest I
At   the   riv - er   I   stand, Guide my   feet, hold my

fall;   Take my hand,   pre-cious Lord,   Lead me home.
hand;   Take my hand,   pre-cious Lord,   Lead me home.

Text: Thomas A. Dorsey
Tune: Thomas A. Dorsey

163 Be Still, My Soul

1. Be still, my soul— the Lord is on thy side!
2. Be still, my soul— thy God doth un - der - take
3. Be still, my soul— the hour is has - t'ning on

Bear pa - tient - ly the cross of grief or pain;
To guide the fu - ture as He has the past;
When we shall be for - ev - er with the Lord,

Leave to thy God to or - der and pro - vide—
Thy hope, thy con - fi - dence let noth - ing shake—
When dis - ap - point - ment, grief, and fear are gone,

In ev - 'ry change He faith - ful will re - main.
All now mys - te - rious shall be bright at last.
Sor - row for - got, love's pur - est joys re - stored.

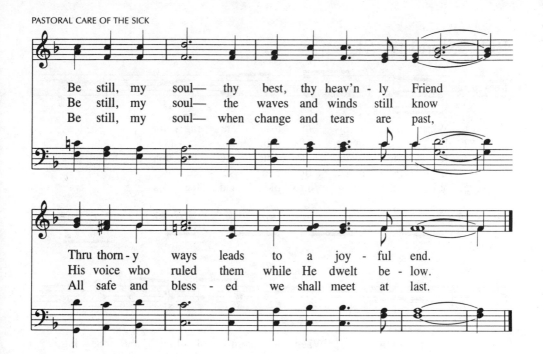

Be still, my soul— thy best, thy heav'n - ly Friend
Be still, my soul— the waves and winds still know
Be still, my soul— when change and tears are past,

Thru thorn - y ways leads to a joy - ful end.
His voice who ruled them while He dwelt be - low.
All safe and bless - ed we shall meet at last.

Text: Katharina von Schlagel; Tr. by Jane L. Borthwick, 1813-1897
Tune: FINLANDIA, Jean Sibelius

164 Stand by Me

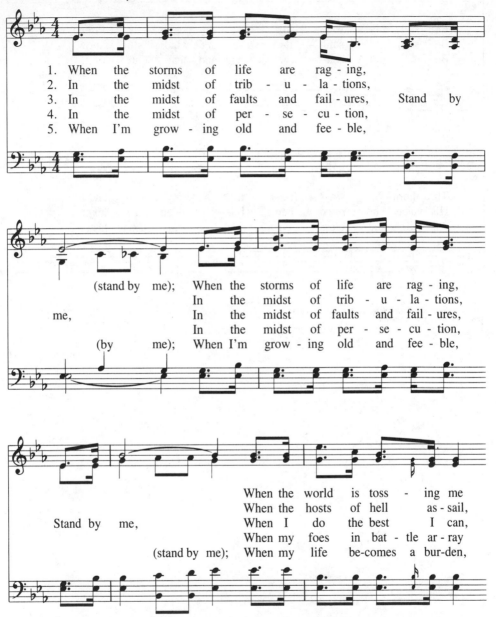

1. When the storms of life are rag - ing,
2. In the midst of trib - u - la - tions,
3. In the midst of faults and fail - ures, Stand by
4. In the midst of per - se - cu - tion,
5. When I'm grow - ing old and fee - ble,

(stand by me); When the storms of life are rag - ing,
In the midst of trib - u - la - tions,
me, In the midst of faults and fail - ures,
In the midst of per - se - cu - tion,
(by me); When I'm grow - ing old and fee - ble,

Stand by me,
(stand by me);
When the world is toss - ing me
When the hosts of hell as - sail,
When I do the best I can,
When my foes in bat - tle ar - ray
When my life be-comes a bur - den,

Like	a	ship	up - on		the	sea;	Thou	who
And	my	strength	be - gins		to	fail,	Thou	who
And	my	friends	mis - un	- der -	stand,		Thou	who
Un -	der -	take	to	stop	my	way,	Thou	who
And	I'm	near -	ing	chill - y	Jor -	dan,	O	Thou

rul -	est	wind	and	wa - ter,			(stand by	me).
nev -	er	lost	a	bat - tle,	Stand	by	me.	
know -	est	all	a - bout me,	Stand	by	me.		
saved		Paul	and	Si - las,				
Lil -	y	of	the	Val - ley,"			(by	me).

Text: C. A. Tindley, 1851-1933
Tune: C. A. Tindley, 1851-1933; Harm. by F. A. Clark

165 A Shelter in the Time of Storm

1. The Lord's our rock, in Him we hide,
2. A shade by day, de-fense by night,
3. The rag-ing storms may 'round us beat,
4. O Rock di-vine, O Ref-uge dear,

A shel-ter in the time of storm;
A shel-ter in the time of storm;
A shel-ter in the time of storm;
A shel-ter in the time of storm;

Se-cure what-ev-er ill be-tide,
No fears a-larm, no fears af-fright,
We'll nev-er leave our safe re-treat,
Be Thou our help-er ev-er near,

A shel-ter in the time of storm.
A shel-ter in the time of storm.
A shel-ter in the time of storm.
A shel-ter in the time of storm.

O, Je - sus is a rock in a wea - ry land, A
wea - ry land, a wea - ry land; O, Je - sus is a
rock in a wea - ry land, A shel - ter in the time of storm.

Text: Vernon J. Charlesworth; Adapt. by Ira D. Sankey, 1840-1908
Tune: Ira D. Sankey, 1840-1908

166 Just When I Need Him

1. Just when I need Him, Je-sus is near, Just when I
2. Just when I need Him, Je-sus is true, Nev-er for-
3. Just when I need Him, Je-sus is strong, Bear-ing my
4. Just when I need Him, He is my all, An-swer-ing

fal - ter, just when I fear; Read-y to help me,
sak - ing all the way thro'; Giv-ing for bur - dens
bur - dens all the day long; For all my sor - row
when up - on Him I call; Ten-der-ly watch-ing

read - y to cheer, Just when I need Him most.
plea-sures a - new, Just when I need Him most.
giv - ing a song, Just when I need Him most.
lest I should fall, Just when I need Him most.

Just when I need Him most, Just when I need Him most;

Je - sus is near to com-fort and cheer, Just when I need Him most.

Text: William C. Poole, 1875-1949
Tune: Charles H. Gabriel, 1856-1932

167 He Touched Me

1. Shack-led by a heav-y bur-den, 'Neath a load of
2. Since I met this bless-ed Sav-ior, Since He cleansed and

guilt and shame; Then the hand of Je-sus touched me,
made me whole; I will nev-er cease to praise Him,

And now I am no long-er the same.
I'll shout it while e-ter-ni-ty rolls. He touched me,

O, He touched me, and O, the joy that floods my

soul; Some-thing hap-pened, and now I

know, He touched me and made me whole.

Text: William J. Gaither, b.1936
Tune: William J. Gaither, b.1936

168 Lead Me, Guide Me

Lead me, guide me, a-long the way,

For if you lead me, I can-not stray.

Lord, let me walk each day with thee.

Lead me, oh Lord, lead me.

PENANCE

I am weak and I need thy strength and power
Help me tread in the paths of right - eous - ness,
I am lost if you take your hand from me,

to help me o - ver my weak - est hour.
Be my aid when Sa - tan and sin op - press.
I am blind with - out thy Light to see,

Help me through the dark - ness thy face to see,
I am put - ting all my trust in thee.
Lord, just al - ways let me thy ser - vant be.

Lead me, oh Lord, lead me.
Lead me, oh Lord, lead me.
Lead me, oh Lord, lead me.

169 Jesus, Lover of My Soul

1. Je - sus, Lov - er of my soul, Let me
2. Oth - er ref - uge have I none: Hangs my
3. Thou, O Christ, art all I want: More than
4. Plen - teous grace with Thee is found, Grace to

to Thy bos - om fly. While the
help - less soul on Thee. Leave, ah,
all in Thee I find; Raise the
cov - er all my sin: Let the

near - er wa - ters roll, While the tem - pest
leave me not a - lone, Still sup - port and
fall - en, cheer the faint: Heal the sick and
heal - ing streams a - bound, Make and keep me

still is high! Hide me, O my
com - fort me! All my trust on
lead the blind. Just and ho - ly
pure with - in. Thou of life the

Sav - ior, hide, Till the storm of
Thee is stayed, All my help from
is Thy name, I am all un-
foun - tain art: Free - ly let me

life is past; Safe in - to the
Thee I bring; Cav - en my de-
right - eous - ness; False and full of
take of Thee; Spring Thou up with-

ha - ven guide, O re - ceive my soul
fense - less head. With the shad - ow of
sin I am, Thou art full of truth
in my heart. Rise to all e - ter-

1.
at last!
Thy wing.
and grace.
ni - ty.

2.

Text: Charles Wesley, 1707-1788, alt.
Tune: Charles Wesley, 1707-1788, and Simeon B. Marsh, 1798-1875

170 Amen!

A - men, A - men,
A - men, Hal - le - lu - jah, praise Je - ho - vah, A-
A - men, Ev - 'ry - bod - y said, A -

men, A -
men, Hal - le - lu - jah, praise Je - ho - vah, A-
men, Ev - 'ry - bod - y said, A -

men, A - men, A - men, men.
men, Ev - 'ry - bod - y said,
men,

(Hum)
The Lord is my Shep - herd, He leads me
John on the Isle of Pat - mos, Looked o - ver in the
I would not be a de - ceiv - er, I'll tell you the
When I was a sin - ner, A sin - ner
Some - times my way is cloud - ed, My path - way
(Hum)

(Hum)

PENANCE

day by day; He feeds me when I'm hun - gry,
Glo - ry - land; He heard the an - gels sing - ing,
rea - son why: I'm a - fraid my Lord might call me,
just like you, I come to the Lord in re - pent - ance,
all con - fused; I set my face to-ward heav - en,

D.C.

And hears me when I pray. Ev-'ry-bod-y said,
And shout - ing Hal - le - lu - jah! A - men. Ev-'ry-bod-y said,
And I would-n't be read - y to die. Ev-'ry-bod-y said,
I be - lieved till I came thro'. Ev-'ry-bod-y said,
De - ter - mined to go thro'. Ev-'ry-bod-y said,

Text: Rev. B. H. Hogan
Tune: Rev. B. H. Hogan and Laura B. Davis; Harm. by E. Edwin Young, © 1963
© Copyright 1935 by Homer A. Rodeheaver. © Copyright 1963 by The Rodeheaver Company (A Div. of WORD, INC.) All Rights Reserved. International Copyright Secured. Used by Permission.

171 I'm So Glad, Jesus Lifted Me

1. I'm so glad, Jesus lift-ed me,
2. Sa - tan had me bound,
3. When I was in trou - ble,

I'm so glad,
Sa - tan had me bound,
When I was in trou - ble,

Je - sus lift - ed me,

I'm so glad,
Sa - tan had me bound,
When I was in trou - ble,

Je - sus lift - ed me, Sing - ing

PENANCE

Glo - ry, Hal - le - lu - jah! Je - sus lift - ed me.

Text: Afro-American Spiritual
Tune: Afro-American Spiritual; Harm. by Richard Smallwood

172 Sinner, Please Don't Let This Harvest Pass

Sin - ner, please don't let this har - vest pass; har - vest

pass; Sin - ner, please don't let this har - vest pass, har - vest

pass; Sin - ner, please don't let this har - vest pass, and

die and lose your soul at last soul at last. **Fine**

1. I know that my Re - deem - er lives, yes, He lives;
2. Sin - ner, O see the cru - el tree, cru - el tree,
3. My God is a might - y man of war, man of war,

I know that my Re - deem - er lives, yes, He lives,
Sin-ner, O see the cru - el tree, cru - el tree,
My God is a might - y man of war, man of war,

I know that my Re - deem - er lives, Sin - ner, please don't
Sin-ner, O see the cru - el tree, Where Christ
My God is a might - y man of war, Sin - ner, please don't

D.S.

let this har - vest pass, har - vest pass, Sin - ner,
died for you and me, you and me, Sin - ner,
let this har - vest pass, har - vest pass, Sin - ner,

Text: Afro-American Spiritual
Tune: Afro-American Spiritual

Amazing Grace 173

1. A - maz - ing grace! how sweet the sound, That
2. 'Twas grace that taught my heart to fear, And
3. The Lord has prom - ised good to me, His
4. Through man - y dan - gers, toils, and snares, I
5. When we've been there ten thou - sand years, Bright

saved and set me free! I once was lost, but
grace my fears re - lieved; How pre - cious did that
word my hope se - cures; He will my shield and
have al - read - y come; 'Tis grace has brought me
shin - ing as the sun, We've no less days to

now am found, Was blind, but now I see.
grace ap - pear The hour I first be - lieved!
por - tion be As long as life en - dures.
safe thus far, And grace will lead me home.
sing God's praise Than when we'd first be - gun.

Text: St. 1-4, John Newton, 1725-1807; St. 5, Ascr. to John Rees, fl.1859
Tune: NEW BRITAIN, CM; *Virginia Harmony*, 1831; Harm by John Barnard, b.1948
Harm. Copyright © 1982 by Hope Publishing Company, Carol Stream, IL 60188. All Rights Reserved. Used by Permission.

174 Yield Not to Temptation

1. Yield not to temp - ta - tion, For yield-ing is sin;
2. Shun e - vil com - pan - ions, Bad lan-guage dis - dain;
3. To those that o'er - com - eth, God giv-eth a crown;

Each vic - t'ry will help you Some oth - er to win;
God's name hold in rev - 'rence, Nor take it in vain;
Thro' faith we will con - quer, Tho' of - ten cast down;

Move hope - ful - ly on - ward, Dark pas - sions sub - due;
Be thought - ful and ear - nest, Kind - heart - ed and true;
He who is our Sav - ior, Our strength will re - new;

Look ev - er to Je - sus, He'll car - ry you through.
Look ev - er to Je - sus, He'll car - ry you through.
Look ev - er to Je - sus, He'll car - ry you through.

Ask the Sav-ior to help you, Com-fort, strength-en and keep you;

He is will-ing to aid you, He will car-ry you through.

Text: Horatio Richmond Palmer, 1834-1907
Tune: Horatio Richmond Palmer, 1834-1907

175 Softly and Tenderly Jesus Is Calling

1. Soft - ly and ten - der - ly Je - sus is call - ing,
2. Why should we tar - ry when Je - sus is plead - ing,
3. Time is now fleet - ing, the mo - ments are pass - ing,
4. O for the won - der - ful love He has prom - ised,

Call - ing for you and for me; See, on the
Plead-ing for you and for me? Why should we
Pass - ing from you and from me; Shad - ows are
Prom-ised for you and for me; Though we have

por - tals He's wait - ing and watch - ing, Watch-ing for
lin - ger and heed not His mer - cies, Mer - cies for
gath - er - ing, death - beds are com - ing, Com - ing for
sinned He has mer - cy and par - don, Par - don for

you and for me. Come home, come home,
you and for me? Come home, come home,
you and for me.
you and for me.

PENANCE

Ye who are wea-ry, come home; Ear-nest-ly, ten-der-ly,

Je - sus is call-ing— Call-ing, "O sin-ner, come home!"

Text: Will L. Thompson, 1847-1909
Tune: Will L. Thompson, 1847-1909

176 Tell Jesus All

1. Are you bur-dened, worn and wea - ry, Heed-ing
2. Would you have your past for - giv - en, And be
3. Are you need - ing one to guide you, Shel - ter

still the temp - ter's call? Is your life each
lift - ed, if you fall? Trust the Friend whose
when the storms ap - pall, Some-one who would

day more drear - y? Just tell Je - sus, tell Him all.
side was riv - en, Just tell Je - sus, tell Him all.
stay be - side you? Just tell Je - sus, tell Him all.

Just tell Je - sus, tell Him all, Tri-als great and tri-als small;

He will share them, free-ly bear them, Just tell Je - sus tell Him all.

Text: James Rowe, 1865-1933
Tune: J. M. Henson

Whey He Day 177

178 Lord, I'm Coming Home

1. I've wan-dered far a-way from God— Now I'm com-ing home;
2. I've wast-ed man-y pre-cious years— Now I'm com-ing home;
3. I've tired of sin and stray-ing, Lord— now I'm com-ing home;
4. My soul is sick, my heart is sore— Now I'm com-ing home;

The paths of sin too long I've trod— Lord, I'm com-ing home.
I now re-pent with bit-ter tears— Lord, I'm com-ing home.
I'll trust Thy love, be-lieve Thy word— Lord, I'm com-ing home.
My strength re-new, my hope re-store— Lord, I'm com-ing home.

Com-ing home, com-ing home, Nev-er-more to roam;

O-pen now Thine arms of love— Lord, I'm com-ing home.

Text: William J. Kirkpatrick, 1838-1921
Tune: William J. Kirkpatrick, 1838-1921

Pass Me Not, O Gentle Savior 179

1. Pass me not, O gentle Savior,
2. Let me at a throne of mercy
3. Trusting only in Thy merit,
4. Thou the Spring of all my comfort,

Hear my humble cry,
Find a sweet relief;
Would I seek Thy face;
More than life to me,

While on others
Kneeling there in
Heal my wounded,
Whom have I on

Thou art calling,
deep contrition,
broken spirit,
earth beside Thee?

Do not pass me by.
Help my unbelief.
Save me by Thy grace.
Whom in heav'n but Thee?

Savior, Savior, Hear my humble cry; While on others Thou art calling, Do not pass me by.

Text: Fanny J. Crosby, 1820-1915
Tune: William H. Doane, 1832-1915

180 Let All Things Now Living

1. Let all things now liv - ing A song of thanks - giv - ing
2. His law he en - forc - es, The stars in their cours - es

To God our cre - a - tor tri - um - phant - ly raise,
The sun in his or - bit o - be - dient - ly shine;

Who fash - ioned and made us, Pro - tect - ed and stayed us,
The hills and the moun - tains, The riv - ers and foun - tains,

Who guid - eth us on to the end of our days.
The deeps of the o - cean pro - claim him di - vine.

His ban - ners are o'er us, His light goes be - fore us,
We too should be voic - ing Our love and re - joic - ing;

A pil - lar of fire shin - ing forth in the night,
With glad ad - o - ra - tion a song let us raise

Till shad - ows have van - ished And dark - ness is ban - ished,
Till all things now liv - ing U - nite in thanks - giv - ing:

As for - ward we trav - el from light in - to light.
"To God in the high - est, ho - san - na and praise!"

Text: Katherine K. Davis, b. 1892, © 1939, E. C. Schirmer Music Co.
Tune: THE ASH GROVE, 6 6 11 6 6 11 D; Welsh Folk Tune; Harm. © 1978, *Lutheran Book of Worship*

181 How Great Thou Art

1. O Lord my God, when I in awe - some won - der
2. When thru the woods and for - est glades I wan - der
3. And when I think that God, His Son not spar - ing,
4. When Christ shall come with shout of ac - cla - ma - tion

Con - sid - er all the worlds Thy hands have made,
And hear the birds sing sweet - ly in the trees,
Sent Him to die, I scarce can take it in—
And take me home, what joy shall fill my heart!

I see the stars, I hear the roll - ing thun - der,
When I look down from loft - y moun - tain gran - deur
That on the cross, my bur - den glad - ly bear - ing,
Then I shall bow in hum - ble ad - o - ra - tion

Thy pow'r thru - out the un - i - verse dis - played!
And hear the brook and feel the gen - tle breeze,
He bled and died to take a - way my sin!
And there pro - claim, my God, how great Thou art!

CREATION

Then sings my soul, my Sav - ior God, to Thee;

How great Thou art, how great Thou art! Then sings my soul, my

Sav - ior God, to Thee; How great Thou art, how great Thou art!

Text: Stuart K. Hine, b.1899
Tune: Stuart K. Hine, b.1899

182 The Awakening

I. O-pen-ing up my
II. O-pen-ing up my

hands to the world you gave me; Reach-ing out my
heart to the world you gave me; Reach-ing out my

arms to the Lord and His won-ders; All that I
spir - it to the Lord and His won-ders; All that I

am, I know it's be - cause of you.
am, I know it's be - cause of you.

All that I am, I lift up to you.
All that I am, I lift up to you.

1. When I re - flect in me, I
2. My heart is filled with love, which is
3. And now I thank you, Lord for

see the emp - ti - ness which I once felt.
shared in a ver - y spe - cial way.
all you have done for me.

And now, through you, I see all I have
For in reach-ing out you sent me so man - y hearts to
And now, I thank you (y) for the

1., 2.

gained in my life. *(to refrain II)*
share in life with. *(to refrain I)*

3.

rit. *a tempo*

sun - shine and the rain. *(to refrain II)*

Text: Ron Broussard
Tune: Ron Broussard; Harm. by Adeline Huss
© 1987, GIA Publications, Inc.

183 God Will Take Care of You

1. Be not dis-mayed what-e'er be-tide,
2. Thru days of toil when heart doth fail,
3. All you may need He will pro-vide,
4. No mat-ter what may be the test,

God will take care of you;
God will take care of you;
God will take care of you;
God will take care of you;

Be-neath His
When dan-gers
Noth-ing you
Lean, wea-ry

wings of love a-bide, God will take care of you.
fierce your path as-sail, God will take care of you.
ask will be de-nied, God will take care of you.
one, up-on His breast, God will take care of you.

God will take care of you, Thru ev-'ry day, O'er all the way;

PROVIDENCE

He will take care of you, God will take care of you.

take care of you.

Text: Civilla D. Martin, 1869-1948
Tune: W. Stillman Martin, 1862-1935

You Are Near   184

Yah-weh, I know You are near, stand-ing

al - ways at my side. You

guard me   from the foe,   and You   lead   me   in

ways   e - ver - last - ing.

1. Lord,   You   have searched   my   heart,   and You
2. Where   can   I   run   from Your   love?   If   I
3. You   know   my   heart   and   its   ways,   You who
4. Mar - vel - ous   to   me   are Your   works;   how pro-

Man.

Text: Ps. 139, Dan Schutte, SJ
Tune: Dan Schutte, SJ; Harm. by Sr. Theophane Hytrek, OSF
© 1979, North American Liturgy Resources

185 God Has Smiled On Me

God has smiled on me, He has set me free.

God has smiled on me, He's been good to me.

Text: Isaiah Jones
Tune: Isaiah Jones, Jr.
© 1973, Davike Music Co.

186 His Eye Is on the Sparrow

1. Why should I feel dis-cour-aged, Why should the shad-ows come, Why should my heart be lone-ly And long for heaven and home, When Je-sus is my por-tion? My con-stant Friend is He: His eye is

2. "Let not your heart be trou-bled," His ten-der word I hear, And rest-ing on His good-ness, I lose my doubts and fears; Though by the path He lead-eth But one step I may see: His eye is

3. When-ev-er I am tempt-ed, When-ev-er clouds a-rise, When song gives place to sigh-ing, When hope with-in me dies, I draw the clos-er to Him, From care He sets me free: His eye is

PROVIDENCE

on the spar - row, And I know He watch - es me; His
on the spar - row, And I know He watch - es me; His
on the spar - row, And I know He watch - es me; His

eye is on the spar - row, And I know He watch - es me.
eye is on the spar - row, And I know He watch - es me.
eye is on the spar - row, And I know He watch - es me.

I sing be - cause I'm hap - py, I
I'm hap - py,

sing be - cause I'm free, For His eye is
I'm free,

on the spar - row, And I know He watch - es me.

Text: Civilla D. Martin, 1860-1948
Tune: Charles H. Gabriel, 1856-1932

187   I Know Who Holds Tomorrow

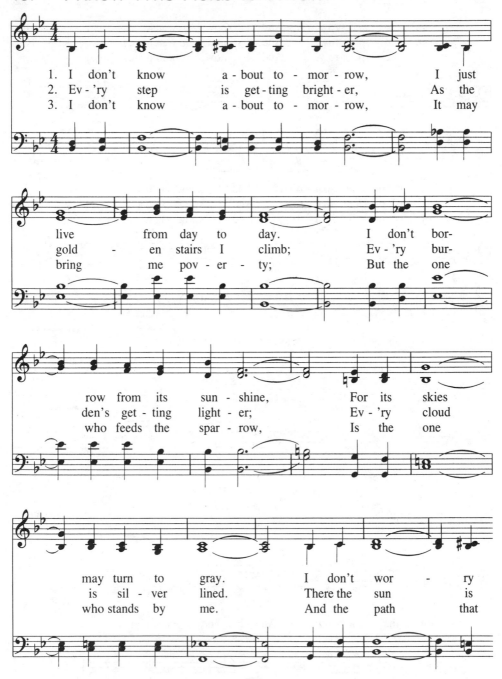

1. I don't know   a - bout to - mor - row,   I just
2. Ev - 'ry   step   is get - ting bright - er,   As the
3. I don't know   a - bout to - mor - row,   It may

live   from day to day.   I don't bor-
gold - en stairs I climb;   Ev - 'ry bur-
bring me pov - er - ty;   But the one

row from its sun - shine,   For its skies
den's get - ting light - er;   Ev - 'ry cloud
who feeds the spar - row,   Is the one

may turn to gray.   I don't wor - ry
is sil - ver lined.   There the sun is
who stands by me.   And the path that

o'er the fu - ture, For I know what
al - ways shin - ing, There no tear will
be my por - tion, May be through the

Je - sus said, And to - day I'll walk be -
dim the eye, At the end - ing of the
flame or flood, But His pres - ence goes be -

side Him, For He knows what is a - head.
rain - bow, Where the moun - tains touch the sky.
fore me, And I'm cov - ered with His blood.

Man - y things a - bout to - mor - row, I don't

seem to un - der - stand; But I know who

holds to - mor - row,   And I   know   who holds my   hand.

188   God Is So Good

1. God   is   so   good,   God   is   so   good,
2. He   cares   for   me,   He   cares   for   me,
3. He's   all   I   need,   He's   all   I   need,

God   is   so   good—   He's   so   good   to   me.
He   cares   for   me—   He's   so   good   to   me.
He's   all   I   need—   He's   so   good   to   me.

Text: Traditional
Tune: Traditional

Let the Heav'n Light Shine on Me 189

Text: Roland M. Carter, b.1942
Tune: Roland M. Carter, b.1942, *Five Choral Responses*
© 1978, Mar-vel Music Co.

190 This Little Light of Mine

1. This lit - tle light of mine I'm gon - na let it
2. Ev - 'ry - where I go, I'm gon - na let it
3. Je - sus gave it to me, I'm gon - na let it

Oh

shine, This lit - tle light of mine
shine, Ev - 'ry - where I go,
shine, Je - sus gave it to me,

Oh

I'm gon - na let it shine; This lit - tle light of
I'm gon - na let it shine; Ev - 'ry - where I
I'm gon - na let it shine; Je - sus gave it to

Oh

mine I'm gon - na let it shine, Let it
go, I'm gon - na let it shine, Let it
me, I'm gon - na let it shine, Let it

Oh

Text: Afro-American Spiritual
Tune: Afro-American Spiritual; Harm. by Horace Clarence Boyer

shine, let it shine, let it shine.
shine, let it shine, let it shine.
shine, let it shine, let it shine.

Text: Afro-American Spiritual
Tune: Afro-American Spiritual; Harm. by Horace Clarence Boyer

Blessing and Honor and Glory and Power 191

Bless-ing and hon - or and glo - ry and pow - er be

yours for ev - er and ev - er. A - men.

Text: Revelation 5:13
Tune: Timothy Gibson, © 1987, Timothy Gibson

192 How Excellent Is Thy Name

I will sing prais - es un - to the Fa - ther

for He's wor - thy to be praised.

1. Lord how ex - cel-lent is thy name in all the earth.

2. Let ev' - ry-thing that has breath, that has breath,

praise the Lord. O Lord, how ex-

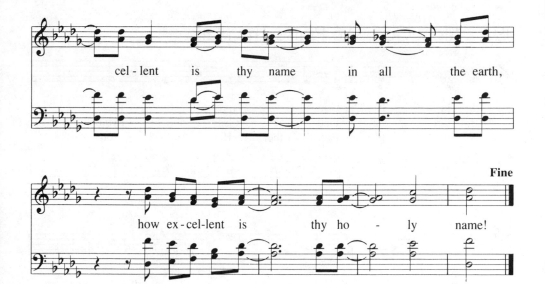

cel - lent is thy name in all the earth,

how ex - cel-lent is thy ho - ly name!

Text: John W. Higdon
Tune: John W. Higdon

193 Holy God, We Praise Thy Name

1. Ho - ly God, we praise thy name!
2. Hark! the loud ce - les - tial hymn
3. Ho - ly Fa - ther, Ho - ly Son,

Lord of all, we bow be - fore thee;
An - gel choirs a - bove are rais - ing;
Ho - ly Spir - it, Three we name thee,

All on earth thy scep - ter claim,
Cher - u - bim and Ser - a - phim
While in es - sence on - ly One,

All in heav'n a - bove a - dore thee;
In un - ceas - ing cho - rus prais - ing,
Un - di - vid - ed God we claim thee,

In - fi - nite thy vast do - main,
Fill the heav'ns with sweet ac - cord:
And a - dor - ing bend the knee,

Ev - er - last - ing is thy reign.
Ho - ly, ho - ly, ho - ly Lord!
While we own the mys - ter - y.

⌐Optional repeat of last eight measures

In - fi - nite thy vast do - main,
Fill the heav'ns with sweet ac - cord,
And a - dor - ing bend the knee,

Ev - er - last - ing is thy reign.
Ho - ly, ho - ly, ho - ly Lord!
While we own the mys - ter - y.

Text: Grosser Gott, wir loben dich; Ascr. to Ignaz Franz, 1719-1790; Tr. by Clarence Walworth, 1820-1900
Tune: GROSSER GOTT, 7 8 7 8 77; *Katholisches Gesangbuch,* Vienna, c.1774

194 Glorious Is the Name of Jesus

Glo - rious is the Name of Je - sus, Prais - es to His

Name. Oh, glo - rious and right - eous and

Ho - ly is His Name. Oh, glo - ri - ous is His

Name. I feel His pres - ence

in this place, His Spir - it has con - trol, Can't you

feel His warm em - brace and all the joy with - in your

soul, Oh, glo - ri - ous is His

Name, Oh, glo - ri - ous is His Name.

Text: R. J. Fryson
Tune: R. J. Fryson
© 1982, Bob Jay Music Co.

195 He Looked beyond My Fault

A - maz - ing grace shall al - ways be my song of praise,

For it was grace that bought my lib - er - ty;

I do not know just why He came to love me so,

He looked be - yond my fault and saw my need.

I shall for - ev - er lift mine eyes to Cal - va - ry,

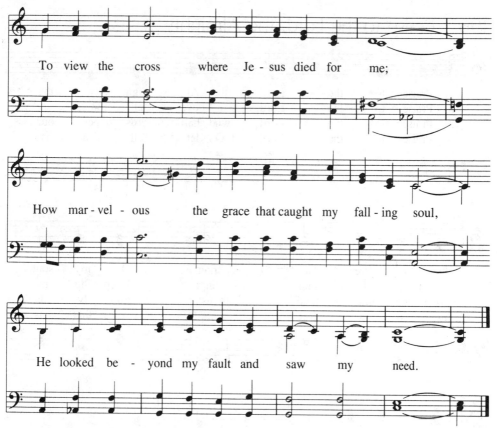

To view the cross where Je - sus died for me;

How mar - vel - ous the grace that caught my fall - ing soul,

He looked be - yond my fault and saw my need.

Text: Dottie Rambo
Tune: LONDONDERRY AIRE, adapt.

196 Praise to the Lord, the Almighty

1. Praise to the Lord, the Al - might - y, the king of cre - a - tion! O my soul, praise him, for he is your health and sal - va - tion! Come, all who hear:

2. Praise to the Lord, a - bove all things so might - i - ly reign - ing; Keep - ing us safe at his side, and so gent - ly sus - tain - ing. Have you not seen

3. Praise to the Lord, who shall pros - per our work and de - fend us; Sure - ly his good - ness and mer - cy shall dai - ly at - tend us. Pon - der a - new

4. Praise to the Lord— O let all that is in us a - dore him! All that has life and breath come now with prais - es be - fore him! Let the "A - men!"

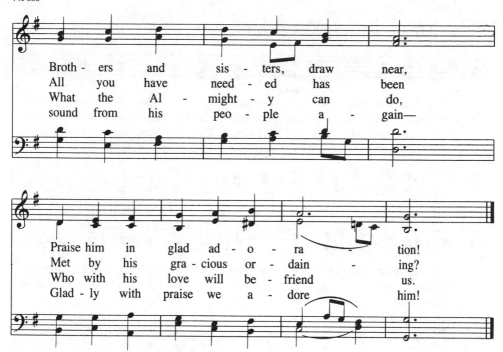

Broth - ers and sis - ters, draw near,
All you have need - ed has been
What the Al - might - y can do,
sound from his peo - ple a - gain—

Praise him in glad ad - o - ra - tion!
Met by his gra - cious or - dain - ing?
Who with his love will be - friend us.
Glad - ly with praise we a - dore him!

Text: *Lobe den Herren, den mächtigen König;* Joachim Neander, 1650-1680; Tr. by Catherine Winkworth, 1827-1878, alt.
Tune: LOBE DEN HERREN, 14 14 47 8; Straslund Gesangbuch, 1665

197 Joyful, Joyful, We Adore You

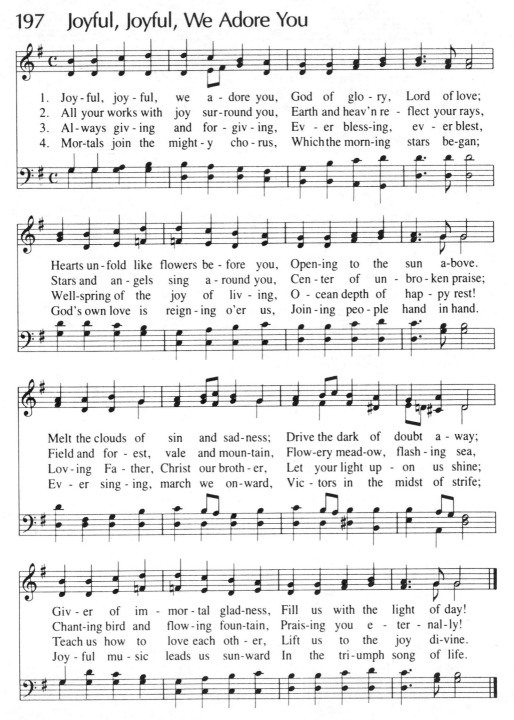

1. Joy-ful, joy-ful, we a-dore you, God of glo-ry, Lord of love;
2. All your works with joy sur-round you, Earth and heav'n re-flect your rays,
3. Al-ways giv-ing and for-giv-ing, Ev-er bless-ing, ev-er blest,
4. Mor-tals join the might-y cho-rus, Which the morn-ing stars be-gan;

Hearts un-fold like flowers be-fore you, Open-ing to the sun a-bove.
Stars and an-gels sing a-round you, Cen-ter of un-bro-ken praise;
Well-spring of the joy of liv-ing, O-cean depth of hap-py rest!
God's own love is reign-ing o'er us, Join-ing peo-ple hand in hand.

Melt the clouds of sin and sad-ness; Drive the dark of doubt a-way;
Field and for-est, vale and moun-tain, Flow-ery mead-ow, flash-ing sea,
Lov-ing Fa-ther, Christ our broth-er, Let your light up-on us shine;
Ev-er sing-ing, march we on-ward, Vic-tors in the midst of strife;

Giv-er of im-mor-tal glad-ness, Fill us with the light of day!
Chant-ing bird and flow-ing foun-tain, Prais-ing you e-ter-nal-ly!
Teach us how to love each oth-er, Lift us to the joy di-vine.
Joy-ful mu-sic leads us sun-ward In the tri-umph song of life.

Text: Henry van Kyke, 1852-1933, alt., © Charles Scribner's Sons
Tune: HYMN TO JOY, 8 7 8 7 D; Arr. from Ludwig van Beethoven, 1770-1827, by Edward Hodges, 1796-1867

Praise My Soul, the King of Heaven   198

1. Praise, my soul, the King of heav - en; To his feet thy
2. Praise him for his grace and fa - vor To our fa - thers
3. Fa - ther - like he tends and spares us; Well our fee - ble
4. An - gels, help us to a - dore him; Ye be - hold him

trib - ute bring; Ran - somed, healed, re - stored, for - giv - en,
in dis - tress; Praise him still the same as ev - er,
frame he knows; In his hands he gent - ly bears us,
face to face; Sun and moon, bow down be - fore him,

Ev - er - more his prais - es sing: Al - le - lu - ia!
Slow to chide, and swift to bless. Al - le - lu - ia!
Res - cues us from all our foes. Al - le - lu - ia!
Dwell - ers all in time and space. Al - le - lu - ia!

Al - le - lu - ia! Praise the ev - er - last - ing King.
Al - le - lu - ia! Glo - rious in his faith - ful - ness.
Al - le - lu - ia! Wide - ly yet his mer - cy flows.
Al - le - lu - ia! Praise with us the God of grace.

Text: Ps. (102) 103; Henry F. Lyte, 1793-1847, alt.
Tune: LAUDA ANIMA, 8 7 8 7 8 7; John Goss, 1800-1880

199 Blessed Assurance

1. Bless-ed as - sur - ance, Je - sus is mine! O what a
2. Per - fect sub - mis - sion, per - fect de - light, Vi - sions of
3. Per - fect sub - mis - sion, all is at rest, I in my

fore - taste of glo - ry di - vine! Heir of sal - va - tion,
rap - ture now burst on my sight; An - gels de - scend - ing,
Sav - ior am hap - py and blest; Watch-ing and wait - ing,

pur - chase of God, Born of His Spir - it, washed in His blood.
bring from a - bove Ech - oes of mer - cy, whis - pers of love.
look - ing a - bove, Filled with His good-ness, lost in His love.

Refrain

This is my sto - ry, this is my song, Prais-ing my

Sav - ior all the day long; This is my sto - ry, this is my song, Prais-ing my Sav - ior all the day long.

Text: Fanny J. Crosby, 1820-1915
Tune: Phoebe P. Knapp, 1839-1908

200 Bless His Holy Name

Bless the Lord, O my soul, and all that is with-
in me, Bless His ho - ly Name.

He has done great things, He has done great things,

D.C.

He has done great things, Bless His ho - ly Name.

Text: Ps. 103; Andraé Crouch
Tune: Andraé Crouch
© 1973, Lexicon Music Inc./Crouch Music
Used by permission. All rights reserved.

Let's Just Praise the Lord 201

Let's just praise the Lord! Praise the Lord! Let's just lift our hearts to heav-en and praise the Lord; Let's just praise the Lord! Praise the Lord! Let's just lift our hearts to heav-en and praise the Lord!

*Alternate lyrics, "voices," "hands," etc.

Text: Gloria Gaither, b.1942, William J. Gaither, b.1936
Tune: William J. Gaither, b.1936

202 Praise the Lord! You Heav'ns, Adore Him

1. Praise the Lord! you heav'ns, a - dore him; Praise him, an - gels, in the height; Sun and moon, re - joice be - fore him; Praise him, all you stars and light. Praise the Lord! for he has spo - ken; Worlds his might - y voice o - beyed;

2. Praise the Lord! for he is glo - rious; Nev - er shall his prom - ise fail; God has made his saints vic - to - rious; Sin and death shall not pre - vail. Praise the God of our sal - va - tion! Hosts on high, his pow'r pro - claim;

3. Wor - ship, hon - or, glo - ry, bless - ing, Lord, we of - fer as our gift. Young and old, your praise ex - press - ing, Our glad songs to you we lift. All the saints in heav'n a - dore you, We would join their glad ac - claim;

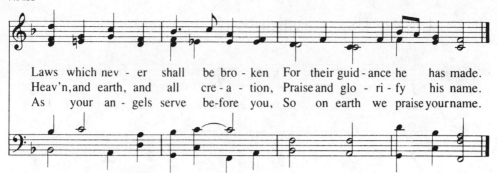

Laws which nev - er shall be bro - ken For their guid - ance he has made.
Heav'n, and earth, and all cre - a - tion, Praise and glo - ri - fy his name.
As your an - gels serve be - fore you, So on earth we praise your name.

Text: Ps. 148: St. 1-2 *Foundling Hospital Collection*, 1796; St. 3, Edward Osler, 1798-1863
Tune: HEAVENLY HOSTS, 8 7 8 7 D; Noel H. Tredinnick, b.1949

203 Let All That Is within Me Cry Holy

Let all that is with-in me cry, "Ho-ly!" Let
all that is with-in me cry, "Ho-ly!" Ho-ly!
Ho-ly! Ho-ly is the Lamb that was slain.

"Worthy," "Jesus," or "Glory" may be substituted for "Holy".
Text: Tr. by Melvin Harrel, *Melody Choruses*, © 1963, Gospel Publishing House
Tune: Anonymous; Harm. by Charles High, © 1978, The Word of God

Praise to the Lord 204

Praise to the Lord! Praise him! Praise to the Lord!

1. Shout to God, all you heav - ens, and
2. Know that God is our Fa - ther; he
3. Mer - ci - ful to us sin - ners, com-
4. Praise him, then, with full voic - es and
5. Praise the Lord with the trum - pet. O

clap your hands you on earth.
made us, we are his own.
pas - sion - ate to us all,
sing to him from the heart!
praise his name with the dance;

En - ter in - to his pre - sence ex-
Come to him with thanks - giv - ing ex-
He has sent his be - lov - ed to
Gath - er, Chris - tians, to - geth - er, to-
cel - e - brate with the cym - bal, ex-

ult - ing and sing - ing for joy!
tol - ling and bless - ing his name.
guide us in jus - tice and peace!
geth - er, to joy - ful - ly sing.
alt him with drum, pipe and string!

Text: The Psalms; Adapted by Paschal Jordan
Tune: Paschal Jordan
© 1984, McCrimmon Publishing Co. Ltd.

205   Come, Ye Thankful People, Come

1. Come, ye thank - ful peo - ple, come, Raise the song of har - vest - home: All is safe - ly gath-ered in, Ere the win - ter storms be - gin; God, our Mak - er, does pro - vide For our wants to be sup - plied; Come to God's own

2. All the world is God's own field, Fruit un - to his praise to yield; Wheat and tares to - geth - er sown, Un - to joy or sor - row grown; First the blade, and then the ear, Then the full corn shall ap - pear: Grant, O har - vest

3. For the Lord our God shall come, And shall take his har - vest home; From his field shall in that day All of- fens - es purge a - way; Give his an - gels charge at last In the fire the tares to cast, But the fruit - ful

4. E - ven so, Lord, quick - ly come To your fi - nal har - vest home; Gath - er all your peo - ple in, Free from sor - row, free from sin; There, for ev - er pu - ri - fied, In your pres - ence to a - bide: Come, with all your

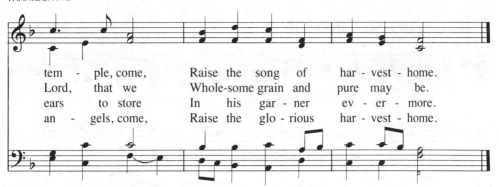

tem - ple, come,   Raise the song of   har - vest - home.
Lord,   that we   Whole-some grain and   pure may   be.
ears   to store   In his gar - ner   ev - er - more.
an - gels, come,   Raise the glo - rious   har - vest - home.

Text: Henry Alford, 1810-1871, alt.
Tune: ST. GEORGE'S WINDSOR, 77 77 D; George J. Elvey, 1816-1893; Harm. by Richard Proulx, b.1937, © 1986, GIA Publications, Inc.

Thank You, Lord   206

1. Thank you,   Lord,   Thank you,   Lord,   Thank you,
2. Been   so   good,   Been   so   good,   Been   so
3. Been   my   friend,   Been   my   friend,   Been   my,

Lord,   I just want to   thank you,   Lord.
good,   I just want to   thank you,   Lord.
Friend,   I just want to   thank you,   Lord.

Text: Traditional
Tune: Traditional; Harm. by J. Jefferson Cleveland, b. 1937, and Verolga Nix, b. 1933, from *Songs of Zion* © 1981 by Abingdon

207 I Am So Grateful

I am so grate-ful that Christ is in
my life. What would my life be with-out Him?
It would be ver-y dark and grim. When I'm sad
He cheers me, When I am lone-ly He will my
com-fort be. That's why I'm grate-ful, tru-ly grate-ful,

I'm so grate-ful that Christ is in my life.

1. When my friends and my foes turn a - gainst me,
2. When my way gets as dark as the mid - night,

And it seems I'm at the end of the road, There's a
And my bod - y is all racked with pain, Christ ap-

still soft voice saying with - in me, There is
pears with His ho - ly light, And by

some - one, some - one great - er who's carry - ing the load.
faith, faith and grace, I'm made whole a - gain.

Text: Gloria Griffin
Tune: Gloria Griffin; Harm. by Roberta Martin, © 1965

208 Now Thank We All Our God

1. Now thank we all our God With hearts and hands and voic - es,
2. O may this gra - cious God Through all our life be near us,
3. All praise and thanks to God The Fa - ther now be giv - en,

Who won-drous things has done, In whom his world re - joic - es;
With ev - er joy - ful hearts And bless - ed peace to cheer us;
The Son, and Spir - it blest, Who reigns in high - est heav - en,

Who, from our moth - ers' arms, Hath blessed us on our way
Pre - serve us in his grace, And guide us in dis - tress,
E - ter - nal, Tri - une God, Whom earth and heav'n a - dore;

With count-less gifts of love, And still is ours to - day.
And free us from all sin, Till heav - en we pos - sess.
For thus it was, is now, And shall be ev - er - more.

Text: *Nun danket alle Gott;* Martin Rinkart, 1586-1649; Tr. by Catherine Winkworth, 1827-1878, alt.
Tune: NUN DANKET, 6 7 6 7 6 6 6 6; Johann Crüger, 1598-1662; Harm. by A. Gregory Murray, OSB, b.1905

Remember Me   209

Re - mem - ber me, re - mem - ber
Fa - ther I stretch my hands to
If thou with - draw thy self from

me, Oh Lord, re - mem - ber me.
thee, no oth - er help I know.
me, Oh whith - er shall I go?

Text: Afro-American Spiritual
Tune: Afro-American Spiritual; Harm. by Leon C. Roberts, from *The Mass of St. Augustine,* © 1981, GIA Publications, Inc.

I Couldn't Hear Nobody Pray   210

O Lord!

And I could - n't hear no - bod - y pray: And I

could - n't hear no - bod - y · pray, O way down yon - der

1.

by my - self And I could - n't hear no - bod - y pray.

2.

1. In the val - ley!
2. Chill - y wa - ters!
3. Hal - le - lu - jah!

pray. A could - n't hear no - bod - y

On my knees!
In the Jor - dan!
Trou - bles o - ver!

pray A could - n't hear no - bod - y

With my bur - den!
Cross - ing o - ver!
In the king - dom!

pray, A could - n't hear no - bod - y

And my Sav - ior!
In - to Ca - naan!
With my Je - sus!

O Lord!
O Lord!
O Lord!

pray, A could - n't hear no - bod - y pray.

Text: Afro-American Spiritual
Tune: Afro-American Spiritual

211 Just a Little Talk with Jesus

1. I once was lost in sin but Je-sus took me in,
2. Some-times my path seems drear, with-out a ray of cheer,
3. I may have doubts and fears, my eyes be filled with tears,

And then a lit-tle light from heav-en filled my soul;
And then a cloud of doubt may hide the light of day;
But Je-sus is a friend who watch-es day and night;

It bathed my heart in love and wrote my name a-bove,
The mists of sin may rise and hide the star-ry skies,
I go to Him in pray'r, He knows my ev-'ry care,

And just a lit-tle talk with Je-sus made me whole.
But just a lit-tle talk with Je-sus clears the way.
And just a lit-tle talk with Je-sus makes it right.

Have a lit-tle talk with Je-sus,

Now let us let us

tell Him all a-bout our trou-bles, Hear our faint-est

He will

cry, an-swer by and by;

and He will Now when you

Feel a lit-tle pray'r wheel turn-ing, know a lit-tle

and you

fire is burn-ing, Find a lit-tle talk with

You will

Je - sus makes it right.

it makes it right.

Text: Cleavant Derricks
Tune: Cleavant Derricks
© Copyright 1965 by Stamps-Baxter Music/BMI. All rights reserved. International copyright secured.
Used by permission of the The Benson Company, Inc., Nashville.

212   Sweet Hour of Prayer

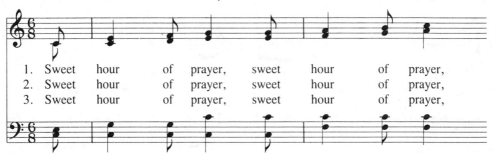

1. Sweet   hour   of   prayer,   sweet   hour   of   prayer,
2. Sweet   hour   of   prayer,   sweet   hour   of   prayer,
3. Sweet   hour   of   prayer,   sweet   hour   of   prayer,

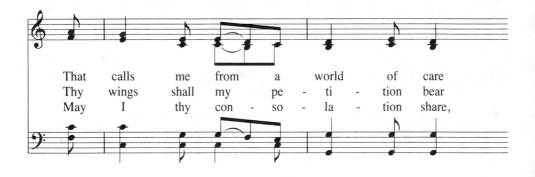

That   calls   me   from   a   world   of   care
Thy   wings   shall   my   pe - ti - tion   bear
May   I   thy   con - so - la - tion   share,

And bids me at my Fa - ther's throne
To Him whose truth and faith - ful - ness
Till from Mount Pis - gah's loft - y height

D.S.– And oft es - caped the tempt - er's snare
D.S.– I'll cast on Him my ev - 'ry care,
D.S.– And shout, while pass - ing thru the air,

Fine

Make all my wants and wish - es known!
En - gage the wait - ing soul to bless;
I view my home and take my flight:

By thy re - turn, sweet hour of prayer.
And wait for thee, sweet hour of prayer.
"Fare - well, fare - well, sweet hour of prayer!"

In sea - sons of dis - tress and grief
And since He bids me seek His face,
This robe of flesh I'll drop, and rise

D.S.

My soul has of - ten found re - lief,
Be - lieve His Word and trust His grace,
To seize the ev - er - last - ing prize,

Text: William W. Walford, 1772-1850
Tune: SWEET HOUR, William B. Bradbury, 1816-1868

213 A Praying Spirit

Lord, give me a pray-ing spir - it, a pray - ing spir - it. Lord, help me to say yes, yes, yes, Lord; yes, yes, Lord. A pray - ing spir - it through - out the day,

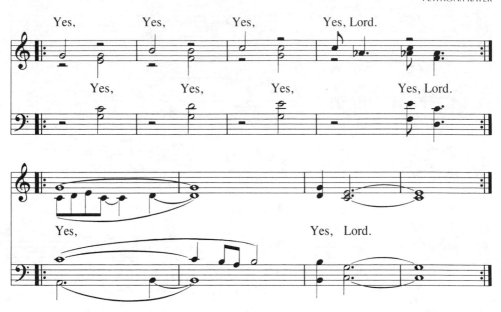

Yes,   Yes,   Yes,   Yes, Lord.

Yes,   Yes,   Yes,   Yes, Lord.

Yes,   Yes, Lord.

Text: Elbernita Clark
Tune: Elbernita Clark

214   What a Friend We Have in Jesus

1. What a friend we have in Je - sus,   All our
2. Have we tri - als and temp - ta - tions?   Is there
3. Are we weak and heav - y lad - en,   Cum - bered

sins and griefs to bear!   What a priv - i - lege to
trou - ble an - y - where?   We should nev - er be dis-
with a load of care?   Pre - cious Sav - ior, still our

car - ry Ev - 'ry -thing to God in prayer! Oh, what
cour - aged, Take it to the Lord in prayer: Can we
ref - uge; Take it to the Lord in prayer: Do thy

peace we of - ten for - feit, Oh, what
find a friend so faith - ful Who will
friends de - spise, for - sake thee? Take it

need-less pain we bear, All be - cause we do not
all our sor - rows share? Je - sus knows our ev - 'ry
to the Lord in prayer; In His arms He'll take and

car - ry Ev - 'ry -thing to God in prayer!
weak - ness, Take it to the Lord in prayer.
shield thee; Thou wilt find a sol - ace there.

Text: Joseph Scriven, 1819-1866
Tune: Charles C. Converse, 1832-1918

215 The Spirit Is Willing

Cantor, then all:

The Spir-it is will-ing says the Lord, the Spir-it is will-ing, the flesh is weak.

Cantor:

1. On the mount of o-lives Je-sus prayed to his Fa-ther:

Slowly

"Fa-ther if it is pos-si-ble let this cup pass from me." The

2. Fa-ther, let not my will, but yours be done. The

3. To his dis-ci-ples Je-sus says: stay a-wake and pray to a-void temp-ta-tion. The

Text: from Matthew 26
Tune: Jacques Berthier, b. 1923
© 1984, Les Presses de Taizé

216 Standin' in the Need of Prayer

1. Not my broth - er, nor my sis - ter, but it's me, O Lord,
2. Not the preach - er, nor the dea - con, but it's me, O Lord,
3. Not my fa - ther, nor my moth - er, but it's me, O Lord,
4. Not the stran - ger, nor my neigh - bor, but it's me, O Lord,

Stand-in' in the need of prayer; Not my broth - er, nor my sis - ter,
Stand-in' in the need of prayer; Not the preach - er, nor the dea - con,
Stand-in' in the need of prayer; Not my fa - ther, nor my moth - er,
Stand-in' in the need of prayer; Not the stran - ger, nor my neigh-bor,

but it's me, O Lord, Stand - in' in the need of prayer.
but it's me, O Lord, Stand - in' in the need of prayer.
but it's me, O Lord, Stand - in' in the need of prayer.
but it's me, O Lord, Stand - in' in the need of prayer.

It's me, it's me, O Lord, Stand - in' in the need of prayer;
It's me,

It's me, it's me, O Lord, Stand-in' in the need of prayer.

It's me,

Text: Afro-American Spiritual
Tune: Afro-American Spiritual

O Lord, Hear My Prayer 217

O Lord, hear my pray'r. O Lord, hear my pray'r, when I call

an-swer me. O Lord, hear my pray'r. O Lord, hear my pray'r.

Come and lis-ten to me. O me.

Text: Ps.(101) 102
Tune: Jacques Berthier, b.1923
©1982, Les Presses de Taizé

218 Come by Here

1. Come by here, Lord, come by here,
2. Some-body needs you, Lord, come by here,
3. Looking for a bless-ing, Lord, come by here,

Come by here, Lord, come by here,
Some-body needs you, Lord, come by here,
Looking for a bless-ing, Lord, come by here,

Come by here, Lord, come by here,
Some-body needs you, Lord, come by here,
Looking for a bless-ing, Lord, come by here,

O Lord, come by here.

Text: Afro-American Spiritual
Tune: Afro-American Spiritual; Harm. by Richard Smallwood
©1975 Richwood Music

Lead Me, Lord   219

Lead me, Lord, lead me in Thy right-eous-ness,

Make Thy way plain be - fore Thy face. A - men.

Text: Ps. 5:8
Tune: Samuel S. Wesley, 1810-1876

220 Every Time I Feel the Spirit

Ev - 'ry time I feel the spir - it, mov - ing in my heart, I will pray. Ev - 'ry-time I feel the spir - it, mov - ing in my heart, I will pray.

Up - on the moun - tain my Lord spoke,
All a - round me looked so shine,
Jor - dan riv - er, chilly and cold,

D.C.

(Out of) His mouth came fire and smoke.
Asked my Lord if all was mine.
Chills the bod - y but not the soul.

Text: Afro-American Spiritual
Tune: Afro-American Spiritual

My Faith Looks Up to Thee   221

1. My faith looks up to Thee, Thou Lamb of
2. May Thy rich grace im - part Strength to my
3. While life's dark maze I tread, And griefs a-
4. When ends life's tran - sient dream, When death's cold,

Cal - va - ry, Sav - ior di - vine! Now hear me
faint - ing heart, My zeal in - spire; As Thou hast
round me spread, Be Thou my guide; Bid dark - ness
sul - len stream Shall o'er me roll; Blest Sav - ior,

while I pray, Take all my guilt a - way,
died for me, O may my love to Thee
turn to day, Wipe sor - row's tears a - way,
then, in love, Fear and dis - trust re - move;

O let me from this day Be whol - ly Thine!
Pure, warm and change - less be, A liv - ing fire!
Nor let me ev - er stray From Thee a - side.
O bear me safe a - bove, A ran - somed soul!

Text: Ray Palmer, 1808-1887
Tune: Lowell Mason, 1792-1872

222 Lord, Make Me More Holy

1. Lord, make me more ho - ly, Lord make me more ho - ly,
2. Lord, make me more faith - ful, Lord make me more faith - ful,
3. Lord, make me more hum - ble, Lord, make me more hum - ble,
4. Lord, make me more right - eous, Lord, make me more right - eous,

Lord make me more ho - ly, un - til we meet a - gain.
Lord make me more faith - ful, un - til we meet a - gain.
Lord, make me more hum - ble, un - til we meet a - gain.
Lord, make me more right - eous, un - til we meet a - gain.

Ho - ly, ho - ly, ho - ly, un - til we meet a - gain.
Faith - ful, faith - ful, faith - ful, un - til we meet a - gain.
Hum - ble, hum - ble, hum - ble, un - til we meet a - gain.
Right-eous, right-eous, right - eous, un - til we meet a - gain.

Text: Afro-American Spiritual
Tune: Afro-American Spiritual

Father, I Stretch My Hands to Thee 223

1. Fa - ther, I stretch my hands to Thee, No oth-
2. What did Thine on - ly Son en - dure, Be - fore
3. Sure - ly Thou canst not let me die, O speak
4. Au - thor of faith! to Thee I lift My wear-

er help I know; If Thou with - draw Thy - self
I drew my breath! What pain, what la - bor to
and I shall live; And here I will un - wear-
y, long - ing eyes: O let me now re - ceive

from me, Ah! whith - er shall I go?
se - cure My soul from end - less death!
ied lie, Till Thou Thy spir - it give.
that gift! My soul with - out it dies.

Text: Afro-American Spiritual
Tune: Afro-American Spiritual

224 God Never Fails

God nev-er fails! God nev-er

fails! He a - bides in me, He gives me

vic - to - ry; No, God nev-er fails!

Just keep the faith and nev-er cease to pray;

Just walk up-right, call Him noon, day or night.

He'll be there, He'll be there, There's no need to

FAITH

wor - ry, for God nev - er fails!

1. I nev - er wor - ry, I nev - er fret;
2. No need to cry, I'm not a - fraid to die;

For God al - might - y has nev - er failed me yet.
I've got my Lord, I know He's on my side.

Tho' re-buked and scorned, I know that I've been re-
Dai - ly I trust Him, nev - er shall I

D.C.

born, for God nev - er fails!
doubt Him, for God nev - er fails!

Text: George Jordan
Tune: George Jordan; Harm. H. Pickard
© 1968, Elmer and Carl Music Publishers, Inc.

225 We've Come This Far by Faith

We've come this far by faith, Lean-ing on the Lord; Trust-ing in his ho-ly word, He's nev-er failed me yet. O can't turn a-round, We've come this far by faith.

1. Don't be dis - cour - aged when trou - ble's in your life, He'll bear your bur - dens and move all mis - er - y and strife. That's why we've

2. Just the other day I heard someone say
He didn't believe in God's word;
But I can truly say that God had made a way
And He's never failed me yet.
That's why we've

226 Yes, God Is Real

1. There are some things I may not know, There are some plac - es I can't go, But I am sure of this one thing, That God is real for I can feel Him deep with - in.

2. Some folks may doubt, some folks may scorn, All can de - sert and leave me a - lone, But as for me I'll take God's part, For God is real and I can feel Him in my heart.

3. I can - not tell just how you felt When Je - sus took your sins a - way, But since that day, yes, since that hour, God has been real for I can feel His ho - ly pow'r.

Yes, God is real, real in my soul; Yes, God is

FAITH

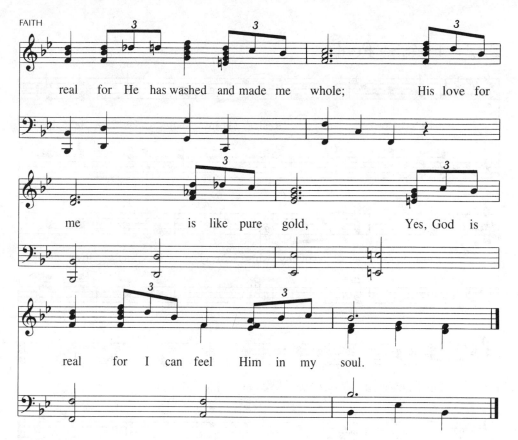

real   for He has washed and made me   whole;   His love for

me   is like pure gold,   Yes, God is

real   for I can feel   Him in my   soul.

Text: Kenneth Morris
Tune: Kenneth Morris
© 1942, Kenneth Morris

227 He's So Real

He's so real, Real in my soul to-day! He has
washed all of my sins a-way. Je-sus' love just
bub-bles o - ver in my soul.

Some peo-ple doubt the Lord; They don't be-
He's done so much for me; One day He

lieve in His word; They try to make you
set me free. And now I

D.C.

think that God is dead.
want the world to know.

Text: Charles H. Nicks, Jr.
Tune: Charles H. Nicks, Jr.
© 1975, Bridgeport Music, Inc.

Through It All   228

1. I've had man - y tears and sor-rows, I've had
2. I've been to lots of plac - es, And I've
3. I thank God for the moun-tains, And I

ques - tions for to - mor-row, There have been times I
seen a lot of fac - es, There have been times I
thank Him for the val - leys, I thank Him for the

did - n't know right from wrong;   But in
felt   so   all   a - lone;   But
storms He brought me through;   For

ev - ery sit - u - a - tion God gave   bless - ed con - so-
in my lone - ly hours, Yes, those   pre - cious lone - ly
if I'd nev - er had a prob - lem I would - n't know that

la - tion That my   tri - als come   to   on - ly
hours, Je - sus   let me know that   I
He could solve them, I'd nev - er know what faith in

make me   strong.
was His   own.   Through it all,
God could do.

Through it all, I've learned to trust in Je-sus, I've learned to trust in God; Through it all, Through it all, I've learned to de-pend up-on His Word.

Text: Andraé Crouch
Tune: Andraé Crouch

229 Lord, Help Me to Hold Out

Lord, help me to hold out,

Lord, help me to hold out,

Lord, help me to hold out un-

til my change comes.

1. comes.
2. comes.

My way may not be eas-y You did not

Text: James Cleveland, b.1932
Tune: James Cleveland, b.1932; Harm. by Kenneth Morris, b.1916
© 1974, Planemar Music Co.

O God, Our Help in Ages Past   230

1. O God, our help in ages past,
2. Un - der the shad - ow of your throne
3. Be - fore the hills in or - der stood,
4. A thou - sand a - ges in your sight

hope for years to come,
saints have dwelt se - cure;
earth re - ceived its frame,
like an eve - ning gone,

Our shel - ter from the
Suf - fi - cient is your
From ev - er - last - ing
Short as the watch that

storm - y blast, And our e - ter - nal home.
arm a - lone, And our de - fense is sure.
you are God, To end - less years the same.
ends the night Be - fore the ris - ing sun.

5. Time like an ever-rolling stream,
   Soon bears us all away;
   We fly forgotten, as a dream
   Dies at the op'ning day.

6. O God, our help in ages past,
   Our hope for years to come,
   Still be our guard while troubles last,
   And our eternal home.

Text: Psalm (89)90; Isaac Watts, 1674-1748
Tune: ST. ANNE, CM; Attr. to William Croft, 1678-1727; Harm. composite from 18th C. versions

231 My Heavenly Father Watches Over Me

1. I trust in God wher-ev-er I may be,
2. He makes the rose and ob-ject of His care,
3. I trust in God, for, in the li-on's den,
4. The val-ley may be dark, the shad-ows deep,

Up-on the land or on the roll-ing sea,
He guides the ea - gle thru the path-less air,
On bat-tle-field, or in the pris-on pen,
But O, the Shep - herd guards His lone-ly sheep;

For, come what may, From day to day,
And sure-ly He Re-mem-bers me, My
Thru praise or blame, Thru flood or flame,
And thru the gloom He'll lead me home,

rit.

heav'n-ly Fa-ther watch-es o - ver me.

a tempo

I trust in

God, I know He cares for me, On moun-tain
He cares for me, On

bleak or on the storm - y sea;
moun-tain bleak or on the sea, the storm - y sea;

Tho' bil-lows roll, He keeps my soul,
tho' bil-lows roll, He keeps my soul,

rit.

My heav'n - ly Fa - ther watch - es o - ver me.

Text: Rev. W. C. Martin
Tune: Chas. H. Gabriel, 1856-1932

232 I Will Trust in the Lord

1. I will trust in the Lord, I will trust in the Lord, I will trust in the Lord 'til I die. I will trust in the
2. Sis-ter, will you trust in the Lord, Sis-ter, will you trust in the Lord, Sis-ter, will you trust in the Lord 'til you die? Sis-ter, will you trust in the
3. Broth-er, will you trust in the Lord, Broth-er, will you trust in the Lord, Broth-er, will you trust in the Lord 'til you die? Broth-er, will you trust in the
4. Dea-con, will you trust in the Lord, Dea-con, will you trust in the Lord, Dea-con, will you trust in the Lord 'til you die? Dea-con, will you trust in the
5. Preach-er, will you trust in the Lord, Preach-er, will you trust in the Lord, Preach-er, will you trust in the Lord 'til you die? Preach-er, will you trust in the

Lord,   I   will   trust   in   the   Lord,   I   will
Lord, Sis-ter, will you trust in the Lord? Sis-ter, will you
Lord, Broth-er, will you trust in the Lord? Broth-er, will you
Lord, Dea-con, will you trust in the Lord? Dea-con, will you
Lord, Preach-er, will you trust in the Lord? Preach-er will you

trust   in   the   Lord   'til   I   die.
trust   in   the   Lord   'til you   die?
trust   in   the   Lord   'til you   die?
trust   in   the   Lord   'til you   die?
trust   in   the   Lord   'til you   die?

Text: Afro-American Spiritual
Tune: Afro-American Spiritual

233 Lead Me, Savior

1. Sav - ior, lead me, lest I stray,
2. Thou the ref - uge of my soul,
3. Sav - ior, lead me, then at last,

1. Sav - ior,   lead me, lest I stray,

Gen - tly lead me all the way;
When life's storm - y bil - lows roll,
When the storm of life is past,

Gen - tly   lead me all the way;

I am safe when by Thy side,
I am safe when Thou art nigh,
To the land of end - less day,

I   am   safe when by Thy side,

I would in Thy love a - bide.
All my hopes on Thee re - ly.
Where all tears are wiped a - way.

I would in Thy love a - bide.

Lead me, lead me, Sav - ior, lead me, lest I

stray; Gen - tly down the stream of time,

lest I stray; *stream of time,*

Lead me, Sav - ior, all the way.

all the way.

Text: Frank M. Davis
Tune: Frank M. Davis

234   I Can Do All Things through Christ

me, strength - ens me.

Text: Elbernita Clark
Tune: Elbernita Clark
© 1980, Bridgeport Music, Inc.

235 I Surrender All

1. All to Je - sus I sur - ren - der,
   I will ev - er love and trust Him,
2. All to Je - sus I sur - ren - der,
   World - ly pleas - ures all for - sak - en,
3. All to Je - sus I sur - ren - der,
   Let me feel the Ho - ly Spir - it
4. All to Je - sus I sur - ren - der,
   Fill me with Thy love and pow - er,

All to Him I free - ly give;
In His pres - ence dai - ly live.
Hum - bly at His feet I bow;
Take me, Je - sus, take me now.
Make me, Sav - ior, whol - ly Thine;
Tru - ly know that Thou art mine.
Lord, I give my - self to Thee;
Let Thy bless - ings fall on me.

I sur - ren - der all,
I sur - ren - der all,

TRUST

I sur-ren-der all,
I sur-ren-der all,
All to Thee, my
bless - ed Sav - ior, I sur-ren - der all.

Text: Judson W. Van de Venter, 1855-1939
Tune: Winfield S. Weeden, 1847-1908

236 'Tis So Sweet to Trust in Jesus

1. 'Tis so sweet to trust in Je - sus,
2. O how sweet to trust in Je - sus,
3. Yes, 'tis sweet to trust in Je - sus,
4. I'm so glad I learned to trust Thee,

Just to take Him at His word, Just to rest up-
Just to trust His cleans - ing blood, Just in sim - ple
Just from sin and self to cease, Just from Je - sus
Pre - cious Je - sus, Sa - vior, Friend; And I know that

on His prom - ise, Just to know, "Thus saith the Lord."
faith to plunge me 'Neath the heal - ing, cleans - ing flood!
sim - ply tak - ing Life and rest and joy and peace.
Thou art with me, Wilt be with me to the end.

Je - sus, Je - sus, how I trust Him! How I've proved Him o'er and o'er!

237 Be Strong!

Be strong! Do not be a - fraid. Our God will come,

will come to save us. Be strong! Do not be a - fraid.

Our God will come, will come to save us.

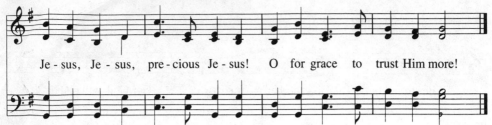

Je - sus, Je - sus, pre - cious Je - sus! O for grace to trust Him more!

Text: Louisa M. R. Stead, c.1850-1917
Tune: William J. Kirkpatrick, 1838-1921

from *Advent Mass*
Music by Edward V. Bonnemère
Word Adaptation by Robert J. Ledogar
Copyright © 1967, 1986 Amity Music Corporation

I Love the Lord 238

1. I love the Lord, He heard my
2. I love the Lord, He heard my

cry and pit - ied ev - 'ry groan.
cry and pit - ied ev - 'ry groan.

Long as I live and trou - bles rise,
O let my heart no more des - pair

I'll has - ten to His throne.
while I have breath to pray.

Text: Afro-American Spiritual
Tune: Afro-American Spiritual; Harm. by Richard Smallwood
Words and Music Richard Smallwood
©1975 Richwood Music

239 Think of His Goodness to You

1. When waves of af - flic - tion sweep o - ver the soul,
2. The world may for - sake you, and those whom you trust
3. Mis - for - tune's dark cloud may hang o - ver the way,
4. When dear ones are tak - en a - way from you here,

And sun - light is hid - den from view, If
May prove to be false and un - true; There's
De - spite your best ef - forts to do; The
You loved with af - fec - tion so true, Look

ev - er you're tempt - ed to fret or com - plain, Just
One you can trust e - ven un - to the end; Just
Sav - ior is guard - ing your treas - ures up there; Just
un - to the Sav - ior for strength to en - dure, And

think of His good - ness to you.
think of His good - ness to you.
think of His good - ness to you.
think of His good - ness to you.

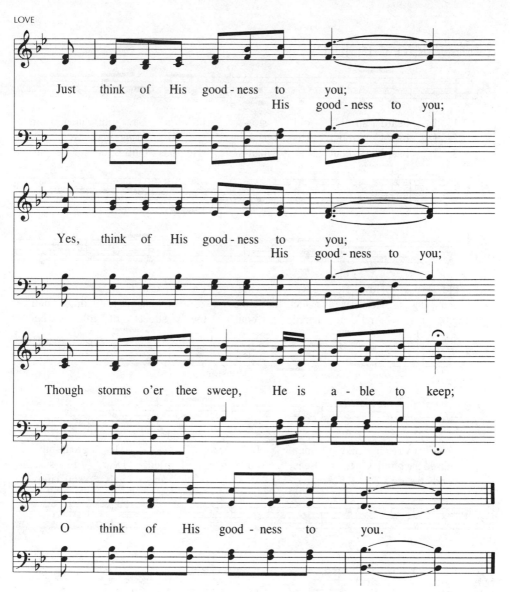

Just think of His good-ness to you;
His good-ness to you;

Yes, think of His good-ness to you;
His good-ness to you;

Though storms o'er thee sweep, He is a-ble to keep;

O think of His good-ness to you.

Text: R. C. Ward
Tune: R. C. Ward

240 Victory in Jesus

1. I heard an old, old sto - ry, how a Sav - ior came from
2. I heard a - bout His heal - ing, of His cleans - ing power re -
3. I heard a - bout a man - sion He has built for me in

glo - ry, How He gave His life on Cal - va - ry to
veal - ing, How He made the lame to walk a - gain and
glo - ry, And I heard a - bout the streets of gold be -

save a wretch like me; I heard a - bout His groan - ing,
caused the blind to see; And then I cried, "Dear Je - sus,
yond the crys - tal sea; A - bout the an - gels sing - ing

of His pre - cious blood's a - ton - ing, Then I re -
come and heal my bro - ken spir - it," And some - how
and the old re - demp - tion sto - ry, And some sweet

pent - ed of my sins and won the vic - to - ry.
Je - sus came and brought to me the vic - to - ry.
day I'll sing up there the song of vic - to - ry.

O vic - to - ry in Je - sus, my Sav - ior, for - ev - er!

He sought me and bought me with His re - deem - ing blood; He

loved me ere I knew Him, and all my love is due Him—

He plunged me to vic - to - ry be - neath the cleans - ing flood.

Text: Eugene M. Bartlett, 1885-1941
Tune: Eugene M. Bartlett, 1885-1941
© 1967, Albert E. Brumley and Sons

241 God Is Love

1. God is love, God is peace,
2. God is love, God is peace,

God is all that we need.
Please, Lord, come by here.

Gave His joy and gave His peace to
We need you to come by here right

me,
now,

He's my all. Sent His son
O Lord. By your deeds,

die for me: on - ly love could this be.
Lord, you see, you are what we need.

you all the way, when in your heart to him you learn to pray,

not just one day but each and ev' - ry day,

then you'll know not to stray.
keep me, dear Lord, to - day!

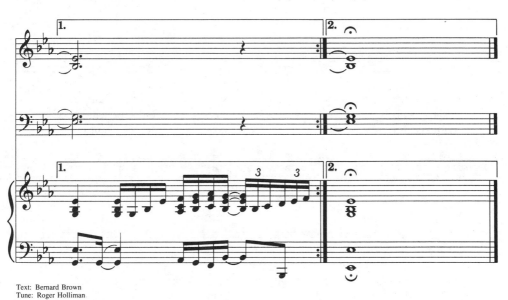

Text: Bernard Brown
Tune: Roger Holliman
© 1987, GIA Publications, Inc.

242 Great Is Thy Faithfulness

1. Great is Thy faith-ful-ness, O God my Fa-ther,
2. Sum-mer and win-ter, and spring-time and har-vest,
3. Par-don for sin and a peace that en-dur-eth,

There is no shad-ow of turn-ing with Thee;
Sun, moon and stars in their cours-es a-bove,
Thine own dear pres-ence to cheer and to guide;

Thou chang-est not, Thy com-pas-sions, they fail not,
Join with all na-ture in man-i-fold wit-ness,
Strength for to-day and bright hope for to-mor-row,

As Thou hast been Thou for-ev-er wilt be.
To Thy great faith-ful-ness, mer-cy and love.
Bless-ings all mine, with ten thou-sand be-side!

Great is Thy faith-ful-ness! Great is Thy faith-ful-ness!

Morn-ing by morn-ing new mer-cies I see;

All I have need-ed Thy hand hath pro-vid-ed,

rallentando

Great is Thy faith-ful-ness, Lord un-to me!

Text: Thomas O. Chisholm, 1866-1960
Tune: William M. Runyan, 1870-1957

243 I Know the Lord's Laid His Hands on Me

O I know the Lord, I know the Lord,

I know the Lord's laid his hands on me, O hands on me.

1. Did	ev - er	you	see	the	like	be -	fore?
	Je - sus	preach - ing		to	the		poor.
2. O	was - n't	that	a	hap -	py		day,
	Je - sus	washed	my	sins	a -		way?
3.	Some	seek the	Lord	and	don't	seek him	right,
	fool	all	day	and	pray	at	night,
4.	My	Lord's	done	just	what	he	said,
	healed	the	sick	and	raised	the	dead,

I know the Lord's laid his hands on me, King
I know the Lord's laid his hands on me. O
I know the Lord's laid his hands on me, When
I know the Lord's laid his hands on me. O
I know the Lord's laid his hands on me, They
I know the Lord's laid his hands on me. O
I know the Lord's laid his hands on me, He's
I know the Lord's laid his hands on me. O

Text: Afro-American Spiritual
Tune: Afro-American Spiritual

244 Is There Anybody Here Who Loves My Jesus

Is there an-y-bod-y here who loves my Je-sus? An-y-bod-y

here who loves my Lord?   I want to know if you love my

Je-sus;   I want to know if you love my Lord.

This world's a wil - der - ness of woe,
Re - li - gion is a bloom - ing rose,
When I was blind and could not see,
When ev - 'ry star re - fuses to shine,

LOVE

D.C.

So   let   us   all   to   glo   -   ry   go.
And   none   but   them   who   feel   it   know.
King   Je   -   sus   brought   the   light   to   me.
I   know   King   Je   -   sus   will   be   mine.

Text: Afro-American Spiritual
Tune: Afro-American Spiritual

245 My Soul Loves Jesus

1. My soul loves Je - sus, my soul
2. He's a won-der in my soul, He's a won-der
3. My soul seeks to please Him, my soul

loves Je - sus, my soul loves Je - sus;
in my soul, He's a won-der in my soul;
seeks to please Him, my soul seeks to please Him;

bless His name. My soul loves Je - sus,
bless His name. He's a won-der in my soul,
bless His name. My soul seeks to please Him,

my soul loves Je - sus, my soul
He's a won-der in my soul, He's a won - der
my soul seeks to please Him, my soul

LOVE

loves Je - sus, bless His name.
in my soul, bless His name.
seeks to please Him, bless His name.

Text: Charles H. Mason
Tune: Charles H. Mason

246 More Love to Thee, O Christ

1. More love to Thee, O Christ, More love to Thee!
2. Once earth-ly joy I craved, Sought peace and rest;
3. Then shall my ev - ery breath Sing out Your praise;

Hear Thou the prayer I make On bend - ed knee;
Now Thee a - lone I seek, Give what is best;
This be the on - ly song My heart shall raise;

This is my ear - nest plea:
This all my prayer shall be: More love, O Christ, to
This still my prayer shall be:

Thee, More love to Thee, More love to Thee! A - men.

Text: Elizabeth P. Prentiss, 1818-1878
Tune: MORE LOVE TO THEE, William H. Doane, 1832-1915

I've Got the Joy, Joy, Joy 247

1. I've got the joy, joy, joy, joy,
2. I've got the peace that pass - eth un - der - stand - ing,
3. I've got the love of Je - sus, love of Je - sus,
4. For there is there - fore now no con - dem - na - tion,

Down in my heart, Down in my heart, Down in my
Down in my heart, Down in my heart, Down in my
Down in my heart, Down in my heart, Down in my
Down in my heart, Down in my heart, Down in my

heart; I've got the joy joy, joy, joy,
heart; I've got the peace that pass - eth un - der - stand - ing,
heart; I've got the love of Je - sus, love of Je - sus,
heart; For there is there - fore now no con - dem - na - tion,

Down in my heart, Down in my heart to stay.
Down in my heart, Down in my heart to stay.
Down in my heart, Down in my heart to stay.
Down in my heart, Down in my heart to stay.

Text: George W. Cooke
Tune: George W. Cooke

248 In the Garden

1. I come to the gar-den a-lone, While the dew is
2. He speaks, and the sound of His voice Is so sweet the
3. I'd stay in the gar-den with Him Though the night a-

still on the ros - es; And the voice I hear, fall-ing
birds hush their sing - ing; And the mel - o - dy that He
round me be fall - ing; But He bids me go thru the

on my ear, The Son of God dis - clos - es.
gave to me With - in my heart is ring - ing.
voice of woe, His voice to me is call - ing.

And He walks with me, and He talks with me, And He

JOY

tells me I am His own, And the joy we share as we tar - ry there, None oth - er has ev - er known.

Text: C. Austin Miles, 1868-1946
Tune: C. Austin Miles, 1868-1946

249 O Happy Day!

1. O hap-py day that fixed my choice On Thee, my
2. O hap-py bond that seals my vows To Him who
3. 'Tis done, the great trans-ac-tion's done— I am my
4. Now rest, my long - di - vid - ed heart, Fixed on this

Sav - ior and my God! Well may this glow - ing heart re-
mer - its all my love! Let cheer-ful an - thems fill His
Lord's and He is mine; He drew me, and I fol - lowed
bliss - ful cen - ter, rest; Nor ev - er from my Lord de-

joice And tell its rap - tures all a - broad.
house, While to that sa - cred shrine I move.
on, Charmed to con - fess the voice di - vine.
part, With Him of ev - 'ry good pos - sessed.

Hap - py day, hap - py day, When Je - sus washed

my sins a - way! He taught me how to watch and pray

And live re - joic - ing ev - 'ry day; Hap - py day,

hap - py day, When Je - sus washed my sins a - way!

Text: Philip Doddridge, 1702-1751
Tune: Edward F. Rimbault

250 In My Father's House

1. Come and go with me to my Fa-ther's house, to my Fa-ther's house, to my Fa-ther's house. Come and go with me to my Fa-ther's house, where there's joy, joy, joy!

Any of the following verses, or spontaneous verses, may be used.

2. It's not very far to my Father's house...
3. Jesus is the Way to my Father's house...
4. Jesus is the Light in my Father's house...
5. All is peace and love in my Father's house...
6. We will dance and sing in my Father's house...
7. We will praise the Lord in my Father's house...

Text: Anonymous
Tune: Anonymous; Harm. by Charles High, © 1978, The Word of God

Jesus, Savior, Pilot Me 251

1. Je - sus, Sav - ior, pi - lot me, O - ver life's tem-
2. As a moth - er stills her child, Thou canst hush the
3. When at last I near the shore, And the fear - ful

pes - tuous sea: Un - known waves be - fore me roll,
o - cean wild; Bois-t'rous waves o - bey Thy will
break-ers roar 'Twixt me and the peace - ful rest—

Hid - ing rocks and treach-'rous shoal; Chart and com - pass
When Thou say'st to them, "Be still!" Won-drous Sov - 'reign
Then, while lean - ing on Thy breast, May I hear Thee

come from Thee— Je - sus, Sav - ior, pi - lot me!
of the sea, Je - sus, Sav - ior, pi - lot me!
say to me, "Fear not— I will pi - lot thee!"

Text: Edward Hopper, 1816-1888
Tune: John E. Gould, 1822-1875

252 I've Got a Feeling

1. I've got a feel - ing, ev - 'ry
2. Je - sus al - read - y told me, ev - 'ry
3. The Ho - ly Ghost has con - firmed it, ev - 'ry

thing's gon - na be al - right. O
thing's gon - na be al - right. O
thing's gon - na be al - right. O the

I've got a feel - ing ev - 'ry-
Je - sus al - read - y told me ev - 'ry-
Ho - ly Ghost has con - firmed it, ev - 'ry-

thing's gon - na be al - right. O
thing's gon - na be al - right. O
thing's gon - na be al - right. O the

8va

I've got a feel - ing ev - 'ry-
Je - sus al - read - y told me, ev - 'ry-
Ho - ly Ghost has con - firmed it, ev - 'ry-

thing's gon - na be al - right, be al-
thing's gon - na be al - right, be al-
thing's gon - na be al - right, be al-

right, be al - right, be al - right.
right, be al - right, be al - right.
right, be al - right, be al - right.

Text: Traditional
Tune: Traditional

253 Jesus, You Brought Me All of the Way

Je - sus, You brought me all the way.

You car - ry my bur - dens ev - er - y day

You are such a won - der - ful Sav - ior, I've nev - er

known you to fail me yet, for you brought me, thank God,

all the way, for You brought me, thank God, all the

way, for You brought me, thank God, all the way,

for You brought me, thank God, all the way, Je-sus,

You brought me all the way, Trou-bles and

tri - als seem to block my way.

I find it some-times dif - fi - cult to pray.

But there is one thing I can tru - ly say:

That you brought me, thank God, all the way.

Text: Traditional
Tune: Traditional; Arr. © 1987, Kenneth Louis

254 He Knows Just How Much You Can Bear

1. We are our heav - en - ly Fa - ther's chil - dren
2. Think of the times you've asked the ques - tion
3. Just praise His name al - though you're bur - dened,

And we all know that He loves us one and all;
Down in your heart now just what shall I do?
For there are bless - ings He's be - stowed on you;

Yet there are times when we find we an - swer
Then you con - fide in your friends and loved ones,
In ev - 'ry way we must nev - er doubt Him,

An - oth - er's voice and call; If we are will - ing,
But they have trou - bles, too; There is a God who
These trials we must go through; Try to en - dure a

He will teach us, His voice on - ly to o-
rules earth and heav'n, In Him there's re - lief from
lit - tle long - er, And don't for - get that for

bey no mat - ter where, and He knows,
ev - 'ry pain or care, for He knows,
each of us He cares and He knows,

Yes, He knows, Just how much we can bear.

Though the load gets heav - y, You're nev - er left a-

lone to bear it all; Ask for the strength and

keep on toil-ing, tho' the tear-drops fall.

You have the joy of this as - sur - ance:

The heav - en - ly Fa - ther will al - ways an - swer

prayer and He knows, Yes, He knows

Just how much you can bear. bear.

Text: Roberta Martin
Tune: Roberta Martin
© 1941, Roberta Martin

Come, Ye Disconsolate 255

1. Come, ye dis - con - so - late, wher - e'er ye lan - guish—
2. Joy of the des - o - late, light of the stray - ing,
3. Here see the Bread of Life, see wa - ters flow - ing

Come to the mer - cy - seat, fer - vent - ly kneel;
Hope of the pen - i - tent, fade - less and pure!
Forth from the throne of God, pure from a - bove;

Here bring your wound - ed hearts, here tell your an - guish:
Here speaks the Com - fort - er, ten - der - ly say - ing,
Come to the feast of love— come ev - er know - ing

Earth has no sor - row that heav'n can - not heal.
"Earth has no sor - row that heav'n can - not cure."
Earth has no sor - row but heav'n can re - move.

Text: St. 1-2, Thomas Moore, 1779-1852; St. 3, Thomas Hastings, 1784-1872
Tune: Samuel Webbe, 1740-1816

256 It Is Well with My Soul

1. When peace, like a riv - er, at - tend - eth my
2. Tho' Sa - tan should buf - fet, tho' tri - als should
3. My sin— oh, the bliss of this glo - ri - ous
4. And, Lord, haste the day when the faith shall be

way, When sor - rows like sea - bil - lows roll;
come, Let this blest as - sur - ance con - trol,
thought— My sin— not in part, but the whole—
sight, The clouds be rolled back as a scroll,

What - ev - er my lot, Thou hast taught me to
That Christ has re - gard - ed my help - less es -
Is nailed to the cross and I bear it no
The trump shall re - sound and the Lord shall de -

say, It is well, it is well with my soul.
tate, And has shed His own blood for my soul.
more, Praise the Lord, praise the Lord, O my soul!
scend, E - ven so— it is well with my soul.

It is well with my soul,
It is well with my
soul,
It is well, it is well with my soul.

Text: Horatio G. Spafford, 1828-1888
Tune: Philip P. Bliss, 1838-1876

257 Leaning on the Everlasting Arms

1. What a fel - low - ship, what a joy di - vine,
2. O how sweet to walk in this pil - grim way,
3. What have I to dread, what have I to fear,

Lean - ing on the ev - er - last - ing arms;
Lean - ing on the ev - er - last - ing arms;
Lean - ing on the ev - er - last - ing arms?

What a bless - ed - ness, what a peace is mine,
O how bright the path grows from day to day,
I have bless - ed peace with my Lord so near,

Lean - ing on the ev - er - last - ing arms. Lean-
Lean - ing on

ing, lean - ing, Safe and se - cure from
Je - sus, lean - ing on Je - sus,

all a - larms; Lean - ing, lean-
Lean - ing on Je - sus, lean - ing on

ing, Lean - ing on the ev - er - last - ing arms.
Je - sus,

Text: Elisha A. Hoffman, 1839-1929
Tune: Anthony J. Showalter, 1858-1924

258 Come Out the Wilderness

1. Tell me, how did you feel when you
2. Well, I loved ev - 'ry - bod - y when I
3. Well, my soul was so hap - py when I

come out the wil - der - ness, come out the wil - der - ness,

come out the wil - der - ness? How did you feel when you
Loved ev - 'ry - bod - y when I
Soul was so hap - py when I

come out the wil - der - ness? Lean - ing on the Lord,

I'm a lean - ing on the Lord, I'm a lean - ing on the Lord,

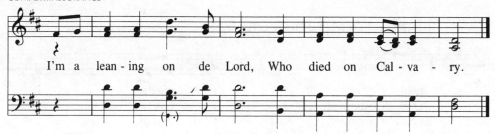

I'm a lean-ing on de Lord, Who died on Cal - va - ry.

Text: Afro-American Spiritual
Tune: Afro-American Spiritual

259 Until I Found the Lord

1. Lord, I cried, I cried, I
2. Lord, I moaned, I moaned, I
3. Lord, I prayed, I prayed, I

I cried, yes, I cried, I cried all night long.
I moaned, yes, I moaned, I moaned all night long.
I prayed, yes, I prayed, I prayed all night long.

cried,
moaned,
prayed,

Un-il I found the Lord. My soul

I cried, yes, I cried un-til I found the Lord.
I moaned, yes, I moaned un-til I found the Lord.
I prayed, yes, I prayed un-til I found the Lord.

O my soul, O my soul,

Just could-n't rest con-tent-ed, just could-n't rest con-tent-ed,

O

Un - til I found the Lord.

Just - could-n't rest con - tent - ed un - til I found the Lord.

Text: Clara Ward, 1924-1973
Tune: Clara Ward, 1924-1973
© 1971, Cherry Blossom Music Co.

260 Without Him I Could Do Nothing

1. With - out him I could do noth - ing, With - out him
2. With - out him I could be dy - ing, With - out him

I'd sure - ly fail; With - out him I would be
I'd be en - slaved; With - out him life would be

drift - ing Like a ship with - out a sail.
hope - less, But with Je - sus, thank God, I'm saved.

Je - sus, O Je - sus, Do you know him to - day?

You can't turn him a - way. O Je - sus, O

Je - sus, With - out him, how lost I would be.

Text: Mylon R. LeFevre, b.1945
Tune: Mylon R. LeFevre, b.1945
© 1963, LeFevre Sing Publishing Co.

261 Take the Name of Jesus with You

1. Take the name of Je - sus with you, Child of
2. Take the name of Je - sus ev - er As a
3. O the pre - cious name of Je - sus! How it
4. At the name of Je - sus bow - ing, Fall - ing

sor - row and of woe; It will joy and com - fort
shield from ev - 'ry snare; When temp - ta - tions round you
thrills our souls with joy, When his lov - ing arms re -
pros - trate at his feet, King of kings in heav'n we'll

give you, Take it then wher - e'er you go.
gath - er, Breathe that ho - ly name in pray'r.
ceive us, And his songs our tongues em - ploy.
crown him, When our jour - ney is com - plete.

Pre - cious name, O how sweet!
Pre - cious name, O how sweet!

Hope of earth and joy of heav'n; Pre-cious name,

Pre-cious name,

O how sweet! Hope of earth and joy of heav'n.

O how sweet, how sweet!

Text: Lydia Baxter, 1809-1874
Tune: PRECIOUS NAME; William H. Doane, 1832-1915

262 Hush, Hush, Somebody's Callin' Mah Name

Hush. Hush. Some-bod - y's call - in' mah

name. Hush. Hush. Some-bod - y's

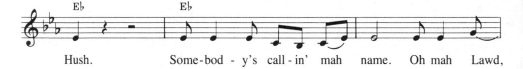

call - in' mah name (yame, yame). Hush.

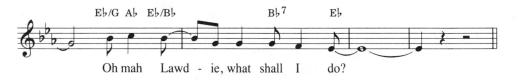

Hush. Some-bod - y's call - in' mah name. Oh mah Lawd,

Oh mah Lawd - ie, what shall I do?

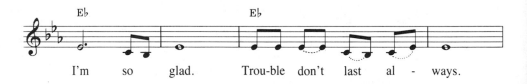

I'm so glad. Trou-ble don't last al - ways.

I'm so glad. Trou-ble don't last al -

ways, yea, yea, yea. I'm so glad.

Trou-ble don't last al - ways. Oh mah Lawd,

Oh mah Lawd - ie, what shall I do?

2. Sounds like Jesus. Somebody's callin' mah name, . . .
3. Soon one mornin', death'll come creepin' in mah room, . . .
4. I'm so glad. Ah got mah religion in time, . . .
5. I'm so glad. I'm on mah journey home, . . .

Text: Afro-American Spiritual
Tune: Afro-American Spiritual; Arr. by J. Jefferson Cleveland, b. 1937, and Verolga Nix, b. 1933, from *Songs of Zion*,
© 1979 by Abingdon

263 I Want Jesus to Walk with Me

1. I want Je-sus to walk with me;
2. In my tri - als, Lord, walk with me;
3. When I'm in trou - ble, Lord, walk with me;

I want Je - sus to walk with me;
In my tri - als, Lord, walk with me;
When I'm in trou - ble, Lord, walk with me;

All a - long my pil - grim jour - ney,
When my heart is al - most break - ing,
When my head is bowed in sor - row,

Lord, I want Je - sus to walk with me.
Lord, I want Je - sus to walk with me.
Lord, I want Je - sus to walk with me.

Text: Afro-American Spiritual
Tune: Afro-American Spiritual; Harm. by J. Jefferson Cleveland, b.1937, and Verolga Nix, b.1933, from *Songs of Zion*, © 1981 by Abingdon

Ride On, Jesus, Ride   264

Ride on, Je-sus, ride. Ride on, Je-sus, ride.

Ride on, Je-sus, con-quering King. Ride on, Je-sus, ride.

King Je-sus rides on a milk white horse. Ride on Je-sus,
My Je-sus left-ed his throne a-bove. Ride on, Je-sus,

ride. The riv-er Jor-dan He did cross. Ride on Je-sus, ride.
ride. See his mer-cy and his love. Ride on, Je-sus, ride.

Text: Afro-American Spiritual
Tune: Afro-American Spiritual; Arr. by Barbara Jackson Martin

265 He's a Mighty Good Leader

1. He's a might-y good lead-er, He's a might-y good lead-er, He's a might-y good lead-er, Je-sus Christ, God's Son, God's Son, God's Son, He's a might-y good lead-er, He's a might-y good lead - er, He's a
2. He is my Cap-tain, He is my Cap-tain, He is my Cap-tain, Je-sus Christ, God's Son, God's Son, God's Son, He is my Cap-tain, He is my Cap - tain, He
3. In the time of trou-ble, In the time of trou-ble, Je-sus Christ, God's Son, God's Son, God's Son, In the time of trou-ble, In the time of trou - ble, In the

might - y good   lead - er,   Je - sus   Christ,   God's   Son.
is   my   Cap - tain,   Je - sus   Christ,   God's   Son.
time   of   trou - ble,   Je - sus   Christ,   God's   Son.

Text: Afro-American Spiritual
Tune: Afro-American Spiritual

266 Jesus Is All the World to Me

1. Je - sus is all the world to me, My life, my joy, my
2. Je - sus is all the world to me, My friend in tri - als
3. Je - sus is all the world to me, And true to Him I'll
4. Je - sus is all the world to me, I want no bet - ter

all; He is my strength from day to day, With-
sore; I go to Him for bless - ings, and He
be; Oh, how could I this friend de - ny, When
friend; I trust Him now, I'll trust Him when Life's

out Him I would fall: When I am sad, to
gives them o'er and o'er: He sends the sun - shine
He's so true to me? Fol - low - ing Him I
fleet - ing days shall end: Beau - ti - ful life with

Him I go, No oth - er one can cheer me so;
and the rain, He sends the har - vest's gold - en grain;
know I'm right, He watch - es o'er me day and night;
such a friend, Beau - ti - ful life that has no end;

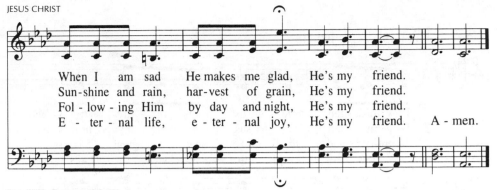

When I am sad He makes me glad, He's my friend.
Sun-shine and rain, har-vest of grain, He's my friend.
Fol - low - ing Him by day and night, He's my friend.
E - ter - nal life, e - ter - nal joy, He's my friend. A - men.

Text: Will L. Thompson, 1847-1909
Tune: Will L. Thompson, 1847-1909

267 I Must Tell Jesus

1. I must tell Je - sus all of my tri - als,
2. I must tell Je - sus all of my trou - bles,
3. Tempt-ed and tried, I need a great Sav - ior,
4. O how the world to e - vil al - lures me!

I can - not bear these bur - dens a - lone;
He is a kind, com - pas - sion - ate Friend;
One who can help my bur - dens to bear;
O how my heart is tempt - ed to sin!

In my dis - tress He kind - ly will help me,
If I but ask Him, He will de - liv - er,
I must tell Je - sus, I must tell Je - sus,
I must tell Je - sus, and He will help me

He ev - er loves and cares for His own.
Make of my trou - bles quick - ly an end.
He all my cares and sor - rows will share.
O - ver the world the vic - t'ry to win.

JESUS CHRIST

I must tell Je - sus! I must tell Je - sus! I can - not bear my bur-dens a - lone; I must tell Je - sus! I must tell Je - sus! Je-sus can help me, Je-sus a - lone.

Text: Elisha A. Hoffman, 1839-1929
Tune: Elisha A. Hoffman, 1839-1929

268 Jesus, I Love You

Je - sus, I love you for your ten-der care

Je - sus, I love you, I'll own you an - y where,

Je - sus, I love you 'cause you brought me through;

Je - sus I love you oh, yes I do.

Je - sus I love you, in you I will a - bide,
Je - sus I love you, be - cause your name's so sweet,
Je - sus I love you, on you I can de - pend,
Je - sus I love you, I love your pow'r di - vine,
Je - sus I love you, I need Thee ev - 'ry hour,

Je - sus I love you, safe in your arms I'll hide;
Je - sus I love you, you've made my life com - plete;
Je - sus I love you, my sor - rows you'll at - tend;
Je - sus I love you, I'll love you all the time;
Je - sus I love you, I need Thy sav - ing pow'r;

Je - sus, I love you, you're love's so sweet and true;
Je - sus, I love you, you're true tho' friends are few;
Je - sus, I love you, be - cause you love me too;
Je - sus, I love you, in me Thy love im - bue;
Je - sus, I love you, you'll all my fears sub - due;

Je - sus I love you Oh, yes I do.

Text: Kenneth Morris
Tune: Kenneth Morris
© 1972, Kenneth Morris

269 Jesu, Joy of Man's Desiring

1. Je - su, joy of man's de - sir - ing, Ho - ly
2. Through the way where hope is guid - ing, Hark what

wis - dom love most bright, Drawn by Thee our
peace - ful mu - sic rings Where the flock in

souls as - pir - ing Soar to un - cre - at - ed
Thee con - fid - ing Drink of joy from death - less

light. Word of God, our flesh that fash - ioned
springs. Theirs is beau - ty's fair - est pleas - ure,

with   the   fire   of   life   im -   pas - sioned.
theirs   is   wis -   dom's   ho -   liest   treas - ures,

Striv - ing   still   to   truth   un -   known,
Thou   dost   e -   ven   lead   Thine   own

Soar - ing,   dy - ing   round   Thy   throne.
In   the   love   of   joys   un - known.   A - men.

Text: Martin Janus
Tune: Johann Schop; Harm. by J. S. Bach

270 Rise Again

1. Go - a - head— drive the nails in My hands, Laugh at
Me where I stand; Go a - head and say it is - n't
Me— The day will come when you will see!

'Cause I'll rise a - gain— There's no pow'r on
'Cause I'll rise a - gain— There's no pow'r on
'Cause I'll rise a - gain— There's no pow'r on

earth can tie Me down! Yes, I'll rise a - gain—
earth can tie Me down! Yes, I'll rise a - gain—
earth can keep Me back! Yes, I'll come a - gain—

To verses 2,3

Last time

Death can't keep Me in the ground!
Death can't keep Me in the ground!
Come to take My peo - ple back!

2. Go a - head and mock My name— My
3. Go a - head and say I'm dead and gone— But

love for you is still the same; Go a - head and
you will see that you were wrong. Go a - head and

D.S.

bur - y, Me— But ver - y soon I will be free!
try to hide the Son— But all will see that I'm the one!

Text: Dallas Holm
Tune: Dallas Holm

271 Spirit Song

1. Oh, let the Son of God en-fold you, with His Spir-it and His love, let Him fill your heart and sat-is-fy your soul. Oh, let Him have the things that hold you, and His Spir-it like a dove, will de-scend up-on your life, and make you

2. Oh, come and sing this song with glad-ness, as your hearts are filled with joy, lift your hands in sweet sur-ren-der to His name. Oh, give Him all your tears and sad-ness, give Him all your years of pain, and you'll en-ter in-to life in Je-sus'

Text: John Wimber
Tune: John Wimber
© 1979, Mercy Publishing, Maranatha! Music

272 I'd Rather Have Jesus

1. I'd rath - er have Je - sus than sil - ver or gold,
2. I'd rath - er have Je - sus than your ap - plause,
3. He's fair - er than lil - ies of rar - est bloom,

I'd rath - er be His than have rich - es un - told;
I'd rath - er be faith - ful to His dear cause;
He's sweet - er than hon - ey from out the comb;

I'd rath - er have Je - sus than hous - es or lands,
I'd rath - er have Je - sus than world - wide fame,
He's all that my hun - ger - ing spir - it needs,

I'd rath - er be led by His nail - pierced hand.
I'd rath - er be true to His ho - ly name.
I'd rath - er have Je - sus and let Him lead.

Than to be the king of a vast do - main Or be held in sin's dread sway; I'd rath - er have Je - sus than an - y - thing This world af - fords to - day.

Text: Rhea Miller, © 1950, Chancel Music, Inc.
Tune: George Beverly Shea, © 1966, Chancel Music, Inc.

273 No, Not One!

1. There's not a friend like the lowly Jesus—
2. No friend like Him is so high and holy—
3. There's not an hour that He is not near us—
4. Did ev - er saint find this Friend for - sake Him?
5. Was e'er a gift like the Sav - ior giv - en?

No, not one! no, not one! None else could heal all our
No, not one! no, not one! And yet no friend is so
No, not one! no, not one! No night so dark but His
No, not one! no, not one! Or sin - ner find that He
No, not one! no, not one! Will He re - fuse us a

soul's dis - eas - es— No, not one! no, not one!
meek and low - ly— No, not one! no, not one!
love can cheer us— No, not one! no, not one!
would not take him? No, not one! no, not one!
home in heav - en? No, not one! no, not one!

Je - sus knows all a - bout our strug - gles, He will guide

JESUS CHRIST

till the day is done; There's not a friend like the

low - ly Je - sus— No, not one! no, not one!

Text: Johnson Oatman, Jr., 1856-1922
Tune: George C. Hugg, 1848-1907

274 In Times Like These

1. In times like these you need a Sav - ior, In times like
2. In times like these you need the Bi - ble, In times like
3. In times like these I have a Sav - ior, In times like

these you need an an - chor; Be ver - y sure, be ver - y
these O be not i - dle; Be ver - y sure, be ver - y
these I have an an - chor; I'm ver - y sure, I'm ver - y

sure Your an - chor holds and grips the Sol - id Rock!
sure Your an - chor holds and grips the Sol - id Rock!
sure My an - chor holds and grips the Sol - id Rock!

This Rock is Je - sus, Yes, He's the One; This Rock is

Be ver-y sure, be ver-y
Je - sus, The on-ly One! Be ver-y sure, be ver-y
I'm ver-y sure, I'm ver-y

sure Your an-chor holds and grips the Sol-id Rock!
sure Your an-chor holds and grips the Sol-id Rock!
sure My an-chor holds and grips the Sol-id Rock!

Text: Ruth Caye Jones, 1902-1972
Tune: Ruth Caye Jones, 1902-1972

275 Changed Mah Name

1. Ah tol' Je - sus it would be all right if He
2. Je - sus tol' me ah would have to live hum - ble if He
3. Je - sus tol' me that the world would be 'gainst me if He
4. But ah tol' Je - sus it would be all right if He

changed mah name.   Ah tol' Je - sus it would
changed mah name.   Je - sus tol' me ah would
changed mah name.   Je - sus tol' me the world
changed mah name.   But ah tol' Je - sus it would

be all right if He changed mah name.
have to live hum - ble if He changed mah name.
would be 'gainst me if He changed mah name.
be all right if He changed mah name.

Ah tol'   Je - sus   it would   be   all   right,   if   He
Je - sus   tol'   me   ah would   have   to   live   hum - ble   if   He
Je - sus   tol'   me   that the   world would   be   'gainst   me   if   He
But ah   tol'   Je - sus   it would   be   all   right,   if   He

changed   mah   name.
changed   mah   name.
changed   mah   name.
changed   mah   name.

Text: Afro-American Spiritual
Tune: Afro-American Spiritual; Arr. by Verolga Nix, b. 1933, from *Songs of Zion*, © 1981 by Abingdon

276 I Shall Not Be Moved

I shall not be, I shall not be moved. I shall not be,

I shall not be moved; Like a tree plant-ed by the wa - ter,

I shall not be moved. (be moved.)

1.	When my cross is heav - y,	I shall not be moved,	
2. The	church of God is march - ing,	I shall not be moved,	The
3. King	Je - sus is our Cap - tain,	I shall not be moved,	King
4. Come	on and join the ar - my,	I shall not be moved,	Come
5.	Fight - ing sin and Sa - tan,	I shall not be moved,	
6.	When my bur - den's heav - y,	I shall not be moved,	
7. Don't	let the world de - ceive you,	I shall not be moved,	Don't
8.	If my friends for - sake me,	I shall not be moved,	

When my cross is heav - y, I shall not be moved; Like a
church of God is march - ing, I shall not be moved; Like a
Je - sus is the Cap - tain, I shall not be moved; Like a
on and join the ar - my, I shall not be moved; Like a
Fight - ing sin and Sa - tan, I shall not be moved; Like a
When my bur - den's heav - y, I shall not be moved; Like a
let the world de - ceive you, I shall not be moved; Like a
If my friends for - sake me, I shall not be moved; Like a

Text: Afro-American Spiritual
Tune: Afro-American Spiritual

277 Is Your All on the Altar

1. You have longed for sweet peace and for faith to in-
2. Would you walk with the Lord in the light of His
3. O we nev - er can know what the Lord will be-
4. Who can tell all the love He will send from a-

crease, And have ear - nest - ly, fer - vent - ly prayed;
Word, And have peace and con - tent - ment al - ways?
stow Of the bless - ings for which we have prayed
bove, And how hap - py our hearts will be made;

But you can - not have rest or be per - fect - ly blest
You must do His sweet will to be free from all ill,
Till our bod - y and soul He doth ful - ly con - trol,
Of the char - i - ty sweet we shall share at His feet

Un - til all on the al - tar is laid.
On the al - tar your all you must lay.
And our all on the al - tar is laid.
When our all on the al - tar is laid.

Is your all on the al - tar of sac - ri - fice laid?

Your heart does the Spir - it con - trol?

You can on - ly be blest and have peace and sweet rest

As you yield Him your bod - y and soul.

Text: Elisha A. Hoffman, 1839-1929
Tune: Elisha A. Hoffman, 1839-1929

278 Make Me a Blessing

1. Out in the high-ways and by-ways of life,
2. Tell the sweet sto-ry of Christ and His love,
3. Give as 'twas giv-en to you in your need,

Man-y are wea-ry and sad;
Tell of His power to for-give;
Love as the Mas-ter loved you;

Car-ry the sun-shine where dark-ness is rife,
Oth-ers will trust Him if on-ly you prove
Be to the help-less a help-er in-deed,

Mak-ing the sor-row-ing glad.
True, ev-ery mo-ment you live.
Un-to your mis-sion be true.

Make me a bless - ing, Make me a bless - ing,

Out of my life May Je - sus shine;

Make me a bless - ing, O Sav - ior, I pray,

Make me a bless - ing to some - one to - day.

Text: Ira B. Wilson, 1880-1950
Tune: George S. Schuler, 1882-1973

279 Give Me a Clean Heart

Give me a clean heart so I may serve Thee.

Lord, fix my heart so that I may be used by Thee.

For I'm not wor - thy of all these bless - ings.

Give me a clean heart and I'll fol-low Thee.

1. I'm not ask-ing for the rich-es of the land.
I am up and some-times I am down.

I'm not ask-ing for the proud to know my
Some-times I am al-most lev-el to the

name.
ground.

Please give me, Lord, a clean heart, that
Please give me, Lord, a clean heart, that

I may fol-low Thee. Give me a clean heart, a
I may fol-low Thee. Give me a clean heart, a

clean heart and I will fol-low Thee. 2. Some-times
clean heart and I will fol-low Thee.

2. Some-times

Text: Margaret J. Douroux, © 1970
Tune: Margaret J. Douroux, © 1970; Harm. by Albert Denis Tessier

Give Me Jesus 280

1. I heard my moth-er say, I heard my moth-er
2. Dark mid-night was my cry, Dark mid-night was my
3. Oh, When I come to die, Oh, when I come to

say, I heard my moth-er say, Give me Je - sus.
cry, Dark mid-night was my cry, Give me Je - sus.
die, Oh, when I come to die, Give me Je - sus.

Give me Je - sus, Give me Je - sus,

You may have all this world, Give me Je - sus.

Text: Afro-American Spiritual
Tune: Afro-American Spiritual; Harm. by Verolga Nix, b.1933, from *Songs of Zion*, (c) 1981 by Abingdon

281 I Am on the Battlefield for My Lord

I am on the bat-tle-field for my Lord, I'm
on the bat-tle-field for my Lord; And I prom-ised Him that
I would serve Him till I die. I'm on the bat-tle-
field for my Lord.

1. I was a - lone and
2. I left my friends and
3. Now when I met my

i - dle, I was a sin-ner too, I heard a voice from
kin - dred Bound for the Prom-ised Land, The grace of God up-
Sav - ior, I met Him with a smile, He healed my wound - ed

heav - en   Say   there   is   work   to   do,   I
on   me,   The   Bi - ble   in   my   hand,   In
spir - it,   And   owned   me   as   His   child,   A-

took   the   Mas - ter's   hand,   And   I   joined   the   Chris - tian
dis - tant   lands   I   trod,   Cry - ing   sin - ner   come   to
round   the   throne   of   grace,   He - ap - points   my   soul   a

D.C.

band,   I'm   on   the   bat - tle - field   for   my   Lord.
God,   I'm   on   the   bat - tle - field   for   my   Lord.
place,   I'm   on   the   bat - tle - field   for   my   Lord.

Text: Sylvana Bell and E. V. Banks
Tune: Afro-American Spiritual; Harm. by Thomas A. Dorsey, b.1899

282 Good News

1. When Je - sus worked here on earth
2. The eld - ers of the syn - a - gogue
3. The way he lived was proof of it:
4. So pass it on to - day, good friend:

he preached in his home - town
were shocked by Mar - y's son,
he qui - et - ed our strife.
the mes - sage is the same.

I - sa - iah's hopes now ful - filled,
that he was des - tined to be
The cross it - self he would not flee
De - liv - 'rance Christ a - lone can give,

those claims of great re - nown.
the Christ for ev - 'ry - one.
e'en though it cost his life.
for this to earth he came.

To bring good news to need - y, to make the blind to see,

Text: Howard S. Olson
Tune: Almaz Belihu; Yemissrach Dimts Literature Program, Ethiopia
© 1977, Augsburg Publishing House

283 Here I Am, Lord

1. I, the Lord of sea and sky, I have heard My
2. I, the Lord of snow and rain, I have borne My
3. I, the Lord of wind and flame, I will tend the

peo - ple cry. All who dwell in dark and sin
peo - ple's pain. I have wept for love of them,
poor and lame. I will set a feast for them,

My hand will save.
They turn a - way.
My hand will save.

I who made the stars of night,
I will break their hearts of stone,
Fin - est bread I will pro - vide

I will make their
give them hearts for
till their hearts be

dark - ness bright.
love a - lone.
sat - is - fied.

Who will bear My light to them?
I will speak My word to them.
I will give My life to them.

molto rit.

Whom shall I send? Here I
Whom shall I send?
Whom shall I send?

a tempo

am, Lord. Is it I, Lord?

I have heard You call - ing in the

Text: Isaiah 6; Dan Schutte, SJ. © 1981, Daniel L. Schutte and North American Liturgy Resources
Tune: Dan Schutte, SJ; Harm. by Michael Pope, SJ, Dan Schutte, SJ, and John Weissrock; © 1983, Daniel L. Schutte and North American Liturgy Resources

284 Yes, Lord

Yes, yes, yes, yes, yes, yes, yes, Lord, yes, Lord, yes, Lord, yes, Lord, yes, Lord, yes, Lord.

1. My soul says yes, my soul says yes,
2. Yes to your will, yes to your will,

my soul says yes, my soul says yes,
yes to your will, yes to your will,

my soul says   yes,   my soul says   yes.
yes   to your will,   yes   to your will.

3. Yes, to your way . . .   6. We thank you, Lord . . .
4. Yes, I'll obey . . .   7. Come the more . . .
5. We praise you, Lord . . .   8. In my soul . . .

Text: Charles H. Mason
Tune: Charles H. Mason

285 Done Made My Vow to the Lord

Done made my vow to the Lord, And I nev-er will turn back, Oh I will go, I shall go to see what the end will be.

1. Some - times I'm up, some - times I'm down;
2. When I was a mourn - er just like you;

1. See what the end will be, But still my soul is
2. See what the end will be, I prayed and prayed 'til

D.C.

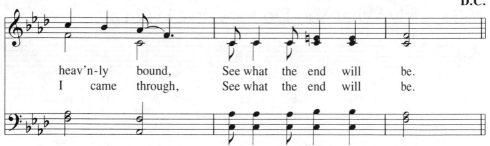

heav'n-ly bound, See what the end will be.
I came through, See what the end will be.

Text: Afro-American Spiritual
Tune: Afro-American Spiritual; Harm. by Evelyn Davidson White

286 Only What You Do for Christ Will Last

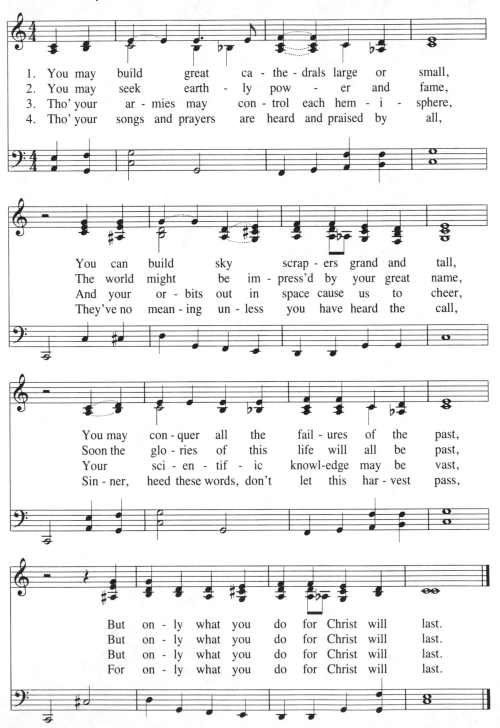

1. You may build great ca-the-drals large or small,
2. You may seek earth-ly pow-er and fame,
3. Tho' your ar-mies may con-trol each hem-i-sphere,
4. Tho' your songs and prayers are heard and praised by all,

You can build sky scrap-ers grand and tall,
The world might be im-press'd by your great name,
And your or-bits out in space cause us to cheer,
They've no mean-ing un-less you have heard the call,

You may con-quer all the fail-ures of the past,
Soon the glo-ries of this life will all be past,
Your sci-en-tif-ic knowl-edge may be vast,
Sin-ner, heed these words, don't let this har-vest pass,

But on-ly what you do for Christ will last.
But on-ly what you do for Christ will last.
But on-ly what you do for Christ will last.
For on-ly what you do for Christ will last.

Text: Raymond Rasberry
Tune: Raymond Rasberry
© 1963, Raymond Rasberry

287 Come to Jesus

1. Come to Je - sus, Come to Je - sus, Come to
2. He will save you, He will save you, He will

Je - sus just now; Just now come to Je - sus,
save you just now; Just now He will save you,

Come to Je - sus just now.
He will save you just now. A - men.

3. He is able.
4. He is willing.
5. Come, confess Him.

6. Come, obey Him.
7. He will hear you.
8. He'll forgive you.

9. He will cleanse you.
10. Jesus loves you.
11. Only trust Him.

Text: Afro-American Spiritual
Tune: Afro-American Spiritual

288 I Am Praying for You

1. I have a Sav - ior, He's plead - ing in glo - ry,
2. I have a Fa - ther; to me He has giv - en
3. I have a robe: 'tis re - splen - dent in white - ness,
4. When Je - sus has found you, tell oth - ers the sto - ry,

EVANGELIZATION

A dear, lov-ing Sav-ior, tho' earth-friends be few;
A hope for e-ter-ni-ty, bless-ed and true;
A-wait-ing in glo-ry my won-der-ing view;
That my lov-ing Sav-ior is your Sav-ior, too;

And now He is watch-ing in ten-der-ness o'er me,
And soon will He call me to meet Him in heav-en,
Oh, when I re-ceive it all shin-ing in bright-ness,
Then pray that your Sav-ior may bring them to glo-ry,

And, oh, that my Sav-ior were your Sav-ior, too.
But, oh, that He'd let me bring you with me, too!
Dear friend, could I see you re-ceiv-ing one, too!
And prayer will be an-swered—'twas an-swered for you!

For you I am pray-ing, For you I am pray-ing,

For you I am pray-ing, I'm pray-ing for you.

Text: S. O'Malley Cluff
Tune: Ira D. Sankey, 1840-1908

289 He Has Done Great Things for Me

He has done great things for me, Great things,

Great things! He has done great things for me.

1.,2. **Last time**

Sa - tan had me bound, my soul was in lost and found.

Je - sus came and He gave me life, I'm so

glad that He saved my soul and I'll

tell it Ev-e-ry where I go.

1. I'm gonna be a witness for him,
   Witness, witness,
   I'm gonna be a witness for him.

2. I'm gonna let my little light shine,
   Shine, shine
   I'm gonna let my little light shine.

3. He has made a way for me,
   Made a way, made a way,
   He has made a way for me.

4. He will see you safely through,
   Safely through, safely through,
   He will see you safely through.

5. He will give you joy and peace of mind,
   Joy and peace, joy and peace,
   He will give you joy and peace of mind.

6. He will give you victory,
   Victory, victory,
   He will give you victory.

Text: Jesse Dixon
Tune: Jesse Dixon; Harm. by Shirley Berkeley

Glory, Glory, Hallelujah   290

Glo-ry, glo-ry, hal-le-lu-jah!

Since I laid my bur-den down,
I feel bet-ter, so much bet-ter,
Feel like shout-ing "Hal-le-lu-jah!"
I am climb-ing Ja-cob's lad-der,
Ev-'ry round goes higher and high-er,

Glo-ry, glo-ry, hal-le-lu-jah!

Since I laid my bur-den down.
I feel bet-ter, so much bet-ter.
Feel like shout-ing "Hal-le-lu-jah!"
I am climb-ing Ja-cob's lad-der.
Ev-'ry round goes higher and high-er.

Text: Afro-American Spiritual
Tune: Afro-American Spiritual; Harm. by J. Jefferson Cleveland, b.1937, and Verolga Nix, b.1933, from *Songs of Zion*, © 1981 by Abingdon

291 Lift Ev'ry Voice and Sing

1. Lift ev-'ry voice and sing, Till earth and heav-en ring,
2. Ston-y the road we trod, Bit-ter the chas-t'ning rod,
3. God of our wea-ry years, God of our si-lent tears,

Ring with the har-mo-nies of lib-er-ty;
Felt in the days when hope un-born had died;
Thou who hast brought us thus far on the way;

Let our re-joic-ing rise High as the lis-t'ning skies,
Yet with a stead-y beat, Have not our wear-y feet
Thou who hast by thy might, Led us in-to the light,

Let it re-sound loud as the roll-ing sea.
Come to the place for which our peo-ple sighed?
Keep us for ev-er in the path, we pray.

Sing a song full of the faith that the dark past has taught us,
We have come o-ver a way that with tears has been wa-tered'
Lest our feet stray from the plac-es, our God, where we met thee,

Sing a song full of the hope that the pres-ent has brought
We have come, tread-ing our path thro' the blood of the slaugh-
Lest our hearts, drunk with the wine of the world, we for-get

us; Fac-ing the ris-ing sun Of our new day be-
tered; Out from the gloom-y past, Till now we stand at
thee; Shad-owed be-neath thy hand, May we for ev-er

gun, Let us march on till vic-to-ry is won.
last Where the bright gleam of our bright star is cast.
stand, True to our God, True to our na-tive land.

Text: James W. Johnson, 1871-1938
Tune: ANTHEM, 66 10 66 10 14 14 66 10; J. Rosamund Johnson, 1873-1954

292 Go Down, Moses

1. When Is - rael was in E - gypt's land,
2. The Lord told Mo - ses what to do,
3. They jour - neyed on at God's com - mand,
4. Oh, let us all from bond - age flee,

Let my peo - ple go; Op - pressed so hard they
Let my peo - ple go; To lead the chil-dren of
Let my peo - ple go; And came at length to
Let my peo - ple go; And let us all in

could not stand, Let my peo - ple go.
Is - rael through, Let my peo - ple go.
Ca - naan's land, Let my peo - ple go.
Christ be free, Let my peo - ple go.

Go down, Mo - ses, way down in E - gypt's land;

Tell old Phar - aoh to let my peo - ple go.

Text: Afro-American Spiritual
Tune: GO DOWN MOSES, Irregular; Afro-American Spiritual; Harm. from *English Praise*, 1975. © 1975, Oxford University Press

293   Free At Last

Free at last, free at last, I thank God I'm
free at last; Free at last, Free at last,
I thank God I'm free at last. O free at last.

'Way down yon - der in the grave - yard walk, I thank God I'm
On a my knees when the light passed by, I thank God I'm
Some of these morn - ings, bright and fair, I thank God I'm

free at last, Me and my Je - sus goin' to
free at last, Thought my soul would
free at last, Goin' meet King Je - sus

D.C.

meet and talk, I thank God I'm free at last, O
rise and fly, I thank God I'm free at last, O
in the air, I thank God I'm free at last, O

Text: Afro-American Spiritual
Tune: Afro-American Spiritual

We've Come a Long Way, Lord   294

We've come a long way, Lord, A might-y long

way, We've come a long way, Lord, A

might-y long way, We've borne our bur-dens in the

heat of the day, But we know the Lord has

made the way, We've come a long way, Lord,

A might - y long way.

1. I've been in the val - ley and I prayed night and
   tri - als each and ev - 'ry

day,   I've been   in   the   val - ley   and   I
day,   I've had   hard   tri - als   each and

prayed night and   day;   I've been   in   the   val - ley and I
ev - 'ry   day;   I've had   hard   tri - als each and

prayed night and   day, And I   know the Lord has made the   way.
ev - 'ry   day, But I   know the Lord has made the   way.

We've come a long   way   Lord,   A might - y long

1.   **2.**   **D.S.**

way.   2. I've had hard   way.   We've come a long

Text: Traditional; Adapt. by Kennteth Morris
Tune: Traditional; Adapt. and harm. by Kenneth Morris, © 1968, Martin and Morris Music, Inc.

295 Keep the Dream Alive

1. Mar - tin's dream for all of us so set his soul a-
2. In our land let free - dom ring was Mar - tin's great de-
3. Those so filled with in - ner light, so filled with no - ble

fire And lift - ed him to soar - ing heights That
sire And as he marched a - mong the poor So
dreams, Must feel the wrath of Sa - tan's might To

he might with his God con - spire To change the course of
man - y did his dream in - spire To self es - teem and
teth - er and to slay. It seems the Christ a - gain is

his - to - ry That all be fam - 'ly, all be free.
dig - ni - ty in strug - gle for our lib - er - ty.
cru - ci - fied. Let Mar - tin's dream not be de - nied.

Keep the dream a - live. Keep the dream a - live.

We will have the vic - to - ry, Just keep the dream a - live.

Text: Robert Manuel
Tune: Robert Manuel
© 1986, Robert Manuel

296 He Had a Dream

We Shall Overcome   297

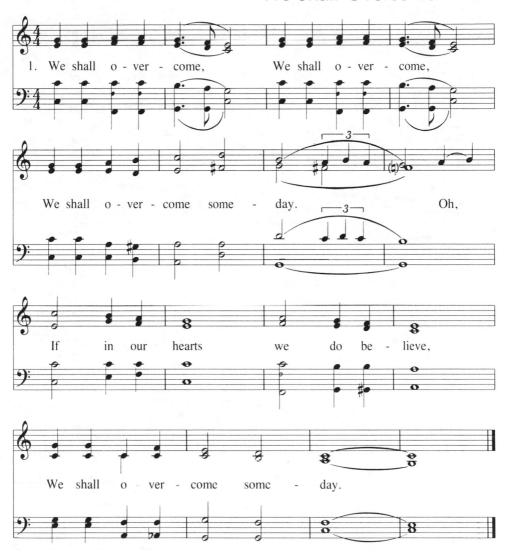

1. We shall o - ver - come, We shall o - ver - come, We shall o - ver - come some - day. Oh,

If in our hearts we do be - lieve,

We shall o - ver - come some - day.

2. We'll walk hand in hand . . .
3. We shall all have peace . . .
4. We are not afraid . . .
5. God is on our side . . .

Text: Traditional
Tune: Traditional; Harm. by J. Jefferson Cleveland, b. 1937, from *Songs of Zion*, © 1981 by Abingdon

298 Oh, Freedom

1. Oh, free-dom, oh, free-dom, oh,
2. No more moan-ing, no more moan-ing, no more
3. There'll be sing-ing, there'll be sing-ing, there'll be

free-dom o - ver me,
moan-ing o - ver me, And be-
sing-ing o - ver me,

me, o - ver me, And be

fore I'd be a slave, I'll be bur-ied in my grave,

And go home to my Lord, and be free.

4. There'll be shoutin', . . .
5. There'll be prayin', . . .

Text: Afro-American Spiritual
Tune: Afro-American Spiritual; Harm. by Evelyn Davidson White

I've Got Peace Like a River 299

1. I've got peace like a riv-er, I've got peace like a
2. I've got joy like a foun-tain, I've got joy like a
3. I've got love like an o-cean, I've got love like an

riv - er, I've got peace like a riv - er in my
foun-tain, I've got joy like a foun-tain in my
o - cean, I've got love like an o-cean in my

soul. I've got riv - er in my soul.
soul. I've got foun-tain in my soul.
soul. I've got o - cean in my soul.

Text: Afro-American Spiritual
Tune: Afro-American Spiritual

300 Let There Be Peace on Earth

Let there be peace on earth, and let it be - gin with

me. Let there be peace on earth, the peace that was

meant to be. With God as our Fa - ther,

fam - 'ly all are we. Let us walk with each

oth - er in per - fect har - mon - y.

Let peace be - gin with me; let this be the mo - ment now. With ev - 'ry step I take, let this be my sol - emn vow: To take each mo - ment, and live each mo - ment in peace e - ter - nal - ly! Let there be peace on earth, and let it be - gin with me.

301 In Christ There Is No East or West

1. In Christ there is no east or west, In
2. In him shall true hearts ev - 'ry - where Their
3. Join hands, dis - ci - ples in the faith, What-
4. In Christ now meet both east and west, In

him no south or north, But one great fam - 'ly
high com - mun - ion find; His ser - vice is the
e'er your race may be! Who serve each oth - er
him meet south and north, All Christ - ly souls are

bound by love Through - out the whole wide earth.
gold - en cord Close - bind - ing hu - man - kind.
in Christ's love Are sure - ly kin to me.
one in him, Through - out the whole wide earth.

Text: Gal. 3:28; John Oxenham, 1852-1941, © American Tract Society
Tune: MC KEE, CM; Afro-American; Adapted by Harry T. Burleigh, 1866-1949

I Just Came to Praise the Lord   302

1. I just came to praise the Lord, I just came to
2. I just came to thank the Lord, I just came to
3. I just came to love the Lord, I just came to

praise the Lord; I just came to praise His
thank the Lord; I just came to praise His
love the Lord; I just came to praise His

ho - ly name, I just came to praise the Lord.
ho - ly name, I just came to thank the Lord.
ho - ly name, I just came to love the Lord.

Text. Wayne Romero
Tune: Wayne Romero
© 1975, Paragon Music

303 I Was Glad

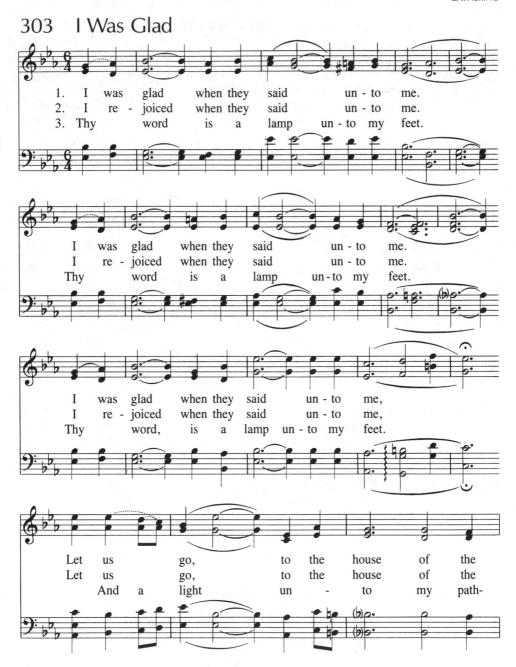

1. I was glad when they said un-to me.
2. I re-joiced when they said un-to me.
3. Thy word is a lamp un-to my feet.

I was glad when they said un-to me.
I re-joiced when they said un-to me.
Thy word is a lamp un-to my feet.

I was glad when they said un-to me,
I re-joiced when they said un-to me,
Thy word, is a lamp un-to my feet.

Let us go, to the house of the
Let us go, to the house of the
And a light un - to my path-

Lord. (House of the Lord.) All na - tions may come
Lord. (House of the Lord.) All na - tions may come
way. (My path - way.) My feet shall stand

to the house of the Lord to kneel at the
to the house of the Lord to kneel at the
in the gates of the Lord as I sing of His

al - tar in prayer and leave all
al - tar in prayer and leave all
prais - es so sweet. His word is

bur - dens, each sor - row and woe. And re - joice
bur - dens, each sor - row and woe. And re - joice
hid - den, with - in my heart. As a guide

when they say, Let us go there. (Let us go there.)
when they say, Let us go there. (Let us go there.)
and a lamp un - to my feet. (Un - to my feet.)

Text: Anna Crockett Ford
Tune: Anna Crockett Ford; Harm. by Virginia Davis and Anna Crockett Ford
© 1967, Anna Crockett Ford

304 All People That on Earth Do Dwell

1. All peo - ple that on earth do dwell,
2. Know that the Lord is God in - deed;
3. O en - ter then his gates with praise;
4. For why? the Lord our God is good:
5. To Fa - ther, Son, and Ho - ly Ghost,

Sing to the Lord with cheer - ful voice;
With - out our aid he did us make;
Ap - proach with joy his courts un - to;
His mer - cy is for ev - er sure;
The God whom heaven and earth a - dore,

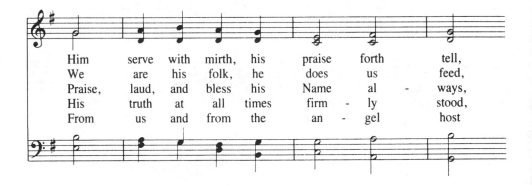

Him serve with mirth, his praise forth tell,
We are his folk, he does us feed,
Praise, laud, and bless his Name al - ways,
His truth at all times firm - ly stood,
From us and from the an - gel host

Come we be - fore him, and re - joice.
And for his sheep he does us take.
For it is seem - ly so to do.
And shall from age to age en - dure.
Be praise and glo - ry ev - er - more.

Text: Psalm (99)100; William Kethe, d. c.1593; Doxology, Thomas Ken, 1637-1711
Tune: OLD HUNDREDTH, LM; Louis Bourgeois, c.1510-1561; alt. harm. by John Dowland, 1562-1626

Praise God from Whom All Blessings Flow 305

Praise God, from whom all blessings flow;
Praise Him, all creatures here below;
Praise Him above, you heav'nly host:
Praise Father, Son and Holy Ghost.

306 Praise God from Whom All Blessings Flow

Slowly, with feeling

Praise God from whom all bless - ings flow,

Praise Him all crea - tures here be - low.

Praise Him a - bove ye heav - en - ly host,

Praise Fa - ther, Son and Ho - ly Ghost.

Peo - ple and realms of ev - 'ry tongue
Sing to the Lord with cheer - ful voice,

Dwell on His love with sweet - est song,
Come ye be - fore Him and re - joice,

To Him shall end - less prayer be made,
All peo - ple that on earth do dwell,

And end - less prais - es crown His head.
Serve Him with mirth, His prais - es tell.

A - men, A - men.

Text: Isaac Watts, 1675-1748; and William Keathe, d.1593; Adapt. by Thomas Ken, 1637-1711
Tune: John Hatton, d.1793; Adapt. by George Coles; Harm. by Roberta Martin, 1912-1969, © 1968

307 We Gather Together

1. We gath - er to - geth - er to ask the Lord's bless - ing;
2. Be - side us to guide us, our God with us join - ing,
3. We all do ex - tol you our lead - er tri - um - phant,

He chas - tens and has - tens his will to make known;
Whose king - dom calls all to the love which en - dures.
And pray that you still our de - fend - er will be.

The wick - ed op - press - ing now cease from dis - tress - ing:
So from the be - gin - ning the fight we were win - ning:
Let your con - gre - ga - tion es - cape trib - u - la - tion:

Sing prais - es to his name; he for - gets not his own.
You, Lord, were at our side; all glo - ry be yours!
Your name be ev - er praised! O Lord, make us free!

Text: *Wilt heden nu treden;* Tr. by Theodore Baker, 1851-1934, alt., © J. Curwen and Sons
Tune: KREMSER, 12 11 12 11; *Neder-landtsch Gedenckclanck,* 1626; Harm. by Edward Kremser, 1838-1914

God Be with You   308

God be with you, God be with you, God be

with you 'till we meet a - gain, O God be with you,

God be with you, God be with you till we meet a - gain.

Till we meet (till we meet), Till we meet (till we meet), Till we

meet our spir - its keep, Till we meet (till we meet), Till we

meet (till we meet), our souls in love do keep, O till we

meet (till we meet), Till we meet (till we meet), keep us

hum - ble at Thy feet, God be with us till we

meet a - gain.
1. If we nev - er - more shall meet you,
2. If your way is dark and drear - y,
3. Joy will un - fold like a flow - er,

If we nev - er - more shall greet you,
Cast your ev - 'ry care on Je - sus, God be
If you trust Him ev - 'ry hour,

GOING FORTH

with you till we meet a - gain, Keep on work - ing
Songs of joy

for the Mas - ter, He'll be with you here and af - ter,
when in sor - row, He's a joy for you to - mor - row,
will sur - round you, Ho - ly an - gels sing a - round you,

He's a com - fort

D.C.

God be with you till we meet a - gain.

309 God Be with You

1. God be with you till we meet a - gain;
2. God be with you till we meet a - gain;
3. God be with you till we meet a - gain;
4. God be with you till we meet a - gain;

By His
'Neath His
When life's
Keep love's

coun - sels guide, up - hold you,
wings pro - tect - ing hide you,
per - ils thick con - found you,
ban - ner float - ing o'er you,

With His
Dai - ly
Put His
Smite death's

sheep se - cure - ly fold you:
man - na still pro - vide you:
arms un - fail - ing round you:
threat-'ning wave be - fore you:

God be with you till we

meet a - gain. Till we meet, till we meet, Till we

GOING FORTH

meet at Je - sus' feet, Till we meet,

till we meet,

till we meet God be with you till we meet a - gain.

Text: Jeremiah E. Rankin, 1828-1904
Tune: William G. Tomer, 1832-1896

310　Woke Up this Morning

1. O I woke up this morn - ing with my mind, And it was
2. Can't hate your neigh - bor in your mind, If you keep it
3. Makes you love ev - 'ry - bod - y with your mind, When you keep it
4. The dev - il can't catch you in your mind, If you keep it
5. Je - sus is the cap - tain in your mind, When you keep it

stayed, Stayed on Je - sus. Woke up this morn - ing with my
stayed, Stayed on Je - sus. Can't hate your neigh - bor in your
stayed, Stayed on Je - sus. Love ev - 'ry - bod - y with your
stayed, Stayed on Je - sus. Dev - il can't catch you in your
stayed, Stayed on Je - sus. Je - sus is the cap - tain in your

mind, And it was stayed, Stayed on Je - sus,
mind, If you keep it stayed, Stayed on Je - sus,
mind, When you keep it stayed, Stayed on Je - sus,
mind, If you keep it stayed, Stayed on Je - sus,
mind, When you keep it stayed, Stayed on Je - sus,

Woke up this morn - ing with my mind, And it was stayed,
Can't hate your neigh - bor in your mind, If you keep it stayed,
Love ev - 'ry - bod - y with your mind, When you keep it stayed,
Dev - il can't catch you in your mind, If you keep it stayed,
Je - sus is the cap - tain in your mind, When you keep it stayed,

Stayed on Je - sus, Hal - le - lu, Hal - le-
Hal - le - lu,

lu, Hal - le - lu, Hal - le - lu - jah.

Text: Afro-American Spiritual
Tune: Afro-American Spiritual

311 I Will Rejoice

Text: Grayson W. Brown
Tune: Grayson W. Brown; Harm. by Larry Adams © 1979, North American Liturgy Resources

An Evening Prayer   312

1. If I have wound-ed an-y soul to-day,
2. If I have ut-tered i-dle words or vain,
3. If I have been per-verse, or hard, or cold,
4. For-give the sins I have con-fessed to Thee;

If I have caused one foot to go a-stray,
If I have turned a-side from want or pain,
If I have longed for shel-ter in the fold,
For-give the se-cret sins I do not see;

If I have walked in my own will-ful way,
Lest I of-fend some oth-er thru the strain,
When Thou hast giv-en me some fort to hold,
O guide me, love me, and my keep-er be.

1.2.3. | **D.C.** | **4.**

Dear Lord, for-give (for-give)!   A-men (A-men).

Text: C. M. Battersby
Tune: Charles H. Gabriel, 1856-1932

313 Abide with Me

1. A - bide with me— fast falls the e - ven - tide,
2. Swift to its close ebbs out life's lit - tle day,
3. I need Thy pres - ence ev - 'ry pass - ing hour—
4. Hold Thou Thy word be - fore my clos - ing eyes,

The dark - ness deep - ens— Lord, with me a - bide;
Earth's joys grow dim, its glo - ries pass a - way;
What but Thy grace can foil the temp - ter's pow'r?
Shine thru the gloom and point me to the skies;

When oth - er help - ers fail and com - forts flee,
Change and de - cay in all a - round I see—
Who like Thy - self my guide and stay can be?
Heav'n's morn - ing breaks and earth's vain shad - ows flee—

Help of the help - less, O a - bide with me!
O Thou who chang - est not, a - bide with me!
Thru cloud and sun - shine, O a - bide with me!
In life, in death, O Lord, a - bide with me!

Text: Henry F. Lyte, 1793-1847
Tune: EVENTIDE; William H. Monk, 1823-1887

Fix Me, Jesus 314

Oh, fix me; Oh, fix me;
(Je - sus) (Je - sus)

Oh, fix me; fix me, Je - sus, fix me.

Fix me for my long white robe.
Fix me for my jour - ney home. Fix me, Je - sus, fix me.

D.C.

Fix me for my star - ry crown.
Fix me for my dy - ing bed. Fix me, Je - sus, fix me.

Text: Afro-American Spiritual
Tune: Afro-American Spiritual; Arr. by Verolga Nix, b. 1933, from *Songs of Zion*, © 1981 by Abingdon

315 Want to Go to Heaven When I Die

1. Want to go to Heav - en when I die,
2. Want to see my moth - er when I die,
3. Want to see my fa - ther when I die,
4. Want to see my sis - ter when I die,
5. Want to see my Je - sus when I die,

Want to go to Heav - en when I die,
Want to see my moth - er when I die,
Want to see my fa - ther when I die,
Want to see my sis - ter when I die,
Want to see my Je - sus when I die,

Want to go to Heav - en when I die; Good Lord,
Want to go see moth - er, when I die; Good Lord,
Want to see my fa - ther, when I die; Good Lord,
Want to see my sis - ter, when I die; Good Lord,
Want to see my Je - sus, when I die; Good Lord,

when I die, Good Lord, when I die,

Good Lord, when I die, Good Lord, when I

die, Good Lord, when I die.

Shout o - ver!

Text: Afro-American Spiritual
Tune: Afro-American Spiritual

316 Come, We That Love the Lord

1. Come, we that love the Lord, And let our joys be
2. Let those re - fuse to sing Who nev - er knew our
3. Then let our songs a-bound And ev - ery tear be

known; Join in a song with sweet ac - cord, Join
God; But chil - dren of the heaven - ly King, But
dry; We're march - ing thru Em - man - uel's ground, We're

in a song with sweet ac - cord And thus sur-
chil - dren of the heaven - ly King May speak their
march - ing thru Em - man - uel's ground To fair - er

round the throne, And thus sur - round the throne.
joys a - broad, May speak their joys a - broad.
worlds on high, To fair - er worlds on high.

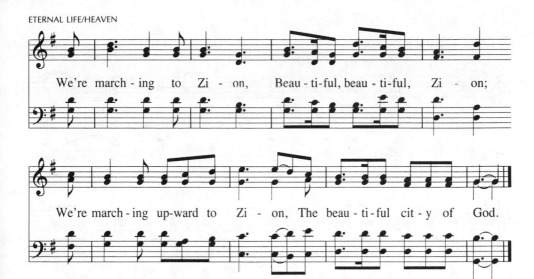

We're march-ing to Zi - on, Beau - ti-ful, beau - ti-ful, Zi - on;

We're march - ing up-ward to Zi - on, The beau - ti-ful cit - y of God.

Text: Isaac Watts, 1674-1748, Robert Lowry, 1826-1899
Tune: Robert Lowry, 1826-1899

317 Good News

Good news! The char - i - ot's com - ing. Good news! The

char - i - ot's com - ing. Good news! The char - i - ot's com - ing,

And I don't want it to leave - a me be - hind.

There's a long white robe in the heav - en, I know.

A

There's a long white robe in the heav - en, I know

A

long white robe in the heav - en, I know. There's a

long white robe in the heav - en, I know.

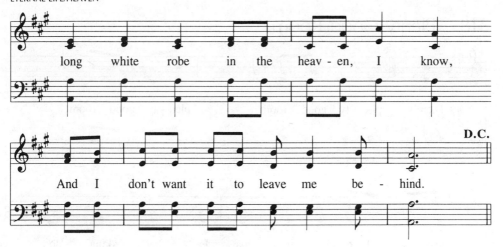

long white robe in the heav - en, I know,

D.C.

And I don't want it to leave me be - hind.

2. pair of wings . . .

3. pair of shoes . . .

4. starry crown . . .

5. golden harp . . .

Text. Afro-American Spiritual
Tune: Afro-American Spiritual

318 Plenty Good Room

There's plen-ty good room, plen-ty good room,

plen-ty good room in ma Fa-ther's king-dom,

Plen-ty good room, plen-ty good room, just

choose your seat and sit down. There's

sit down, sit down, sit down.

Text: Afro-American Spiritual
Tune: Afro-American Spiritual; Harm. by Fredricka R. Young, b.1928, © 1963

319 Steal Away to Jesus

Steal a-way, steal a-way, steal a-way to Je-sus!

Steal a-way, steal a-way home, I ain't got long to stay here.

My Lord, he calls me, He calls me by the thun-der; The
Green trees are bend-ing, Poor sin-ners stand a trem-bling; The
My Lord, he calls me, He calls me by the light-ning; The

D.C.

trum-pet sounds with-in my soul; I ain't got long to stay here.

Text: Afro-American Spiritual
Tune: Afro-American Spiritual

My Country, 'Tis of Thee 320

1. My coun - try, 'tis of thee, Sweet land of
2. My na - tive coun - try, thee, Land of the
3. Let mu - sic swell the breeze, And ring from
4. Our fa - thers' God, to thee, Au - thor of

lib - er - ty, Of thee I sing; Land where my
no - ble, free; Thy name I love; I love thy
all the trees Sweet free - dom's song; Let mor - tal
lib - er - ty, To thee we sing; Long may our

fa - thers died, Land of the pil - grim's pride,
rocks and rills, Thy woods and tem - pled hills;
tongues a - wake; Let all that breathe par - take;
land be bright With free - dom's ho - ly light;

From ev - 'ry moun - tain - side Let free - dom ring!
My heart with rap - ture thrills, Like that a - bove.
Let rocks their si - lence break, The sound pro - long.
Pro - tect us by thy might, Great God, our King.

Text: Samuel F. Smith, 1808-1895
Tune: AMERICA, 66 4 666 4; *Thesaurus Musicus*, 1744

321 America the Beautiful

1. O beau - ti - ful for spa - cious skies, For am - ber
2. O beau - ti - ful for pil - grim feet, Whose stern, im-
3. O beau - ti - ful for he - roes proved In lib - er-
4. O beau - ti - ful for pa - triot dream That sees be-

waves of grain, For pur - ple moun-tain maj - es - ties
pas - sioned stress A thor - ough-fare for free - dom beat
at - ing strife, Who more than self their coun - try loved,
yond the years Thine al - a - bas - ter cit - ies gleam,

A - bove the fruit - ed plain! A - mer - i - ca! A-
A - cross the wil - der - ness! A - mer - i - ca! A-
And mer - cy more than life! A - mer - i - ca! A-
Un - dimmed by hu - man tears! A - mer - i - ca! A-

mer - i - ca! God shed his grace on thee, And crown thy
mer - i - ca! God mend thine ev - 'ry flaw, Con - firm thy
mer - i - ca! May God thy gold re - fine, Till all suc-
mer - i - ca! God shed his grace on thee, And crown thy

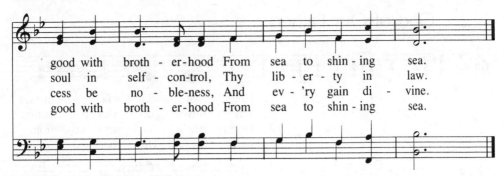

good with   broth - er-hood From   sea   to   shin - ing   sea.
soul   in   self - con-trol, Thy   lib - er - ty   in   law.
cess   be   no - ble-ness, And   ev - 'ry gain di - vine.
good with   broth - er-hood From   sea   to   shin - ing   sea.

Text: Katherine L. Bates, 1859-1929
Tune: MATERNA, CMD; Samuel A. Ward, 1848-1903

322 God of Our Fathers

1. God of our fa - thers, whose al - might - y hand Leads forth in beau - ty all the star - ry band Of shin - ing worlds in splen - dor thru the skies,

2. Thy love di - vine hath led us in the past, In this free land by Thee our lot is cast; Be Thou our rul - er, guard - ian, guide, and stay,

3. From war's a - larms, from dead - ly pes - ti - lence, Be Thy strong arm our ev - er - sure de - fense; Thy true re - li - gion in our hearts in - crease,

4. Re - fresh Thy peo - ple on their toil - some way, Lead us from night to nev - er - end - ing day; Fill all our lives with love and grace di - vine,

Our grate-ful songs be - fore Thy throne a - rise.
Thy word our law, Thy paths our cho - sen way.
Thy boun-teous good - ness nour - ish us in peace.
And glo - ry, laud, and praise be ev - er Thine!

Text: Daniel C. Roberts, 1841-1907
Tune: NATIONAL HYMN, 10 10 10 10; George W. Warren, 1828-1902

323 Star-Spangled Banner

1. O say can you see by the dawn's ear - ly light,
2. On the shore, dim - ly seen thro' the mists of the deep,
3. O thus be it ev - er when free - men shall stand

What so proud - ly we hailed at the twi-light's last gleam-ing,
Where the foe's haugh-ty host in dead si - lence re - pos - es,
Be - tween their loved homes and the war's des - o - la - tion!

Whose broad stripes and bright stars, through the per - il - ous fight,
What is that which the breeze, o'er the tow - er - ing steep,
Blest with vic - t'ry and peace, may the heav'n - res - cued land

O'er the ram - parts we watched, were so gal - lant - ly stream-ing?
As it fit - ful - ly blows half con - ceals, half dis - clos - es?
Praise the Pow'r that hath made and pre - served us a na - tion!

And the rock - ets' red glare, the bombs burst - ing in air,
Now it catch - es the gleam of the morn-ing's first beam,
Then con - quer we must, when our cause it is just,

Gave proof through the night that our flag was still there.
In full glo - ry re - flect - ed now shined on the stream,
And this be our mot - to, "In God is our trust."

O say does that Star-Spang - led Ban - ner yet wave
'Tis the Star-Spang - led Ban - ner O long may it wave
And the Star-Spang - led Ban - ner in tri - umph shall wave

O'er the land of the free and the home of the brave?
O'er the land of the free and the home of the brave!
O'er the land of the free and the home of the brave!

Text: Francis S. Key, 1779-1843
Tune: STAR SPANGLED BANNER, Irregular; John S. Smith, 1750-1836

The composers or sources of refrains, psalm tones, and certain other brief musical elements are identified throughout by their initials. They are:

RJB, Robert J. Batastini;
LB, Laurence Bevenot, OSB;
JRC, J. Robert Carroll;
JG, Joseph Gelineau, SJ;
HH, Howard Hughes, SM;
RP, Richard Proulx;
CW, Chrysogonus Waddell, OCSO;

Christian Initiation of Adults

The passage of an adult into the Christian community takes place over an extended period of time. The members of the local church, the catechists and sponsors, the clergy and the diocesan bishop take part in the journey from inquiry through the catechumenate to baptism, confirmation and eucharist. The candidates are invited by example to pray, reflect on the scriptures, to fast and to join in the community's practice of charity. They are to learn the way of Jesus from the members of the church.

This journey of the candidates and community is marked by liturgical rites; thus the community publicly acknowledges, encourages and strengthens the candidates. The first of these is the rite of becoming catechumens. It concludes the sometimes lengthy period during which those who have come to ask about the way of the church and the life of a Christian have heard the gospel proclaimed and seen it practiced. Those who then feel called to walk in this way of Christ's church ask to begin the journey toward baptism. If the church judges the inquirers ready, they are accepted into the order of catechumens.

Those who have entered the catechumenate are already part of the household of Christ. During this time the catechumens are to hear and reflect on God's word, to learn the teachings and practices of the church, to become gradually accustomed to the ways of prayer and discipline in the church, to observe and to join in the good works of Christians. Ordinarily the catechumens are present on Sunday for the liturgy of the word but are dismissed after the homily—to continue prayer and study with their catechists—since they cannot join in the eucharist.

Rites of exorcism and blessing may be celebrated during the catechumenate. Through such rites the church prays that the catechumens will be purified, strengthened against all evil and thus eagerly grow in faith and good works. The very presence of the catechumens—at the Sunday liturgy, in these special rites and in everyday life—is itself a source of strength and blessing to the faithful.

Each year as Lent begins, the bishop, with the help of the local pastor and others involved with the catechumens, is to call those catechumens who are judged ready to prepare themselves for baptism at the Easter Vigil. Thus the catechumens become the "elect", the chosen, and for the forty days of Lent they make preparations: praying, fasting, doing good works. All the faithful join them in this. On several Sundays in Lent the rites of scrutiny take place when the assembled church prays over the elect. During Lent also the catechumens may publicly receive the words of the church's creed and of the Lord's Prayer.

Good Friday and Holy Saturday are days of prayer, fasting and preparation for the rites of the Easter Vigil. On the night between Saturday and Sunday, the church assembles to keep vigil and listen to many readings from scripture. Then the catechumens are called forward for baptism and confirmation.

The newly baptized, now called neophytes, take a special place in the Sunday eucharist throughout the fifty days of Eastertime. This is a time for their full incorporation into the local community.

All of these stages of initiation take place in the midst of the community. In various rites, the faithful affirm their support for the catechumens. The daily lives of the faithful show the Christian life to the inquirers and catechumens. In turn, the faithful are strengthened and challenged in their faith by the presence of the catechumens.

Those who seek to belong to the Roman Catholic church and who are already baptized may take some part in the catechumenate but they are not baptized again. Rather, they are received into the full communion of the Roman Catholic Church.

325 ACCEPTANCE INTO THE ORDER OF CATECHUMENS

INTRODUCTORY RITES

The presider greets the assembly: candidates, sponsors, members of the parish. The candidates are asked what it is that they seek and each replies. Before or during this rite an appropriate psalm may be sung.

CANDIDATES' FIRST ACCEPTANCE OF THE GOSPEL

The presider solemnly asks if the candidates are ready to begin walking this way of the gospel. The sponsors and all present are asked if they stand ready to assist the candidates as they strive to know and follow Christ. All respond: **We are.**

SIGNING OF THE CANDIDATES WITH THE CROSS

The sign of the cross marks the candidates for their new way of life. The presider signs each on the forehead saying:

N., receive the cross on your forehead.
It is Christ himself who now strengthens you
with this sign of his love.
Learn now to know him and follow him.

Sponsors and others also sign the candidates. Ears and eyes and other senses may also be signed. The presider prays that the catechumens may share in the saving power of the cross.

INVITATION TO THE CELEBRATION OF THE WORD OF GOD

The assembly may go into the church for the liturgy of the word singing an appropriate psalm.

LITURGY OF THE WORD   326

There may be one or more readings from scripture, together with a responsorial psalm. After the homily, a book containing the scriptures may be given to the new catechumens for their study and prayer throughout the time of the catechumenate.

INTERCESSIONS

All join in prayer for the new catechumens.

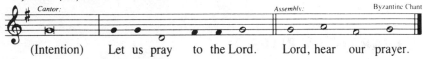

(Intention)   Let us pray   to the Lord.   Lord, hear   our   prayer.

If the eucharist is to be celebrated, the catechumens are first dismissed.

RITES OF THE CATECHUMENATE   327

DISMISSAL OF THE CATECHUMENS

When the catechumens are present at Mass, they are usually dismissed after the homily. Only when they have been baptized are they able to join the faithful for the liturgy of the eucharist. After their dismissal, the catechumens remain together and are joined by their catechists or others to pray and reflect on the scripture.

CELEBRATIONS OF THE WORD OF GOD

On Sundays, after the catechetical sessions, before the liturgical seasons and at other times the catechumens and others may join for liturgy: song, reading of scripture, psalmody, prayer and silence are normally part of such a service.

MINOR EXORCISMS

At appropriate times during the catechumenate, the catechists or other ministers may lead the community in prayers of exorcism over the catechumens. These prayers acknowledge the struggle against evil and ask that God strengthen the catechumens.

BLESSINGS OF THE CATECHUMENS

Prayers of blessing and the laying on of hands may take place whenever the catechumens gather for instruction or other purposes. Catechists or other ministers ask these blessings over the catechumens.

ANOINTINGS AND PRESENTATIONS

During the catechumenate or during Lent, the candidates may be anointed with the oil of catechumens as a sign of strength given for their struggle to live the gospel. At some point in this time they are publicly presented with the church's treasury of prayer and faith, the Our Father and the Creed.

RITE OF ELECTION OR ENROLLMENT OF NAMES

SCRUTINIES

PREPARATORY RITES

SACRAMENTS OF INITIATION

PERIOD OF MYSTAGOGIA

"Mystagogia" refers to the fifty-day period of postbaptismal celebration when the newly baptized are gradually drawn by the community into the fullness of Christian life and prayer. The newly baptized retain a special place in the assembly and are mentioned in the prayers of intercession. A special celebration, on Pentecost or just before, may mark the conclusion of the whole period of initiation.

The Baptism of Children

Children are baptized in the faith of the church: of parents, godparents, the local parish, the church throughout the world, the saints. Bringing their children for baptism, the parents profess their commitment to make a home where the gospel is lived. And the godparents and all members of the community promise to support the parents in this. Thus the children enter the waters of baptism and so are joined to this people, all baptized into the death and resurrection of Christ.

Baptism is celebrated above all at the Easter Vigil, but also on other Sundays, for Sunday is the Lord's day, the day when the church gathers to proclaim the paschal mystery. Baptism may take place at the Sunday Mass and is always to be celebrated in an assembly of members of the church.

RECEPTION OF THE CHILDREN

The parents and godparents are welcomed by all. The presider asks the names of the children and questions the parents about their own expectations and willingness to take on the responsibilities this baptism brings. The godparents are asked if they are ready to assist the parents to become Christian mothers and fathers.

With joy, then, the presider, the parents and godparents make the sign of the cross on the child's forehead: "I claim you for Christ our Savior by the sign of his cross."

All then go in procession to the place where the scriptures will be read. The following antiphon, or a hymn, may be sung during this procession.

Calvin Hampton, 1984
Acc. by Chris De Blasio, 1985

There is one God, one Fa-ther of all. There is one God, one Fa-ther of all. He is o-ver all, and

through all, he lives in all of us. There is one God, one
Fa-ther of all. All of us are one, u-nit-ed in Christ Je-sus. There is one God, one Fa-ther of all.

330 LITURGY OF THE WORD

FIRST READINGS

One or more passages from scripture are read. At the conclusion of each:

Reader: This is the Word of the Lord.

Assembly: **Thanks be to God.**

RESPONSORIAL PSALM

The following psalm may follow the first reading.

Ps. (26)27, 1.4.8-9.13-14 / 759-2
RP

The Lord is my light and my sal-va-tion.

The Lord is my light and my help;
whom shall I fear?
The Lord is the stronghold my life;
before whom shall I shrink? ℟.

There is one thing I ask of the Lord,
for this I long,
to live in the house of the Lord,
all the days of my life,
to savor the sweetness of the Lord,
to behold his temple. ℟.

It is your face, O Lord, that I seek;
hide not your face.
Dismiss not your servant in anger;
you have been my help.
Do not abandon or forsake me,
O God my help! ℟.

I am sure I shall see the Lord's
goodness
in the land of the living.
Hope in him, hold firm and take
heart.
Hope in the Lord! ℟.

GOSPEL

Before the gospel reading, this acclamation is sung:

Al - le - lu - ia, al - le - lu - ia, al - le - lu - ia,

During Lent:

Praise to you, Lord Je-sus Christ, king of end-less glo-ry!

Deacon (or priest): The Lord be with you.

    Assembly: **And also with you.**

      Deacon: A reading from the holy gospel according to N.

    Assembly: **Glory to you, Lord.**

After the reading:

      Deacon: This is the gospel of the Lord.

    Assembly: **Praise to you, Lord Jesus Christ.**

GENERAL INTERCESSIONS

All join in prayer for the church, the needs of the world, the poor, the children to be baptized and their parents.

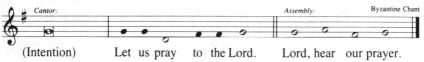

(Intention) Let us pray to the Lord. Lord, hear our prayer.

This prayer concludes with the litany of the saints which may include the patron saints of the children and of the local church.

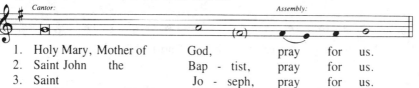

  1. Holy Mary, Mother of God, pray for us.
  2. Saint John the Bap - tist, pray for us.
  3. Saint Jo - seph, pray for us.
  4. Saint Peter and Saint Paul, pray for us.

The names of other saints may be added here. The litany concludes:

  5. All you saints of God, pray for us.

334 PRAYER OF EXORCISM AND ANOINTING

The presider stands before the parents with their infants and prays that God deliver these children from the power of evil. The children may be anointed with the oil of catechumens, an anointing which makes them strong for their struggle against evil in their lives. The presider lays hands on each child to show the love and concern the Church has for them. If there is a procession to the baptistry, the following may be sung.

We come to you, Lord Je-sus, fill us with your life.

Ronald Arnatt, 1984

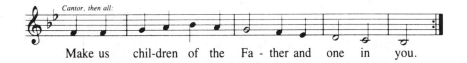

Make us chil-dren of the Fa-ther and one in you.

335 SACRAMENT OF BAPTISM

BLESSING AND INVOCATION OF GOD OVER BAPTISMAL WATER

When all are gathered at the font, the presider leads a blessing of the water, unless the baptismal water has already been blessed.

RENUNCIATION OF SIN AND PROFESSION OF FAITH

The presider then questions the parents and godparents, and they make a renunciation of sin and evil and profess their faith. The assembly listens to their responses. The presider then invites all to give their assent to this profession of faith:

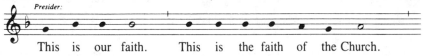

This is our faith. This is the faith of the Church.

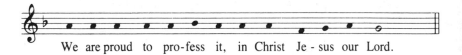

We are proud to pro-fess it, in Christ Je-sus our Lord.

Danish

A - men, a - men, a - men.

BAPTISM

336

One by one, the infants are brought to the font by their parents. There the parents express their desire to have their child baptized in the faith of the church which they have professed. The infant is then immersed in the water three times (or water is poured over the infant's head three times) as the presider says: "N., I baptize you in the name of the Father, and of the Son, and of the Holy Spirit." All may respond to each baptism with an acclamation.

Howard Hughes, SM, 1977

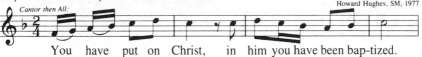

You have put on Christ, in him you have been bap-tized.

Al - le - lu - ia, al - le - lu - ia.

ANOINTING WITH CHRISM

337

The presider anoints each child on the crown of the head with holy chrism, a mixture of oil and perfume. The word "Christ" means "anointed." The baptized child has been "Christ-ed" and the sweet smell of the anointing reminds all of this.

CLOTHING WITH THE BAPTISMAL GARMENT AND GIVING OF THE CANDLE

The infants are then clothed in baptismal garments and a candle for each of the newly baptized is lighted from the paschal candle.

Optional

The presider may touch the ears and mouth of each child: "May Jesus soon touch your ears to receive his word, and your mouth to proclaim his faith."

CONCLUSION AND BLESSING

If baptism is celebrated at Mass, the liturgy continues with the eucharist. Otherwise, all process to the altar, carrying lighted candles. The above acclamation may be sung again during this procession. All then pray the Lord's Prayer, the parents are blessed and the liturgy concludes with a hymn of praise and thanksgiving.

Confirmation

338 Confirmation is a sacrament of initiation. With baptism and eucharist, confirmation climaxes the making of a Christian. It is the seal of baptism, the giving of the Holy Spirit. Adults are confirmed immediately after their baptism at the Easter Vigil. Children who have been baptized as infants are often confirmed some years later. The presider is the bishop or his delegate. The rite is usually celebrated within Mass; the introductory rites are done in the usual way.

339 LITURGY OF THE WORD

FIRST READINGS
One or more passages from scripture are read. At the conclusion of each:

Reader: This is the Word of the Lord.

Assembly: **Thanks be to God.**

RESPONSORIAL PSALM
The following psalm may follow the first reading.

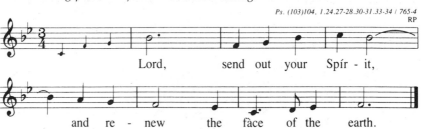

Ps. (103)104, 1.24.27-28.30-31.33-34 / 765-4
RP

Lord, send out your Spír - it, and re - new the face of the earth.

Bless the Lord, my soul!
Lord God, how great you are.
How many are your works, O Lord!
In wisdom you have made them all.
The earth is full of your riches. ℟.

All of these look to you
to give them their food in due
    season.
You give it, they gather it up;
you open your hand, they have their
    fill. ℟.

You send forth your spirit, they are
    created;
and you renew the face of the earth.
May the glory of the Lord last for
    ever!
May the Lord rejoice in his
    works! ℟.

I will sing to the Lord all my life,
make music to my God while I live.
May my thoughts be pleasing to him.
I find my joy in the Lord. ℟.

GOSPEL   340

Before the gospel reading, this acclamation is sung:

Al - le - lu - ia,   al - le - lu - ia,   al - le - lu - ia.

During Lent:

Praise to you, Lord   Je-sus Christ,   king   of   end-less   glo-ry!

Deacon (or priest): The Lord be with you.
    Assembly: **And also with you.**
     Deacon: A reading from the holy gospel according to N.
    Assembly: **Glory to you, Lord.**

After the reading:

    Deacon: This is the gospel of the Lord.
    Assembly: **Praise to you, Lord Jesus Christ.**

SACRAMENT OF CONFIRMATION   341

PRESENTATION OF THE CANDIDATES
The pastor or another minister calls the candidates by name to come forward.
Sponsors may accompany candidates.

HOMILY

RENEWAL OF BAPTISMAL PROMISES

The bishop leads the candidates in the renunciation of sin and evil and the profession of their faith. When the candidates have responded, the bishop proclaims:

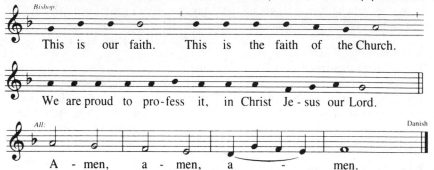

Bishop:

This is our faith. This is the faith of the Church.

We are proud to pro-fess it, in Christ Je-sus our Lord.

All: / Danish

A - men, a - men, a - men.

342 LAYING ON OF HANDS

Over and over the church makes this gesture in the sacraments as a blessing, a sign of solidarity and of love. Here the bishop prays for the coming of the Holy Spirit on those confirmed.

ANOINTING WITH CHRISM

Chrism is a mixture of oil and perfume that has been blessed by the bishop at the end of Lent. The meaning of "Christ" is "the anointed," so in this gesture the candidate is anointed, sealed, to follow in the way of Christ. The bishop rubs the chrism into the forehead of each candidate and says: "N., be sealed with the gift of the Holy Spirit," and the newly confirmed person responds: "Amen." The bishop then says, "Peace be with you," and the newly confirmed person responds, "And also with you." The assembly may join in song during the anointing.

After the anointing, the liturgy continues with the intercessions and the liturgy of the eucharist. If confirmation is celebrated apart from Mass, the intercessions are followed by the Lord's Prayer, the blessing, and the concluding hymn.

Holy Communion
Outside Mass

When for good reason communion cannot be received at Mass, the faith- **343**
ful may share in the paschal mystery through the liturgy of the word and
the reception of holy communion.

INTRODUCTORY RITES
An appropriate hymn or psalm may be sung.

344

GREETING
If the minister is a priest or deacon, the usual form of greeting is used:
Assembly: **And also with you.**

If the minister is not a priest or deacon, another form of greeting may be used:

Assembly: **Blessed be God forever.**

PENITENTIAL RITE
The minister invites silent reflection and repentance. After some silence:
Assembly: **I confess to almighty God,**
and to you, my brothers and sisters,
that I have sinned through my own fault
in my thoughts and in my words,
in what I have done,
and in what I have failed to do;
and I ask blessed Mary, ever virgin,
all the angels and saints,
and you, my brothers and sisters,
to pray for me to the Lord our God.

345 CELEBRATION OF THE WORD OF GOD

FIRST READINGS

One or more passages from scripture are read. At the conclusion of each:

   Reader: This is the Word of the Lord.

Assembly: **Thanks be to God.**

RESPONSORIAL PSALM

The following psalm (or another appropriate psalm) may follow the first reading.

Psalm (33)34, 2-3.4-5.6-7.8-9
RP

Taste and see the good - ness of the Lord.

I will bless the Lord at all times,
his praise always on my lips;
in the Lord my soul shall make its
  boast.
The humble shall hear and be
  glad. ℟.

Glorify the Lord with me,
together let us praise his name.
I sought the Lord and he answered
  me;
from all my terrors he set me
  free. ℟.

Look towards him and be radiant;
let your faces not be abashed.
This poor man called; the Lord heard
  him
and rescued him from all his
  distress. ℟.

The angel of the Lord is encamped
around those who revere him, to
  rescue them.
Taste and see that the Lord is good.
He is happy who seeks refuge in
  him. ℟.

346 GOSPEL

Before the gospel reading, this acclamation is sung:

Cantor, then all:
Chant Mode VI

Al - le - lu - ia, al - le - lu - ia, al - le - lu - ia.

During Lent:

Cantor, then all:
Frank Schoen, 1970

Praise to you, Lord Je - sus Christ, king of end - less glo - ry!

Reader: The Lord be with you.

Assembly: **And also with you.**

Reader: A reading from the holy gospel according to N.

Assembly: **Glory to you, Lord.**

After the reading:

Reader: This is the gospel of the Lord.

Assembly: **Praise to you, Lord Jesus Christ.**

GENERAL INTERCESSIONS 347

The assembly joins in prayer for the needs of the world, of the poor and of the church.

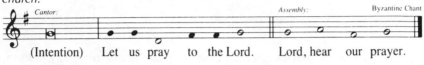

(Intention)   Let us pray   to the Lord.   Lord, hear   our prayer.

HOLY COMMUNION 348

The minister invites all to join in the Lord's Prayer, then to exchange a sign of peace. The minister then raises the Bread and all respond to the invitation.

Assembly: **Lord, I am not worthy to receive you,**
   but only say the word and I shall be healed.

A psalm or hymn may be sung during communion. Afterwards, there may be a period of silence or the singing of a psalm or hymn. The minister then recites a concluding prayer.

CONCLUDING RITE

All are blessed and dismissed.

 Minister: Go in the peace of Christ.

Assembly: **Thanks be to God.**

Reconciliation of Several Penitents

349 The sacrament of penance, also called the sacrament of reconciliation, may be celebrated with one penitent or with many. The latter form, the communal penance service, is a gathering of a few or a large number of Christians. Together they listen to the scriptures, sing psalms and hymns, pray, individually confess their sins and receive absolution, then praise God whose mercy and love are greater than our evil. In the rite of penance, the members of the church confront the struggle that was entered at baptism. There has been failure, evil done and good undone, but the penitent church comes again and again to name and renounce its sins and to return to the way of the Lord.

INTRODUCTORY RITES

An appropriate hymn or psalm may be sung.

350 **GREETING**

The presider and people greet each other in these or other words:

Presider: Grace, mercy, and peace be with you from God the Father and Christ Jesus our Savior.

Assembly: **And also with you.**

OPENING PRAYER

After silent prayer, the presider concludes the gathering rite with a solemn prayer.

351 CELEBRATION OF THE WORD OF GOD

FIRST READINGS

One or more passages from scripture are read. At the conclusion of each:

Reader: This is the Word of the Lord.

Assembly: **Thanks be to God.**

RESPONSORIAL PSALM

The following psalm may follow the first reading.

Psalm (50)51, 3-4.5-6.12-13.14-15
HH

Give back to me the joy of your sal - va - tion.

Have mercy on me, God, in your
    kindness.
In your compassion blot out my
    offense.
O wash me more and more from my
    guilt
and cleanse me from my sin. ℞.

My offenses truly I know them;
my sin is always before me.
Against you, you alone, have I
    sinned;
what is evil in your sight I have
    done. ℞.

A pure heart create for me, O God,
Put a steadfast spirit within me.
Do not cast me away from your
    presence,
nor deprive me of your holy
    spirit. ℞.

Give me again the joy of your hélp;
with a spirit of fervor sustain me,
that I may teach transgressors your
    ways
and sinners may return to you. ℞.

GOSPEL 352

Before the gospel reading, this acclamation is sung:

Cantor, then all: Chant Mode VI

Al - le - lu - ia, al - le - lu - ia, al - le - lu - ia.

During Lent:

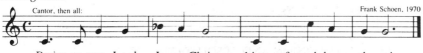

Cantor, then all: Frank Schoen, 1970

Praise to you, Lord Je-sus Christ, king of end-less glo-ry!

Deacon (or priest): The Lord be with you.

    Assembly: **And also with you.**

      Deacon: A reading from the holy gospel according to N.

    Assembly: **Glory to you, Lord.**

After the reading:

      Deacon: This is the gospel of the Lord.

    Assembly: **Praise to you, Lord Jesus Christ.**

HOMILY

EXAMINATION OF CONSCIENCE
In silence or through some other manner all reflect on their lives with sorrow for their sins.

353 SACRAMENT OF PENANCE

GENERAL CONFESSION OF SINS
Kneeling (or with another posture that expresses sorrow,) all join in confession. This form may be used:

I confess to almighty God,
and to you, my brothers and sisters,
that I have sinned through my own fault
in my thoughts and in my words,
in what I have done,
and in what I have failed to do;
and I ask blessed Mary, ever virgin,
all the angels and saints,
and you, my brothers and sisters,
to pray for me to the Lord our God.

354 *Standing, all join in a litany using one of the following responses, or a song asking God's mercy. The Lord's Prayer is then recited or sung.*

| A | **We pray you, hear us.** |

| B | **Lord, be merciful to me, a sinner.** |

| C | **Lord, have mercy.** |

355 **INDIVIDUAL CONFESSION AND ABSOLUTION**
One by one the penitents approach the priest confessors. All confess their sins, accept some fitting act of satisfaction and the counsel of the confessor. Then the priest extends his hands over the penitent's head and speaks the prayer of absolution, concluding: "Through the ministry of the Church may God give you pardon and peace, and I absolve you from your sins in the name of the Father, and of the Son, and of the Holy Spirit." The penitent responds, "Amen."

PROCLAMATION OF PRAISE FOR GOD'S MERCY

356

The presider invites all to give thanks and to show by their lives—and in the life of the whole community—the grace of repentance. A psalm, canticle or hymn may be sung to proclaim God's mercy.

Isaiah 12:1-6
RJB

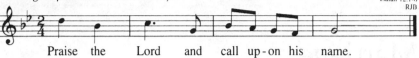

Praise the Lord and call up-on his name.

I thank you, Lord, you were angry with me
but your anger has passed and you give me comfort. ℞.

Truly, God is my salvation,
I trust, I shall not fear.
For the Lord is my strength, my song,
he became my savior.
With joy you will draw water
from the wells of salvation. ℞.

Give thanks to the Lord, give praise to his name!
Make his mighty deeds known to the peoples!
Declare the greatness of his name,
sing a psalm to the Lord!
For he has done glorious deeds,
make them known to all the earth! ℞.

People of Zion, sing and shout for joy
for great in your midst is the Holy One of Israel. ℞.

CONCLUDING PRAYER OF THANKSGIVING

357

This prayer is spoken by the presider.

BLESSING AND DISMISSAL

The presider blesses all present and the deacon or other minister dismisses the assembly. All respond:

Thanks be to God.

Marriage

358   Many rituals of various kinds and origins surround a wedding. These rites of preparation and of celebration are ways for the couple, the families and friends to share in and to strengthen the making of a marriage. The marriage rite itself is the covenant made by bride and groom, the consent each gives to and accepts from each other. The church assembles to witness and bless this union.

INTRODUCTORY RITES

PROCESSION
The ministers, including bride and groom, enter in procession to appropriate music.

359   **GREETING**
  Presider: In the name of the Father, and of the Son, and of the Holy Spirit.
Assembly: **Amen.**

> A   *Presider:* The grace of our Lord Jesus Christ and the love of God and the fellowship of the Holy Spirit be with you all.
> *Assembly:* **And also with you.**

> B   *Presider:* The grace and peace of God our Father and the Lord Jesus Christ be with you.
> *Assembly:* **Blessed be God, the Father of our Lord Jesus Christ.**
> *or:* **And also with you.**

> C   *Presider:* The Lord be with you. *(Bishop:* Peace be with you.)
> *Assembly:* **And also with you.**

PENITENTIAL RITE

The presider invites the people to recall their sins in silence and repent of them.
After the silence, one of the following forms is used.

A *Assembly:* **I confess to almighty God,**
and to you my brothers and sisters,
that I have sinned through my own fault
in my thoughts and in my words,
in what I have done,
and in what I have failed to do;
and I ask blessed Mary, ever virgin,
all the angels and saints,
and you, my brothers and sisters,
to pray for me to the Lord our God.

B *Presider:* Lord, we have sinned against you:
Lord, have mercy.

Assembly: **Lord, have mercy.**

Presider: Lord, show us your mercy and love.

Assembly: **And grant us your salvation.**

C *The presider or another minister makes a series of invocations according*
to the following pattern.

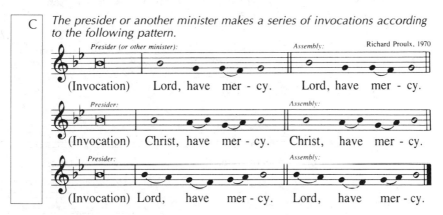

The penitential rite always concludes:

Presider: May almighty God have mercy on us, forgive us our sins, and
bring us to everlasting life.

Assembly: **Amen.**

KYRIE

Unless form C of the penitential rite has been used, the Kyrie follows. The people
repeat each invocation after the presider or other minister.

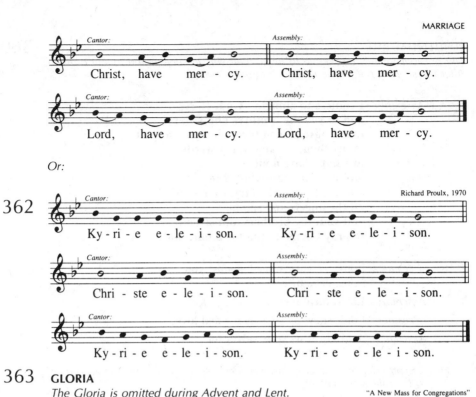

Christ, have mer-cy. *Christ, have mer-cy.*

Lord, have mer-cy. *Lord, have mer-cy.*

Or:

362

Richard Proulx, 1970

Ky - ri - e e - le - i - son. *Ky - ri - e e - le - i - son.*

Chri - ste e - le - i - son. *Chri - ste e - le - i - son.*

Ky - ri - e e - le - i - son. *Ky - ri - e e - le - i - son.*

363 GLORIA

The Gloria is omitted during Advent and Lent.

"A New Mass for Congregations"
Carroll Thomas Andrews, 1970

mf

Glo - ry to God in the high - est, and

peace to his peo - ple on earth. Lord God,

f

heav - en - ly King, al - might - y God and Fa - ther, we

wor - ship you, we give you thanks, we praise you for your

mf

glo - ry. Lord Je - sus Christ, on - ly Son of the

Fa - ther, Lord God, Lamb of God, you take a - way the

sin of the world: have mer - cy on us;

you are seat - ed at the right hand of the Fa - ther:

re - ceive our prayer.

Tempo primo *f*

For you a - lone are the Ho - ly One, you a - lone are the

Lord, you a - lone are the Most High,

Je - sus Christ, with the Ho - ly Spir - it, in the glo - ry of

ff

God the Fa - ther. A - men.

OPENING PRAYER 364

The gathering rites conclude with a silent prayer and a prayer spoken by the presider.

LITURGY OF THE WORD 365

FIRST READINGS

One or more passages from scriptures are read. At the conclusion of each:

Reader: This is the Word of the Lord.

Assembly: **Thanks be to God.**

RESPONSORIAL PSALM

The following psalm may follow the first reading.

Psalm (32)33. 12.18.20.21.22 / 776-1
JRC

Cantor, then all:

The earth is full of the good-ness, the good-ness of the Lord.

They are happy, whose God is the
  Lord,
the people he has chosen as his own.
The Lord looks on those who revere
  him,
on those who hope in his love. ℟.

Our soul is waiting for the Lord.
The Lord is our help and our shield.
In him do our hearts find joy.
We trust in his holy name. ℟.

May your love be upon us, O Lord,
as we place all our hope in you. ℟.

366 GOSPEL

Before the gospel reading, this acclamation is sung:

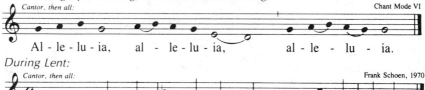

Cantor, then all:

Chant Mode VI

Al - le - lu - ia, al - le - lu - ia, al - le - lu - ia.

During Lent:

Cantor, then all:

Frank Schoen, 1970

Praise to you, Lord Je-sus Christ, king of end-less glo-ry!

Deacon (or priest): The Lord be with you.

  Assembly: **And also with you.**

    Deacon: A reading from the holy gospel according to N.

    Assembly: **Glory to you, Lord.**

After the reading:

    Deacon: This is the gospel of the Lord.

    Assembly: **Praise to you, Lord Jesus Christ.**

HOMILY

367 SACRAMENT OF MARRIAGE

The presider invites the couple to give their consent to each other freely in the presence of the church. When they have done so, the presider receives their consent in the name of the church. The wedding rings, a sign of love and fidelity, are then blessed and exchanged.

GENERAL INTERCESSIONS
368

The church joins in prayer for the needs of the world, for the poor, for the community and for the couple.

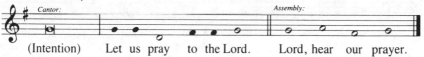

(Intention) Let us pray to the Lord. Lord, hear our prayer.

LITURGY OF THE EUCHARIST
369

PREPARATION OF THE GIFTS

Bread and wine are brought to the table. If there is no music, all may respond to the prayers of preparation:

Assembly: **Blessed be God for ever.**

The preparation concludes with the priest inviting all to pray:

Assembly: **May the Lord accept the sacrifice at your hands**
for the praise and glory of his name,
for our good, and the good of all his church.

EUCHARISTIC PRAYER
370

The presider invites the assembly to join in giving thanks and praise to God for the wonders of creation and the works of salvation.

Sacramentary 1974

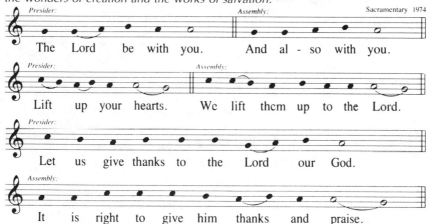

The Lord be with you. And al - so with you.

Lift up your hearts. We lift them up to the Lord.

Let us give thanks to the Lord our God.

It is right to give him thanks and praise.

During the eucharistic prayer, the assembly sings acclamations of praise and thanksgiving. The first is the "Sanctus":

371

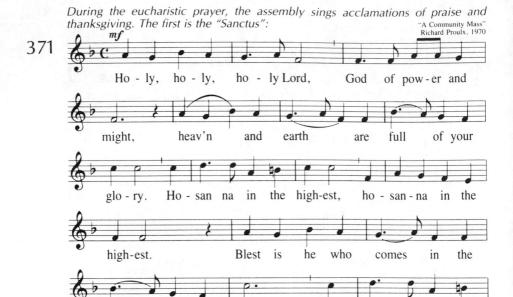

Ho - ly, ho - ly, ho - ly Lord, God of pow-er and might, heav'n and earth are full of your glo - ry. Ho - san - na in the high-est, ho - san-na in the high-est. Blest is he who comes in the name of the Lord. Ho - san - na in the high-est, ho - san - na in the high - est.

The second is the response to the invitation, "Let us proclaim the mystery of faith":

"A Community Mass"
Richard Proulx, 1970

372

Christ has died, Christ is ris - en, Christ will come a - gain.

Finally, the assembly ratifies the entire eucharistic prayer.

373   *Presider:* Through him, with him, in him, in the unity of the Holy Spirit, all glory and honor is yours, almighty Father, for ever and ever.

Danish

A - men, a - men, a - men.

374   **COMMUNION RITE**

The presider invites the assembly to join in the Lord's Prayer.

Robert Snow, 1964
Acc. by Gerard Farrell, OSB, 1984

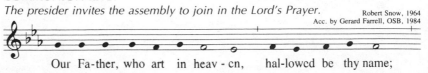

Our Fa-ther, who art in heav - en, hal-lowed be thy name;

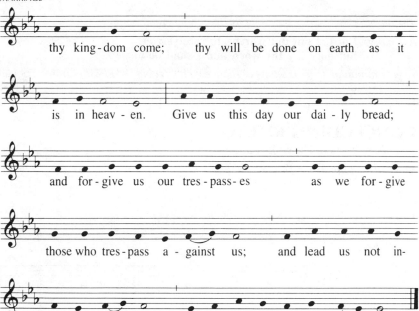

thy king-dom come; thy will be done on earth as it

is in heav - en. Give us this day our dai - ly bread;

and for - give us our tres - pass- es as we for - give

those who tres - pass a - gainst us; and lead us not in-

to temp - ta - tion, but de - liv - er us from e - vil.

In the nuptial blessing, the presider prays that God will surround this couple with love, with peace, with the strength to be faithful to one another and to be an example of kindness to all. After the blessing, all are invited to exchange a sign of peace.

375

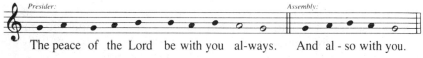

Presider: The peace of the Lord be with you al-ways. *Assembly:* And al - so with you.

As the bread is broken to be shared in communion, the assembly joins in singing the "Lamb of God."

376

Agnus Dei XVIII
Acc. by Gerard Farrell, OSB, 1984

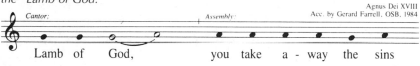

Cantor: Lamb of God, *Assembly:* you take a - way the sins

of the world: have mer - cy on us.

This is sung two or more times. When the bread has been prepared, the "Lamb of God" concludes:

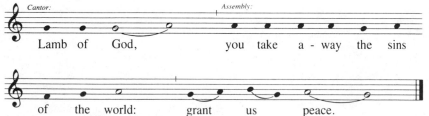

Cantor: Lamb of God, *Assembly:* you take a - way the sins

of the world: grant us peace.

377 *The presider invites the assembly to share holy communion.*

Assembly: **Lord, I am not worthy to receive you,
but only say the word and I shall be healed.**

After communion there is a time of silence which is concluded with a prayer spoken by the presider.

378 CONCLUDING RITE

Presider: The Lord be with you.

Assembly: **And also with you.**

BLESSING
First the couple, then the whole assembly is blessed.

DISMISSAL

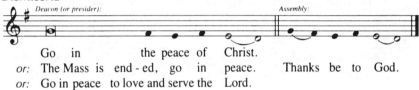

Go in the peace of Christ.
or: The Mass is end - ed, go in peace. Thanks be to God.
or: Go in peace to love and serve the Lord.

The liturgy may conclude with an appropriate song or instrumental music.

[When the rite of marriage is celebrated apart from Mass, all of the above may be used but the "Liturgy of the Eucharist" is omitted. After the prayers of intercession, the nuptial blessing is given. The rite concludes with the Lord's Prayer and the blessing of the couple and the assembly.]

Anointing of the Sick

The sacrament of anointing is celebrated when a Christian's health is seri- 379
ously impaired by sickness or old age. If possible, it is celebrated when
the sick person is able to take part in the rite. When the sick person is
able to receive holy communion, the rite of anointing may be celebrated
within the liturgy of the Mass.

Through the anointing with the blessed oil of the sick, the church
supports those who struggle against illness or injury and continues the
healing work of Christ. The anointing is intended to bring hope and com-
fort to the one anointed and, to the gathered family and friends, a spirit
of support and sharing in the sufferings of our brothers and sisters.

The Mass begins in the usual way, but after the greeting the presider
welcomes the sick.

LITURGY OF THE WORD   380

FIRST READINGS
One or more passages from scripture are read. At the conclusion of each:

Reader: This is the Word of the Lord.

Assembly: **Thanks be to God.**

RESPONSORIAL PSALM

The following psalm may follow the first reading.

Ps.(70)71, 1-2.5-6.8-9.14-15
HH

My God, come quick - ly to help me.

In you, O Lord, I take refuge;
let me never be put to shame.
In your justice rescue me, free me;
pay heed to me and save me. ℟.

It is you, O Lord, who are my hope,
my trust, O Lord, since my youth.
On you I have leaned from my birth,
from my mother's womb you have been my help.
My hope has always been in you. ℟.

My lips are filled with your praise,
with your glory all the day long.
Do not reject me now that I am old;
When my strength fails do not forsake me. ℟.

But as for me, I will always hope
and praise you more and more.
My lips will tell of your justice
and day by day of your help. ℟.

381 GOSPEL

Before the gospel reading, this acclamation is sung:

Chant Mode VI

Al - le - lu - ia, al - le - lu - ia, al - le - lu - ia.

During Lent:

Frank Schoen, 1970

Praise to you, Lord Je-sus Christ, king of end-less glo-ry!

Deacon (or priest): The Lord be with you.

    Assembly: **And also with you.**

      Deacon: A reading from the holy gospel according to N.

    Assembly: **Glory to you, Lord.**

After the reading:

      Deacon: This is the gospel of the Lord.

    Assembly: **Praise to you, Lord Jesus Christ.**

HOMILY

LITURGY OF ANOINTING 382

LITANY

The assembly joins in prayers for the sick and for those who care for them.

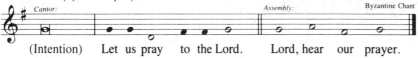

(Intention)   Let us pray   to the Lord.   Lord, hear   our   prayer.

LAYING ON OF HANDS

The presider silently lays hands on the head of each sick person in a gesture of prayer, healing and solidarity.

PRAYER OVER THE OIL

If the oil is already blessed, the presider leads a prayer of thanksgiving over it. After each prayer:

Assembly: **Blessed be God who heals us in Christ.**

If the oil is not blessed, the presider leads the prayer of blessing.

ANOINTING

The presider anoints each sick person on the forehead in a sign of strength and soothing comfort.

Presider: Through this holy anointing may the Lord in his love and mercy
help you with the grace of the Holy Spirit.

Assembly: **Amen.**

The presider anoints the hands of each sick person.

Presider: May the Lord who frees you from sin save you and raise you up.

Assembly: **Amen.**

The presider may anoint other parts of the body.

PRAYER AFTER ANOINTING

The presider prays for those who have been anointed. Then the liturgy of the eucharist is celebrated with special prayers for the sick.

[If the rite of anointing is celebrated outside of Mass, the liturgy begins with the greeting, rite of sprinkling and penitential rite. After the scriptures and homily, the liturgy of anointing is celebrated as above. Then the Lord's Prayer is recited or sung and the rite may conclude with holy communion.]

Funeral Mass

383 The rites which surround the death of a Christian extend from the Viaticum (last communion) and final prayers before death through the wake service and funeral Mass to the burial of the body or ashes. In all of this the community affirms its faith in the communion of saints and the resurrection of the dead. The family and friends are helped in their time of sorrow with prayer and song. Thus they express present grief even as they hold to the church's lasting hope. Following is the rite of the funeral Mass.

INTRODUCTORY RITES

GREETING
One of the following is spoken.

A *Presider:* The grace of our Lord Jesus Christ and the love of God and the fellowship of the Holy Spirit be with you all.
Assembly: **And also with you.**

B *Presider:* The grace and peace of God our Father and the Lord Jesus Christ be with you.
Assembly: **And also with you.**

C *Presider:* The grace and peace of God our Father, who raised Jesus from the dead, be always with you.
Assembly: **And also with you.**

D *Presider:* May the Father of mercies, the God of all consolation, be with you.
Assembly: **And also with you.**

The body is sprinkled with holy water, a reminder of baptism. The family or pall bearers spread the pall over the body, a garment like that which the Christian received at baptism. The funeral procession then moves into the church accompanied by the following song or an appropriate hymn.

Psalm (114) 115
RJB

384

Give him / her e - ter - nal rest, O Lord, and may your light shine on him / her for ev - er.

I love the Lord for he has heard
the cry of my appeal;
for he turned his ear to me
in the day when I called him. ℟.

They surround me, the snares of death,
with the anguish of the tomb;
they caught me, sorrow and distress.
I called on the Lord's name,
O Lord, our God, deliver us. ℟.

How gracious is the Lord, and just;
our God has compassion.
The Lord protects the simple hearts,
I was helpless so he saved me. ℟.

Turn back, my soul, to your rest
for the Lord has been good,
he has kept my soul from death
and my feet from stumbling. ℟.

I will walk in the presence of
the Lord
in the land of the living.
Praise the Father, the Son and
the Holy Spirit,
for ever and ever. ℟.

OPENING PRAYER
385

The presider invites all to pray and leads an opening prayer. All respond: **Amen.**

LITURGY OF THE WORD
386

FIRST READINGS
One or more passages from scripture are read. At the conclusion of each:

Reader: This is the Word of the Lord.

Assembly: **Thanks be to God.**

RESPONSORIAL PSALM

The following psalm may follow the first reading.

Ps.(22) 23, 1-3.3-4.5.6 / 791-1
RP

The Lord is my shep-herd; there is noth-ing I shall want.

The Lord is my shepherd;
there is nothing I shall want.
Fresh and green are the pastures
where he gives me repose.
Near restful waters he leads me,
to revive my drooping spirit. ℟.

He guides me along the right path;
he is true to his name.
If I should walk in the valley of
    darkness
no evil would I fear.

You are there with your crook and
your staff;
with these you give me comfort. ℟.

You have prepared a banquet for me
in the sight of my foes.
My head you have anointed with oil;
my cup is overflowing. ℟.

Surely goodness and kindness shall
    follow me
all the days of my life.
In the Lord's own house shall I dwell
for ever and ever. ℟.

387 GOSPEL

Before the gospel reading, this acclamation is sung:

Chant Mode VI

Al - le - lu - ia, al - le - lu - ia, al - le - lu - ia.

During Lent:

Frank Schoen, 1970

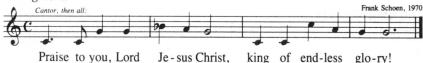

Praise to you, Lord Je - sus Christ, king of end-less glo-ry!

Deacon (or priest): The Lord be with you.

   Assembly: **And also with you.**

     Deacon: A reading from the holy gospel according to N.

   Assembly: **Glory to you, Lord.**

After the reading:

     Deacon: This is the gospel of the Lord.

   Assembly: **Praise to you, Lord Jesus Christ.**

HOMILY

GENERAL INTERCESSIONS   388

All pray for the church, the local community, those in need, the deceased and those who mourn.

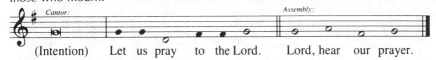

LITURGY OF THE EUCHARIST   389

PREPARATION OF THE ALTAR AND GIFTS

Bread and wine are brought to the table and the deacon or presider prepares these gifts. If there is no music, the prayers of preparation may be said aloud, and all may respond: **Blessed be God for ever.** *The presider then invites all to pray.*

Assembly: **May the Lord accept the sacrifice at your hands
for the praise and glory of his name,
for our good, and the good of all his church.**

The presider says the prayer over the gifts and all respond: **Amen.**

EUCHARISTIC PRAYER   390

This central prayer of the liturgy begins with this dialogue:

The Sanctus acclamation concludes the first part of the eucharistic prayer.

391

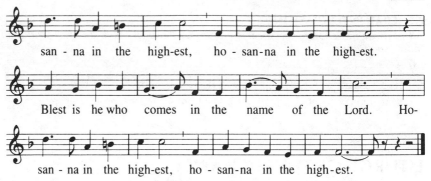

san - na in the high-est, ho - san-na in the high-est.

Blest is he who comes in the name of the Lord. Ho-

san - na in the high-est, ho - san-na in the high-est.

The following acclamation comes in response to the presider's invitation to proclaim the mystery of faith.

"A Community Mass"
Richard Proulx, 1970

392

Christ has died, Christ is ris-en, Christ will come a - gain.

The eucharistic prayer concludes:

393   *Presider:* Through him, with him, in him, in the unity of the Holy Spirit, all glory and honor is yours, almighty Father, for ever and ever.

Danish

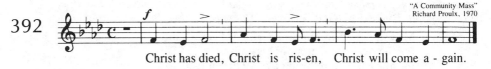

A - men, a - men, a - men.

394   **COMMUNION RITE**

The presider invites the assembly to join in the Lord's Prayer.

Adapt. by Robert Snow, 1964

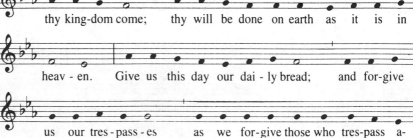

Our Fa-ther, who art in heav - en, hal-lowed be thy name;

thy king-dom come; thy will be done on earth as it is in

heav - en. Give us this day our dai - ly bread; and for-give

us our tres - pass - es as we for-give those who tres-pass a-

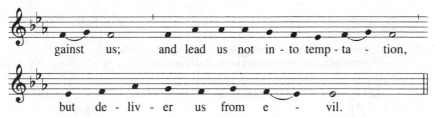

gainst us; and lead us not in - to temp - ta - tion,

but de - liv - er us from e - vil.

Presider: Deliver us, Lord...for the coming of our Savior, Jesus Christ.

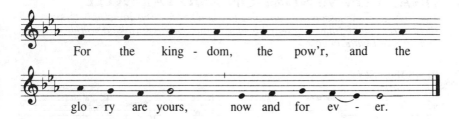

For the king - dom, the pow'r, and the

glo - ry are yours, now and for ev - er.

Following the prayer "Lord, Jesus Christ," the presider invites the sign of peace. **395**

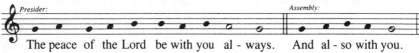

Presider: *Assembly:*

The peace of the Lord be with you al - ways. And al - so with you.

All exchange a sign of peace.

As the bread is broken to be shared in communion, the assembly joins in singing **396**
the "Lamb of God."

Cantor: *Assembly:*   Agnus Dei XVIII

Lamb, of God, you take a - way the sins

of the world: have mer - cy on us.

This is sung two or more times. When the bread has been prepared, the "Lamb of God" concludes:

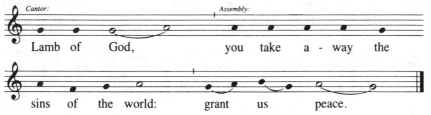

Cantor: *Assembly:*

Lamb of God, you take a - way the

sins of the world: grant us peace.

397 *The presider then invites the assembly to share in the holy communion. All respond to the invitation:*

Assembly: **Lord, I am not worthy to receive you,
but only say the word and I shall be healed.**

A song or psalm may be sung during communion. After communion, a time of silence is observed. The rite concludes with the prayer after communion to which all respond: **Amen.**

398 FINAL COMMENDATION AND FAREWELL

The ministers and assembly surround the body. After the invitation, prayer and silence, one of the following may be sung as the body is sprinkled with holy water and honored with incense.

RESPONSORY

Richard Proulx, 1975

ALTERNATE RESPONSORY

Howard Hughes, SM, 1977

I know that my Re-deem-er lives, and on the last day I shall rise a-gain; in my bod-y I shall look on God, my Sav-ior, in my bod-y I shall look on God, my Sav-ior. I my-self shall see him; my own eyes will gaze on him, my own eyes will gaze on him; in my bod-y I shall look on God, my Sav-ior, in my bod-y I shall look on God, my Sav-ior. This is the hope I cher-ish, this is the hope I cher-ish in my heart; in my bod-y I shall look on God, my Sav-ior, in my bod-y I shall look on God, my Sav-ior.

After the concluding prayer, one of the following songs or an appropriate hymn is sung while the body is being taken away.

400

In Paradisum
ICEL, 1985

TALLIS' CANON, LM
Thomas Tallis, c.1510-1583

1. May saints and an - gels lead you on,
2. Come to the peace of A - bra - ham

Es - cort - ing you where Christ has gone.
And to the sup - per of the Lamb:

Now he has called you, come to him
Come to the glo - ry of the blessed,

Who sits a - bove the ser - a - phim.
And to per - pet - ual light and rest.

401

In Paradisum
Trans. Hymnal Version, 1986

Mode VII
Acc. by Richard Proulx, 1985

In pa - ra - dí - sum de - dú - cant te án -
May choirs of an - gels es - cort you in - to

ge - li: in tu - o ad - vén - tu
par - a - dise: and at your ar - ri - val

su - scí - pi - ant te már - ty - res,
may the mar - tyrs re - ceive and wel - come you;

et per - dú - cant te in ci - vi - tá - tem san - ctam
may they bring you home in - to the ho - ly cit - y,

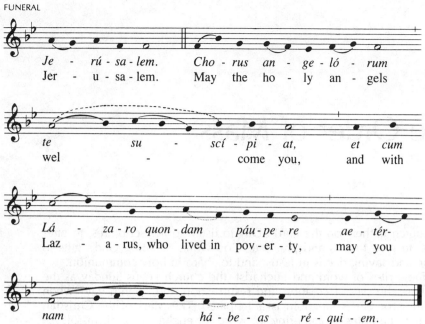

Je - rú - sa - lem. *Cho - rus an - ge - ló - rum*
Jer - u - sa - lem. May the ho - ly an - gels

te su - scí - pi - at, et cum
wel - come you, and with

Lá - za - ro quon - dam páu - pe - re ae - tér-
Laz - a - rus, who lived in pov - er - ty, may you

nam há - be - as ré - qui - em.
have ev - er - last - ing rest.

The Order of Mass

402 Each church gathers on the Lord's Day to listen to the scriptures, to offer prayers, to give thanks and praise to God while recalling God's gifts in creation and saving deeds in Jesus, and to share in holy communion.

In these rites of word and eucharist, the church keeps Sunday as the Lord's Day, the day of creation and resurrection, the "eighth day" when the fullness of God's kingdom is anticipated. The Mass of the Christian community has rites of gathering, of word, of eucharist, of dismissal. All those who gather constitute the assembly. One member of this assembly who has been ordained to the presbyterate, the priesthood, presides by leading the opening and closing prayers and the eucharistic prayer. A member ordained to the diaconate may assist, read the gospel and preach. Other members of the assembly are chosen and trained for various ministries: These are the readers, ushers, musicians, communion ministers. All of these assist the assembly. It is the assembly itself, all those present, that does the liturgy.

The order of Mass which follows is familiar to all who regularly join in this assembly. It is learned through repetition. This order of Mass leaves many things to the local community and to the season of the liturgical year.

INTRODUCTORY RITES
The rites which precede the liturgy of the word assist the assembly to gather as a community. They prepare that community to listen to the scriptures and to celebrate the eucharist together. The procession and entrance song are ways of expressing the unity and spirit of the assembly.

GREETING
After the sign of the cross one of the greetings is given.

  Presider: In the name of the Father, and of the Son, and of the Holy Spirit.

  Assembly: **Amen.**

A *Presider:* The grace of our Lord Jesus Christ and the love of God and the fellowship of the Holy Spirit be with you all.

    Assembly: **And also with you.**

B *Presider:* The grace and peace of God our Father and the Lord Jesus Christ be with you.

    Assembly: **Blessed be God, the Father of our Lord Jesus Christ.**
        or: **And also with you.**

C *Presider:* The Lord be with you. *(Bishop:* Peace be with you.)

    Assembly: **And also with you.**

BLESSING AND SPRINKLING OF HOLY WATER   403

On Sundays, instead of the penitential rite below, the blessing and sprinkling of holy water may be done. The following or another appropriate song is sung.

Joseph Roff, 1984

Cleanse us, O Lord, from all our sins; wash us, and we shall be clean, clean as new snow. snow. I will pour clean wa-ter o-ver you and wash a-way all your sins. snow. A new heart will I give you, says the Lord.

PENITENTIAL RITE   404

The presider invites all to be mindful of human sinfulness and of the great mercy of God. After a time of silence, one of the following forms is used.

A *Assembly:* **I confess to almighty God,**
         and to you, my brothers and sisters,
         that I have sinned through my own fault
         in my thoughts and in my words,
         in what I have done,
         and in what I have failed to do;
         and I ask blessed Mary, ever virgin,
         all the angels and saints,
         and you, my brothers and sisters,
         to pray for me to the Lord our God.

B

Presider: Lord, we have sinned against you:
Lord, have mercy,

Assembly: **Lord, have mercy.**

Presider: Lord, show us your mercy and love.

Assembly: **And grant us your salvation.**

C

The presider or another minister makes a series of invocations according to the following pattern.

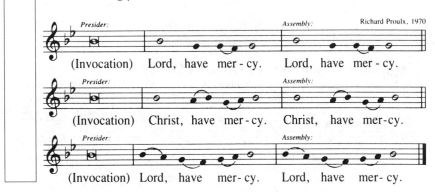

Richard Proulx, 1970

Presider: / *Assembly:*
(Invocation) Lord, have mer - cy. Lord, have mer - cy.

(Invocation) Christ, have mer - cy. Christ, have mer - cy.

(Invocation) Lord, have mer - cy. Lord, have mer - cy.

The penitential rite always concludes:

Presider: May almighty God have mercy on us, forgive us our sins, and bring us to everlasting life.

Assembly: **Amen.**

405 KYRIE

Unless form C of the penitential rite has been used, the Kyrie follows.

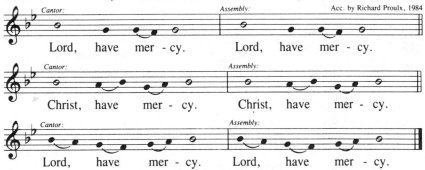

Acc. by Richard Proulx, 1984

Cantor: / *Assembly:*
Lord, have mer - cy. Lord, have mer - cy.

Christ, have mer - cy. Christ, have mer - cy.

Lord, have mer - cy. Lord, have mer - cy.

Or:

406

Acc. by Richard Proulx, 1984

Cantor: / *Assembly:*
Ky - ri - e e - le - i - son. Ky - ri - e e - le - i - son.

Cantor: Chri - ste e - le - i - son. Assembly: Chri - ste e - le - i - son.

Cantor: Ky - ri - e e - le - i - son. Assembly: Ky - ri - e e - le - i - son.

GLORIA

407

The Gloria is omitted during Advent and Lent.

"A New Mass for Congregations"
Carroll T. Andrews, 1970

Glo - ry to God in the high - est, and

peace to his peo - ple on earth. Lord God,

heav - en - ly King, al - might - y God and

Fa - ther, we wor - ship you, we give you thanks, we

praise you for your glo - ry.

Slightly slower
Choir (Congr. ad lib.):

Lord Je - sus Christ, on - ly Son of the Fa - ther,

Lord God, Lamb of God, you take a - way the

sin of the world: have mer - cy on

us; you are seat - ed at the right hand of the

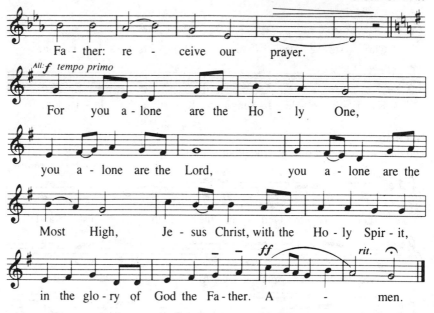

Fa - ther: re - ceive our prayer.

All: **f** *tempo primo*

For you a - lone are the Ho - ly One,

you a - lone are the Lord, you a - lone are the

Most High, Je - sus Christ, with the Ho - ly Spir - it,

ff *rit.*

in the glo - ry of God the Fa - ther. A - men.

408 **OPENING PRAYER**

After the invitation from the presider, all pray for a while. The introductory rites conclude with the proper prayer of the day and the Amen of the assembly.

409 **LITURGY OF THE WORD**

When the church assembles, the book of the scriptures is opened and all listen as lectors and deacon (or presider) read from the places assigned. The first reading is normally from the Hebrew Scriptures, the second from the letters of the New Testament, and the third from the Book of Gospels. Over a three-year cycle, the church reads through the letters and gospels and a portion of the Hebrew Scriptures. During the Sundays of Ordinary Time, the letters and gospels are read in order, each Sunday continuing near the place where the previous Sunday's readings ended. During Advent/Christmas and Lent/Easter, the readings are those which are traditional and appropriate to these seasons.

The church listens to and—through the weeks and years—is shaped by the scriptures. Those who have gathered for Sunday liturgy are to give their full attention to the words of the reader. A time of silence and reflection follows each of the first two readings. After the first reading, this reflection continues in the singing of the psalm. A homily, bringing together the scriptures and the life of the community, follows the gospel. The liturgy of the word concludes with the creed, the dismissal of the catechumens and the prayers of intercession. In the latter, the assembly continues its constant work of recalling and praying for the universal church and all those in need.

This reading and hearing of the word—simple things that they are—are the foundation of the liturgical celebration. The public reading of the scriptures and the rituals which surround this—silence and psalm and acclamation, posture and gesture, preaching and litany of intercession—gather the church generation after generation. They gather and sustain and gradually make of us the image of Christ.

READING I

In conclusion:

   Reader: This is the Word of the Lord.

Assembly: **Thanks be to God.**

After a period of silence, the responsorial psalm is sung.

READING II

In conclusion:

   Reader: This is the Word of the Lord.

Assembly: **Thanks be to God.**

A time of silence follows the reading.

GOSPEL 410

Before the gospel, an acclamation is sung.

Al - le - lu - ia, al - le - lu - ia, al - le - lu - ia.

During Lent one of the following acclamations replaces the alleluia.

A

Praise to you, Lord Je-sus Christ, king of end-less glo - ry!

Or:

   B **Praise and honor to you, Lord Jesus Christ!**

   C **Glory and praise to you, Lord Jesus Christ!**

   D **Glory to you, Word of God, Lord Jesus Christ!**

Deacon (or priest): The Lord be with you.

    Assembly: **And also with you.**

     Deacon: A reading from the holy gospel according to N.

    Assembly: **Glory to you, Lord.**

After the reading:

     Deacon: This is the gospel of the Lord.

    Assembly: **Praise to you, Lord Jesus Christ.**

HOMILY

411 **PROFESSION OF FAITH**

We believe in one God,
  the Father, the Almighty,
  maker of heaven and earth,
  of all that is seen and unseen.

We believe in one Lord, Jesus Christ,
  the only Son of God,
  eternally begotten of the Father,
  God from God, Light from Light,
  true God from true God,
  begotten, not made, one in Being with the Father.
  Through him all things were made.
  For us men and for our salvation he came down from heaven:

All bow at the following words up to: and became man.

  by the power of the Holy Spirit
    he was born of the Virgin Mary, and became man.
  For our sake he was crucified under Pontius Pilate;
    he suffered, died, and was buried.
    On the third day he rose again
      in fulfillment of the Scriptures;
    he ascended into heaven
      and is seated at the right hand of the Father.
  He will come again in glory to judge the living and the dead,
    and his kingdom will have no end.

We believe in the Holy Spirit, the Lord, the giver of life,
  who proceeds from the Father and the Son.
  With the Father and the Son he is worshiped and glorifed.
  He has spoken through the Prophets.
  We believe in one holy catholic and apostolic Church.
  We acknowledge one baptism for the forgiveness of sins.
  We look for the resurrection of the dead,
    and the life of the world to come. Amen.

At Masses with children, the Apostles' Creed may be used: **412**

We believe in God, the Father almighty,
  creator of heaven and earth.

We believe in Jesus Christ, his only Son, our Lord.
  He was conceived by the power of the Holy Spirit
    and born of the Virgin Mary.
  He suffered under Pontius Pilate,
    was crucified, died, and was buried.
  He descended to the dead.
  On the third day he arose again.
  He ascended into heaven,
    and is seated at the right hand of the Father.
  He will come again to judge the living and the dead.

We believe in the Holy Spirit,
  the holy catholic Church,
  the communion of saints,
  the forgiveness of sins,
  the resurrection of the body,
  and the life everlasting. Amen.

GENERAL INTERCESSIONS   **413**

The people respond to each petition as follows, or according to local practice.

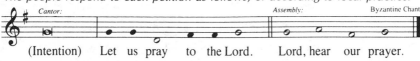

(Intention) Let us pray to the Lord.   Lord, hear our prayer.

LITURGY OF THE EUCHARIST   **414**

To do the eucharist means to give God thanks and praise. When the table has been prepared with the bread and wine, the assembly joins the presider in remembering the gracious gifts of God in creation and God's saving deeds. The center of this is the paschal mystery, the death of our Lord Jesus Christ which destroyed the power of death and his rising which brings us life. That mystery into which we were baptized we proclaim each Sunday at eucharist. It is the very shape of Christian life. We find this in the simple bread and wine which stir our remembering and draw forth our prayer of thanksgiving. "Fruit of the earth and work of human hands," the bread and wine become our holy communion in the body and blood of the Lord. We eat and drink and so proclaim that we belong to one another and to the Lord.

The members of the assembly quietly prepare themselves even as the table is prepared. The presider then invites all to lift up their hearts and join in the eucharistic prayer. All do this by giving their full attention and by singing the acclamations from the "Holy, holy" to the great "Amen." Then the assembly joins in the Lord's Prayer, the sign of peace and the "Lamb of God" litany which accompanies the breaking of bread. Ministers of communion assist the assembly to share the bread and wine. A time of silence and prayer concludes the liturgy of the eucharist.

PREPARATION OF THE ALTAR AND THE GIFTS

Bread and wine are brought to the table and the deacon or presider prepares these gifts. If there is no music, the prayers may be said aloud, and all may respond: **"Blessed be God for ever."** *The presider then invites all to pray.*

Assembly: **May the Lord accept the sacrifice at your hands for the praise and glory of his name, for our good, and the good of all his church.**

The presider says the prayer over the gifts and all respond: **Amen.**

415 EUCHARISTIC PRAYER

The central prayer of the Mass begins with this greeting and invitation between presider and assembly.

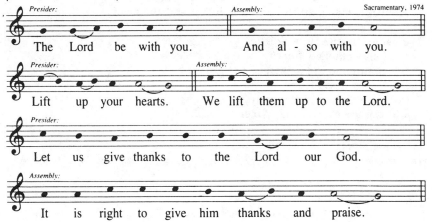

Sacramentary, 1974

Presider: The Lord be with you. Assembly: And al - so with you.

Presider: Lift up your hearts. Assembly: We lift them up to the Lord.

Presider: Let us give thanks to the Lord our God.

Assembly: It is right to give him thanks and praise.

The Sanctus acclamation is sung to conclude the introduction to the eucharistic prayer.

"A Community Mass" Richard Proulx, 1970

416

Ho - ly, ho - ly, ho - ly Lord, God of pow - er and might, heav'n and earth are full of your glo - ry. Ho - san - na in the high - est, ho - san - na in the high - est. Blest is he who comes in the name of the

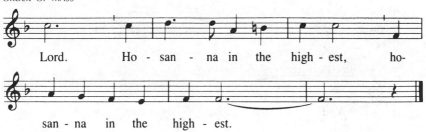

Lord. Ho - san - na in the high - est, ho-

san - na in the high - est.

One of the following acclamations follows the deacon's or presider's invitation: **417**
"Let us proclaim the mystery of faith."

"A Community Mass"
Richard Proulx, 1970

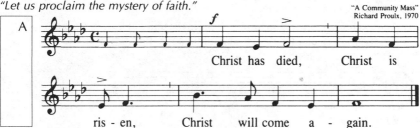

A

Christ has died, Christ is

ris - en, Christ will come a - gain.

John Lee, 1970

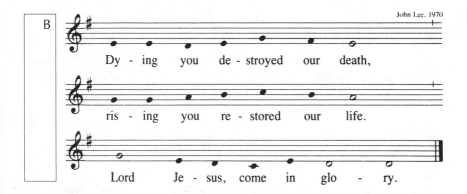

B

Dy - ing you de - stroyed our death,

ris - ing you re - stored our life.

Lord Je - sus, come in glo - ry.

John Lee, 1970

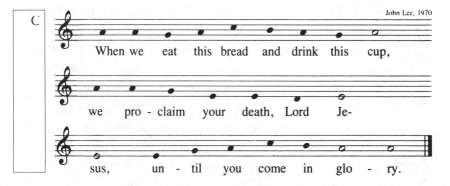

C

When we eat this bread and drink this cup,

we pro - claim your death, Lord Je-

sus, un - til you come in glo - ry.

Adapted from *Genevan Psalter*, 1551
Harm. by Claude LeJeune, 1601

D

Lord, by your cross and re - sur - rec - tion

you have set us free.

You are the Sav-ior of the world.

The eucharistic prayer concludes:

418 *Presider:* Through him, with him, in him, in the unity of the Holy Spirit,
all glory and honor is yours, almighty Father, for ever and ever.

Danish

A - men, a - men, a - men.

419 COMMUNION RITE

The presider invites all to join in the Lord's Prayer.

Robert Snow, 1964
Acc. by Gerard Farrell, OSB, 1984

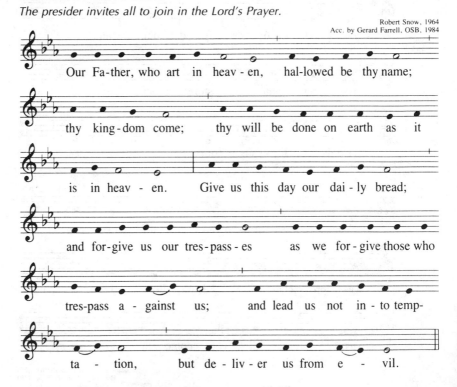

Our Fa-ther, who art in heav - en, hal-lowed be thy name;

thy king-dom come; thy will be done on earth as it

is in heav - en. Give us this day our dai - ly bread;

and for-give us our tres-pass-es as we for-give those who

tres-pass a - gainst us; and lead us not in - to temp-

ta - tion, but de - liv-er us from e - vil.

Presider: Deliver us, Lord...
for the coming of our Savior, Jesus Christ.

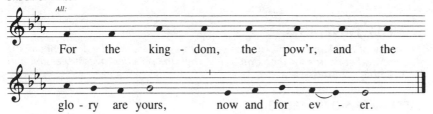

For the king - dom, the pow'r, and the glo - ry are yours, now and for ev - er.

Following the prayer "Lord, Jesus Christ," the presider invites the sign of peace.

420

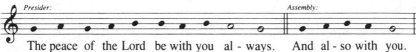

Presider: The peace of the Lord be with you al - ways.
Assembly: And al - so with you.

All exchange a sign of peace.

Then the bread is solemnly broken and the bread and wine prepared for holy communion. The litany "Lamb of God" is sung through the breaking of the bread:

421

Agnus Dei XVIII
Acc. by Gerard Farrell, OSB, 1984

Cantor: Lamb of God, Assembly: you take a - way the sins of the world; have mer - cy on us.

Other invocations, such as "Bread of life" and "Prince of peace" may be added. When the preparation is completed, the litany concludes:

Cantor: Lamb of God, Assembly: you take a - way the sins of the world: grant us peace.

The presider then invites all to share in the holy communion.

422

> *Assembly:* **Lord, I am not worthy to receive you,**
> **but only say the word and I shall be healed.**

Minister of communion: The body of Christ.

> *Or:*

> The blood of Christ.

Communicant: **Amen.**

A song or psalm is ordinarily sung during communion. After communion, a time of silence is observed or a song of thanksgiving is sung. The rite concludes with the prayer after communion to which all respond: **Amen.**

423 CONCLUDING RITE

The liturgy of word and eucharist ends very simply. There may be announcements of events and concerns for the community, then the presider gives a blessing and the assembly is dismissed.

GREETING AND BLESSING

Presider: The Lord be with you.

Assembly: **And also with you.**

<blockquote>

Optional | *When the bishop blesses the people he adds the following:*

Bishop: Blessed be the name of the Lord.

Assembly: **Now and for ever.**

Bishop: Our help is in the name of the Lord.

Assembly: **Who made heaven and earth.**

</blockquote>

The blessing may be in a simple or solemn form. All respond to the blessing or to each part of the blessing: **Amen.**

DISMISSAL

Go in the peace of Christ.
or: The Mass is end - ed, go in peace.   Thanks be to God.
or: Go in peace to love and serve the Lord.

Mass of Saint Augustine

LORD, HAVE MERCY

424
Leon C. Roberts

Lord, have mer - cy, Lord, have mer - cy, Lord, have mer - cy on

425 GLORY TO GOD

Leon C. Roberts

Glo-ry to God in the high - est, and peace to his peo - ple on earth. Glo-ry to God in the high-

cresc.   *cresc.*

est, and   peace to his peo - ple on earth.

C⁷   Fm   E♭/G A♭   B♭ G♭   B♭⁷sus B♭¹³

Choir:
mp *sfz*

Lord   God,   heav-en - ly King,   al - might - y God   and

C/D   D   D♭/F E♭ A♭   F   F⁷

mp *sfz*

All:

Fa - ther,   Glo - ry to God   in the high-

B♭⁷sus B♭¹³ A♭/B♭   B♭⁷   E♭   Gm⁷   B♭/C

Glo - ry to God in the high - est, and
peace to his peo - ple on earth.

Choir:
Lord Je-sus Christ,

on - ly Son of the Fa - ther,

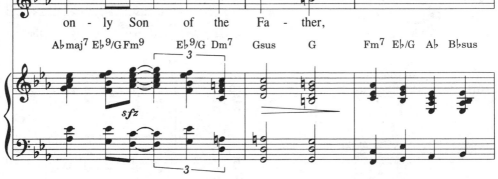

For you a-lone are the Ho-ly One, Glo-ry to God,

you a-lone are the Lord, Glo-ry to God,

you a-lone are the Most High,

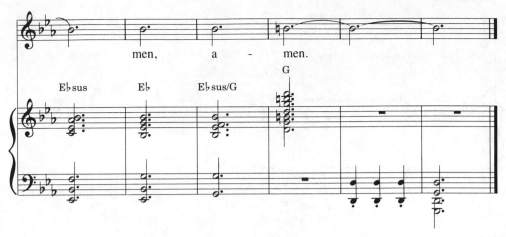

ALLELUIA

Leon C. Roberts

Al - le - lu - ia, al - le - lu - ia, al - le - lu - ia, al - le - lu - ia, al - le - lu - ia, ia.

426 HOLY, HOLY, HOLY

Leon C. Roberts

Ho - ly, ho - ly, ho - ly Lord,

God of pow'r and might, heav-en and earth are

full of your glo - ry. Ho - san - na in the high-

est. Bless-ed is he who comes in the name of the Lord. Ho - san - na in the high - est.

MEMORIAL ACCLAMATION 427

Leon C. Roberts

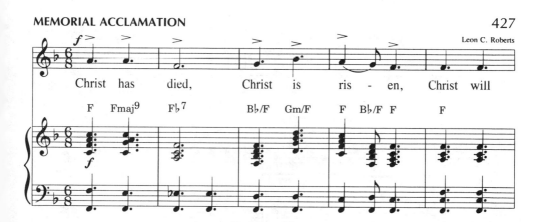

Christ has died, Christ is ris - en, Christ will

come a - gain. Christ has died,

Christ is ris - en, Christ will come a - gain.

428 LAMB OF GOD

Leon C. Roberts

Lamb of God, you take a-

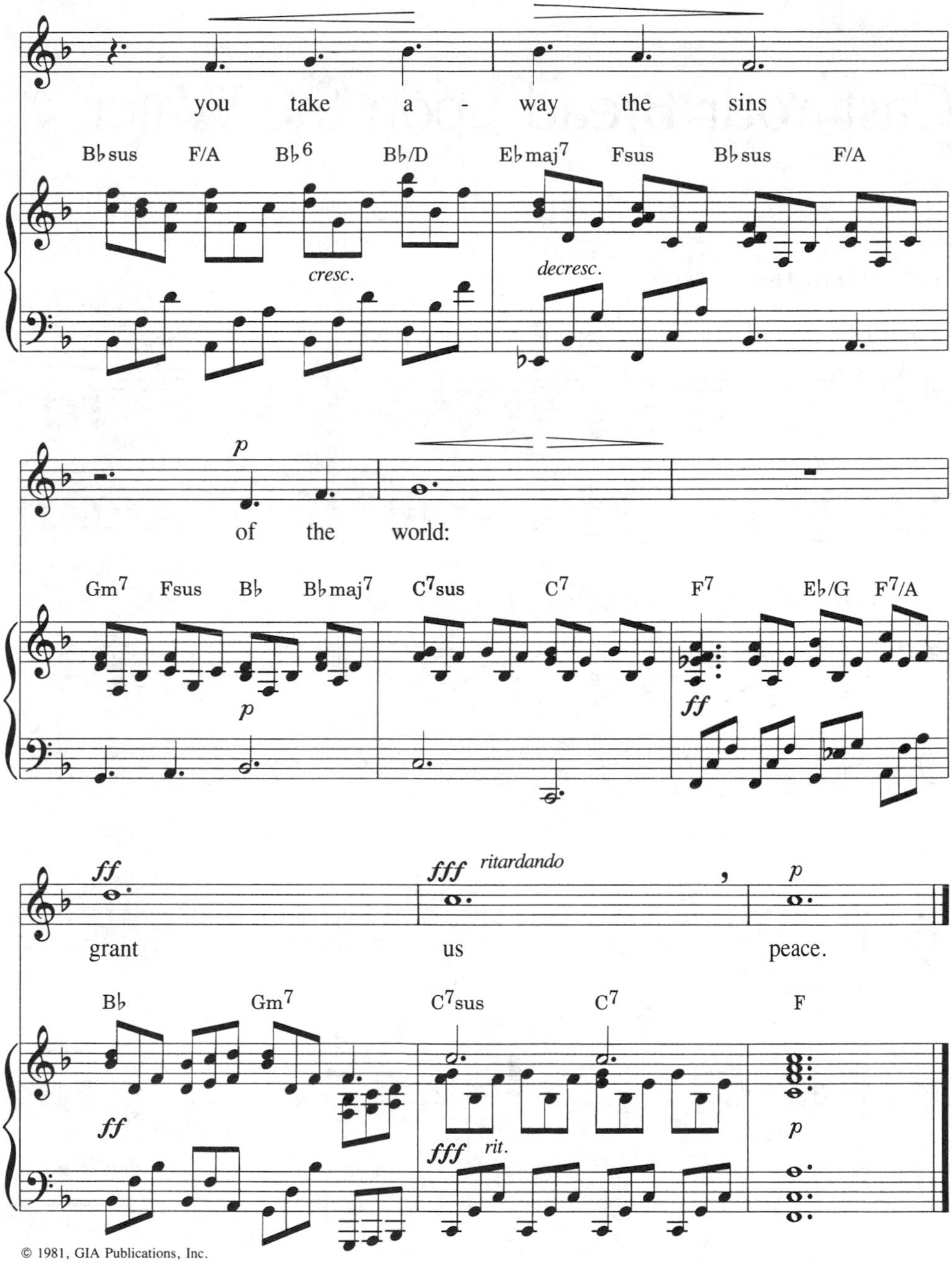

you take a - way the sins
Bb sus F/A Bb6 Bb/D Eb maj7 Fsus Bb sus F/A
cresc.
decresc.
p
of the world:
Gm7 Fsus Bb Bb maj7 C7sus C7 F7 Eb/G F7/A
p
ff
ff
fff
ritardando
p
grant us peace.
Bb Gm7 C7sus C7 F
ff
fff
rit.
p

Cast Your Bread upon the Water

429   LORD, HAVE MERCY

Grayson Warren Brown
Arr. by Val Parker

1. Lord   have   mer-
2. Christ

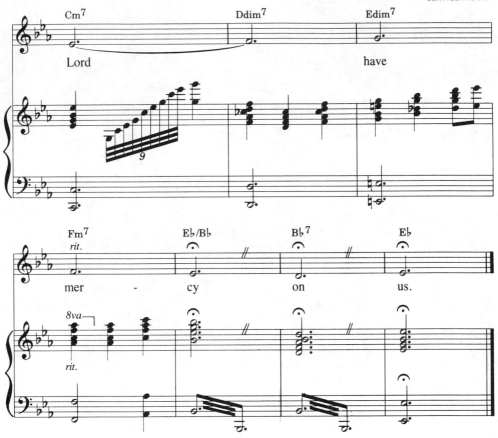

GLORY TO GOD

Grayson Warren Brown
Arr. by Val Parker

Glo - ry to God. Glo - ry to God.

Glo - ry to God in the high - est.

Glo - ry to God. Glo - ry to God, and

peace to his peo-ple on all the earth. earth.

1. A to verses 1,2   **2.** A to verse 3

1. to verses 1,2   **2.** to verse 3

1. Lord God, heav-en-ly king, Al-
2. Lord Je-sus Christ, on-ly Son

might-y God and Fa-ther, we
of the Fa-ther,

wor-ship you, we give you thanks, we
Lord God, Lamb of God, you

ALLELUIA

431

Grayson Warren Brown
Arr. by Val Parker

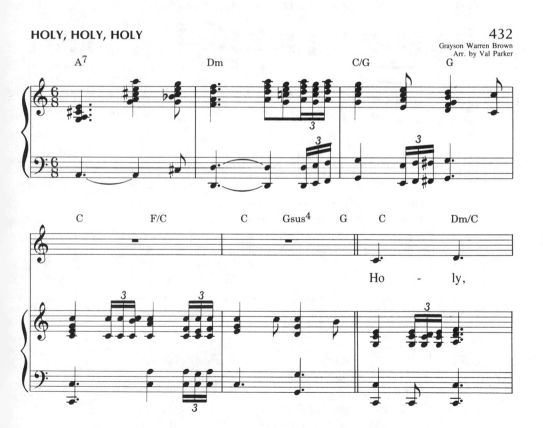

Al - le, Al - le - lu - ia, Al - le, Al - le - lu - ia, Al - le,

Al - le - lu - ia. Al - le, Al - le - lu - ia,

Al - le, Al - le - lu - ia, Al - le, Al - le - lu - ia.

HOLY, HOLY, HOLY

432

Grayson Warren Brown
Arr. by Val Parker

Ho - ly,

433   **MEMORIAL ACCLAMATION**

Grayson Warren Brown
Arr. by Val Parker

Slow and flowing

*Optional %

LAMB OF GOD

Grayson Warren Brown
Arr. by Val Parker

slowly Fadd⁹   F   Csus⁴   C⁷

O

F   Gm/Bb   C   Dm   C⁷/E   F   Cm⁷/G   Am   Bb   D⁷/A   Gdim

Lamb   of   God,   you   take   a - way   the

F/C   F   Gm   F/A   Csus⁴   1,2   C⁷   F/A

sins   of   the   world,   have

Mass Dedicated
to the Brotherhood of Man

LORD, HAVE MERCY

Lord, have mer - cy. Lord, have mer - cy. Lord, have mer - cy.

Christ, have mer - cy. Christ, have mer - cy.

Christ, have mer - cy. Lord, have mer - cy. Lord, have mer - cy.

Lord, have mer - cy.

The accompaniment and choral arrangement for *Mass Dedicated to the Brotherhood of Man* is available from Stimuli, Inc., 17 Erkenbrecher Ave., Cincinnati, OH 45220, and GIA Publications, Inc.

436 **GLORY TO GOD**

437 APOSTLES' CREED

Clarence Jos. Rivers

Allegro

I be-lieve in God, the Fa - ther al-

might - y, cre - a - tor

of heav - en and earth; and in Je - sus Christ,

his on - ly Son, our Lord who was con-

ceived by the Ho - ly Spir - it,

born of the Vir - gin Ma - ry,

suf - fered un - der Pon - tius Pi - late,

was cru - ci - fied, died, and was bur - ied.

He de - scend - ed in - to hell.

Faster

The third day he a - rose a - gain from the

438 HOLY, HOLY, HOLY

Clarence Jos. Rivers

Allegro

Ho - ly, ho - ly,

ho - ly Lord God of hosts,

heav - en and earth are filled with your glo-

ry. Ho - san - na in the high - est.

Bless - ed is he who comes in the name of the

Lord. Ho - san - na in the high - est.

Ho - san - na in the high - est.

Ho - san - na

in the high - est.

MEMORIAL ACCLAMATION 439

Clarence Jos. Rivers

Let us pro - claim the mys-ter-y of faith:

Christ has died, Christ is ris - en,

Christ will come a - gain, al - le - lu - ia!

AMEN 440

Clarence Jos. Rivers

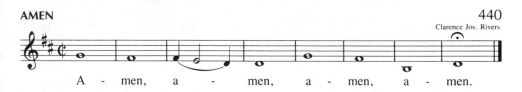

A - men, a - men, a - men, a - men.

LAMB OF GOD 441

Clarence Jos. Rivers

Largo

Lamb of God, you take a - way the sins of the

world, have mer - cy on us. Lamb of God, you

take a - way the sins of the world, have mer - cy on

us. Lamb of God, you take a - way the

sins of the world, grant us peace.

Mass of Saint Thomas More

442   LORD, HAVE MERCY

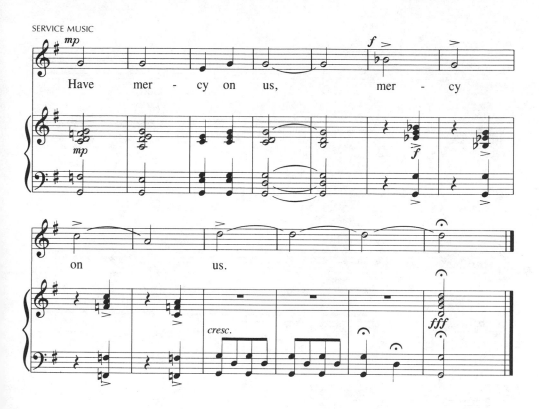

Have mer-cy on us, mer-cy

on us.

GLORY TO GOD

443

Roger L. Holliman

Glo - ry to God in the high-

est, and peace to his peo - ple on earth.

Lord God, heav - en - ly King, al - might - y God and Fa - ther, we wor - ship you, we give you thanks, we

world: have mer - cy on us;

you are seat - ed at the right hand of the

Fa - ther: re - ceive

our prayer.

444 ALLELUIA

Roger L. Holliman

Al - le-, al - le - lu - ia, Al - le, al - le - lu - ia.

445 HOLY, HOLY, HOLY

Roger L. Holliman

Ho - ly, ho - ly, ho - ly Lord, God of pow - er and might, heav'n and earth are full of your glo - ry. Ho-

446 MEMORIAL ACCLAMATION

Moderato (Maestoso)

Roger L. Holliman

Lord, by your cross and re - sur - rec - tion, you have set us free. You are the Sav - ior,

447 **LAMB OF GOD**

Roger L. Holliman

Lamb of God, you take a - way the sins of the world: have mer - cy on us, Lamb of God.

Lamb of God, Lamb of God, grant us peace. Lamb of God, grant us peace.

Missa de Angelis

448 **KYRIE**

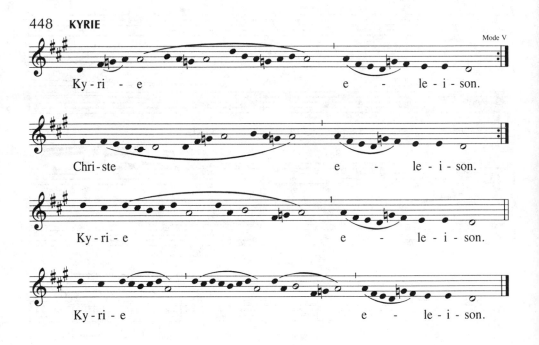

Ky - ri - e   e - le - i - son.

Chri - ste   e - le - i - son.

Ky - ri - e   e - le - i - son.

Ky - ri - e   e - le - i - son.

449 **GLORIA**

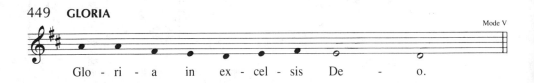

Glo - ri - a   in   ex - cel - sis   De - o.

so - lus San - ctus. Tu so - lus Do - mi - nus.

Tu so - lus Al - tis - si - mus, Je - su Chri - ste.

Cum San - cto Spi - ri - tu, in glo - ri - a De - i

Pa - tris. A - men.

450 CREDO

Mode V

Cre - do in u - num De - um, Pa - trem om - ni - po - ten - tem fa -

cto - rem cae - li et ter - rae, vi - si - bi - li - um om - ni - um

et in - vi - si - bi - li - um. Et in u - num Do - mi - num

Je - sum Chri - stum, Fi - li - um De - i u - ni - ge - ni - tum.

Et ex Pa - tre na - tum an - te om - ni - a sae - cu - la.

De - um de De - o, lu - men de lu - mi - ne, De - um ve - rum

de De - o ve - ro. Ge - ni - tum, non fa - ctum.

con-sub-stan - ti - a-lem Pa - tri: per quem om - ni - a fa - cta sunt.

Qui pro-pter nos ho - mi - nes et pro-pter nost-ram sa - lu - tem

de-scen-dit de cae - lis. Et in-car-na-tus est de Spi - ri - tu

San - cto ex Ma - ri - a Vir - gi - ne, et ho-mo fa-ctus est.

Cru - ci - fi - xus e - ti - am pro no - bis

sub Pon - ti - o Pi - la - to, pas-sus et se - pul - tus est.

Et re-sur-re-xit ter - ti - a di - e, se-cun-dum Scri - ptu ras.

Et a - scen-dit in cae - lum, se-det ad dex-te-ram Pa - tris.

Et i - te-rum ven - tu-rus est cum glo - ri - a, ju - di - ca - re

vi - vos et mor - tu - os, cu - jus re - gni non e - rit fi - nis.

Et in Spi - ri - tum San-ctum, Do - mi - num et vi - vi - fi-can-tem:

qui ex Pa - tre Fi - li - o - que pro - ce - dit. Qui cum

Pa - tre et Fi - li - o si - mul a - do - ra - tur et con-glo-

ri - fi - ca - tur: qui lo - cu - tus est per pro - phe - tas.

Et u - nam, san-ctam, ca - tho - li - cam et a - po - sto - li-

cam Ec - cle - si - am. Con - fi - te - or u - num Ba - ptis-ma

in re - mis - si - o - nem pec - ca - to - rum. Et ex - spe - cto

re - sur - re - cti - o - nem mor - tu - o - rum. Et vi - tam ven-

tu - ri sae - cu - li. A - men.

451 **SANCTUS**

Mode VI

San - ctus, San - ctus, San - ctus

Do - mi - nus De - us Sa - ba - oth.

Ple - ni sunt cae - li et ter - ra glo - ri - a tu - a.

Ho - san - na in ex - cel - sis. Be - ne - di - ctus

qui ve - nit in no - mi - ne Do - mi - ni. Ho - san -

na in ex - cel - sis.

AGNUS DEI

452

Mode VI

A - gnus De - i, qui tol - lis pec - ca - ta mun - di:

mi - se - re - re no - bis. A - gnus De - i,

qui tol - lis pec - ca - ta mun - di: mi - se - re - re no - bis.

A - gnus De - i, qui tol - lis pec - ca - ta

mun - di: do - na no - bis pa - cem.

453 LORD, HAVE MERCY

Edmund C. Broussard

O Lord, have mer - cy. O Lord, have mer - cy.

O Christ, have mer - cy. O Christ, have mer - cy.

O Lord, have mer - cy. O Lord, have mer - cy.

454 LORD, HAVE MERCY

William B. Cooper

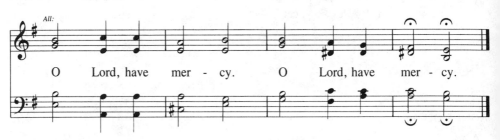

Lord, have mer - cy. Christ, have
Ky - ri - e e - le - i - son. Chri - ste, e-

mer - cy. Lord, have mer - cy.
le - i - son. Ky - ri - e e - le - i - son.

LORD, HAVE MERCY

455

"Mass No. 1 in G"
Avon Gillespie

Lord, have mer - cy. Christ, have mer - cy.

Lord, have mer - cy, have mer - cy, O, Lord.

LORD, HAVE MERCY

456

"Mass No. 2: Santa Catalina"
Avon Gillespie

Lord, have mer - cy. Christ, have mer - cy.

Lord, have mer - cy, have mer- cy.

457 LORD, HAVE MERCY

Clarence Millard Hightower

Lord, have mer - cy. Lord, have mer - cy.

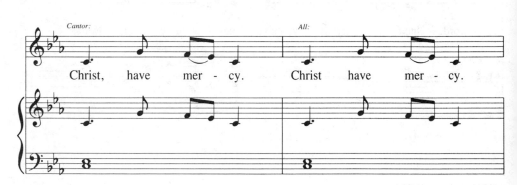

Christ, have mer - cy. Christ have mer - cy.

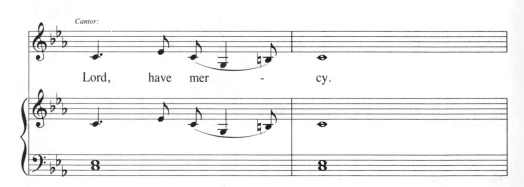

Lord, have mer - cy.

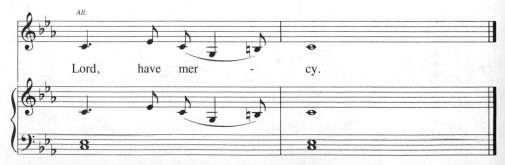

Lord, have mer - cy.

GLORY TO GOD

Norah Duncan, IV

Glo-ry to God in the high-est, and peace to his peo-ple on earth.

Lord God, heav-en-ly King, al-

might-y God and Fa-ther,

we wor-ship you, we give you thanks, we

praise you for your glo-ry.

Refrain

Cantor:

Lord Je - sus Christ, on - ly Son of the Fa - ther, Lord God, Lamb of God, you take a - way the sin of the world: have

mer - cy up - on us;

you are seat - ed at the right hand of the Fa - ther:

re - ceive our prayer.

Refrain

Ostinato (repeats throughout final cantor verse)

Glo - ry to God.

Ostinato

Cantor:

For you a-lone are the Ho-ly One, you a-lone are the Lord, you a-lone are the Most High, Je - sus Christ, with the Ho - ly Spir - it, in the glo - ry of God the Fa - ther. (Glo -ry to God)

Final Refrain

Glo - ry to God in the high- est. A - men, a - men, a - men.

459 HALLELUJAH

460 ALLELUIA

ALLELUIA

John E. Watson

1. Al - le - lu - ia. Al - le - lu-
2. Je - sus is Lord, Je - sus is

ia, al - le - lu - ia, al - le - lu - ia, Oh
Lord, Je - sus is Lord, Je - sus is Lord, yes he

Al - le - lu - ia, al - le - lu-
is, Je - sus is Lord, Je - sus is

ia, al - le - lu - ia, al - le - lu - ia.
Lord, Je - sus is Lord, Je - sus is Lord.

462 ALLELUIA, AMEN

Roland Lafontant

Al - le - lu - ia,   a - men, al - le - lu - ia, a-
Al - le - lu - ia,   a-

men, al - le - lu - ia,   a - men, al - le - lu - ia, a-
men, al - le - lu - ia,   a - men, al - le - lu - ia, a-

men, al - le - lu - ia,   a - men, a - men!
men, al - le - lu - ia,   a - men, a - men, a - men!

463 AMEN

Marjorie Gabriel-Burrow

A - men,   a - men,   a - men,   a - men.

464 AMEN

Anthony E. Jackson

A - men,   a - men,   a - men,   al - le - lu - ia.

ALLELUIA! THE LORD HAS COME

Rawn Harbor

Al - le - lu - ia, al - le - lu - ia, Christ has come to bring sal - va - tion, the Lord has

come to bring sal - va - tion, al - le - lu-

ia, al - le - lu-

ia.

466 **ALLELUIA**

Donald Atkinson

Al - le - lu - ia, al - le - lu - ia, al - le - lu - ia. Al - le - lu - ia, al - le - lu - ia, al - le - lu - ia! al - le - lu - ia, al - le - lu - ia!

LENTEN ACCLAMATION

467

Marjorie Gabriel-Burrow

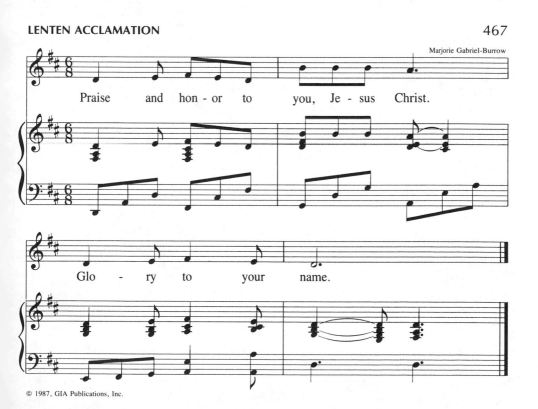

Praise and hon - or to you, Je - sus Christ.

Glo - ry to your name.

468 **AFTER THE GOSPEL**

Roland Lafontant

Deacon or priest:

1. This is the Good News of the Lord.

All:
Refrain

Praise to you, Lord Je - sus Christ.

Deacon or priest:

2. Your word is truth, O Lord, we ac-claim you!

Deacon or priest:

3. By means of your word, O Lord, con - se-crate us.

Refrain (mixed voices)

Praise to you, Lord Je - sus Christ!

© 1987, GIA Publications, Inc.

GENERAL INTERCESSIONS

Moderately slow with rhythmic refrain

Ray East

God is a good God,
Lord of heaven and earth.
Let us humbly bring our
cares before God's throne...

Let us pray to the Lord.

(hum)

All:

O Lord, hear our prayer.

Cantor:

1. For the bishop of Rome,
2. God watch over our land,
3. Wa - ter our faith, Lord,
4. Nour-ish your people Lord,
5. Bring us justice, Lord,
6. Watch o'er our dead, O Lord,

O Lord, hear our prayer. (hum)

D.S.

for our shepherds and teach - ers, let us pray to the Lord.
give our leaders com - pas - sion,
make it bloom in works of love,
hun - gry for your Word and bread,
send your mer - cy and peace,
guard them in the shadow of your wings,

D.S.

470 GENERAL INTERCESSIONS

Joyously with spirit

Ray East

Presider:

If anyone does not have the Spirit of the Risen One, they do not belong tò Chríst.
Moved by the Spirit, let us ask the Father for òur néeds . . .

All:

Send   your   Spir - it, Lord,   hear   our   pray'r.

Send   your   Spir - it, Lord,   hear   our   pray'r.

Cantor:

For	all	the	shep - herds	of	the	Lord
For	all	the	lead - ers	called	to	serve
For	mis - sion - ar - ies		of		the	Lord
For	all	the	chil - dren	of	the	Lord
For the poor	in	spir - it		of	the	Lord
For	those who've died			in	the	Lord

A - men!

let them love those in their care:
let the Spir - it be their guide:
let them pro - claim all your works:
let them tes - ti - fy of you:
let them be a - noint - ed in God's love:
Let them be raised up to the Lord:

A - men!

Let us pray to the Lord.
Let us pray to the Lord.
Let us pray to the Lord.
Let us pray to the Lord.
Let us pray to the Lord.
Let us pray to the Lord.

D.S.

D.S.

GENERAL INTERCESSIONS
471

George Whelpton

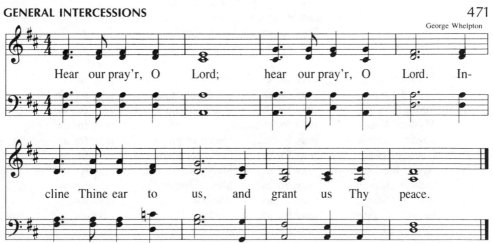

Hear our pray'r, O Lord; hear our pray'r, O Lord. In-

cline Thine ear to us, and grant us Thy peace.

472 LITANY OF THE BLESSED VIRGIN MARY

Calypso

Norbert Farrell

My soul mag-ni-fies the Lord, and my spir-it re-joic-es. Most Ho-ly Mar-y, pray for us. Mo-ther of God, pray for us. Vir-gin of Vir-gins, pray for us. Mo-ther of Christ, pray for us. Mo-ther of di-vine grace, pray for us. Mo-ther of our Sa-vior, pray for us.

Virgin most pure   pray for us.
Virgin most faithful   pray for us.
Virgin most prudent   pray for us.

My soul magnifies the Lord,
and my spirit rejoices.
My soul magnifies the Lord,
and my spirit rejoices.

Mirror of justice	pray for us.	Queen of heaven	pray for us.
Seat of wisdom	pray for us.	Queen of angels	pray for us.
Spiritual vessel	pray for us.	Queen of the Rosary	pray for us.
Mystical Rose	pray for us.	Queen of peace	pray for us.
Tower of David	pray for us.	Queen of prophets	pray for us.
House of Gold	pray for us.	Queen of patriarchs	pray for us.
Ark of the Covenant	pray for us.	Mary, Mother	pray for us.
Gate of Heaven	pray for us.	Mary, Mother	pray for us.
Morning Star	pray for us.	Alleluia!	pray for us.
Refuge of sinners	pray for us.	Alleluia!	Alleluia!
Help of Christians	pray for us.	Alleluia!	
Chorus			

LITANY OF THE SAINTS

Grayson W. Brown
Arr. by Larry Adams

Additional saints and other invocations are added ad libitum.

474 **HOLY, HOLY, HOLY**

"Mass No. 1 in G"
Avon Gillespie

Ho - ly, ho - ly, ho - ly Lord, God of pow - er and

might, heav - en and earth are full of your glo - ry. Ho-

san - na in the high - est. Bless-ed is he who

comes in the name of the Lord. Ho - san - na in the

high - est, ho - san - na in the high - est.

HOLY, HOLY, HOLY

475

"Mass No. 2 in E♭"
Avon Gillespie

Ho - ly, ho - ly, ho - ly Lord, God of pow-er and might, heav-en and earth are full of your glo - ry. Ho- san - na in the high - est. Bless - ed is he who comes in the name of the Lord. Ho - san - na in the high - est, in the high - est.

476   HOLY, HOLY, HOLY

Fernando G. Allen

Ho - ly, ho - ly, ho - ly Lord, God of pow-er and might, heav - en and earth are full of your glo - ry. Ho-san - na in the high - est. (Ho - ly) Bless - ed is he who comes in the name of the Lord. Ho-san - na, ho - san - na in the high - est.

MEMORIAL ACCLAMATION

Marjorie Gabriel-Burrow

Dy - ing you de - stroyed our death, ris - ing you re-

stored our life. Lord Je - sus, come in glo - ry, Lord

Je-sus, come in glo-ry, Lord Je-sus, come in glo-ry a - gain.

478 **MEMORIAL ACCLAMATION**

Marjorie Gabriel-Burrow

Christ has died. Christ is ris-en. Christ will come a-gain.

MEMORIAL ACCLAMATION 479

Donald Atkinson

When we eat this bread and drink this cup, we pro - claim your death, Lord Je - sus, un - til you come in glo - ry.

© 1984, Donald Atkinson from the *Mass of St. Benedict the Moor*

MEMORIAL ACCLAMATION 480

Timothy Gibson

Christ has died. Christ is ris - en. Christ will come a - gain.

© 1987, Timothy Gibson

481 MEMORIAL ACCLAMATION

"Mass of the Divine Word"
Howard Hughes, SM, 1981

we pro - claim your death, Lord Je - sus,

until you come in glo - ry.

until you come in glo - ry.

482 MEMORIAL ACCLAMATION

Clarence Hightower

Christ has died, Christ is ris - en, Christ will come a - gain.

483 MEMORIAL ACCLAMATION

Joe Zamberlin

Christ has died, Christ is ris - en, Christ will come a - gain,

Christ will come a - gain. Je-sus will come,

Christ will come, Je-sus will come a - gain.

AMEN

484

Dresden
John G. Naumann, 1741-1801

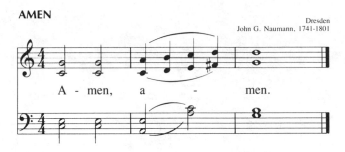

A - men, a - men.

AMEN

485

Peter C. Lutkin

A-
mp

A - men, a-

A - men, a - men, a-

A - men, a - men, a-

men, a - men, a-

cresc.   *dim. poco a poco e rit.*

men, a - men, a - men,

men, a - men, a-

men, a - men, a-

men, a - men, a - men.

pp

a - men, a - men.

men, a - men, a - men.

men, a - men, a-

pp

men, a - men, a - men.

486   AMEN

Arr. Fernando Allen

A - men, a-men, a - men, a - men, a-men, a-men, a - men.

487   AMEN

John Stainer

A - men, a - men, a - men.

488   AMEN

Richard Smallwood

A - men, a - men,

a - men, a - men, a - men.

AMEN   489

A - men, a - men,   a - men,   a - men,   a - men,   a-
men,   a   -   men.   men,   a   -   men.

OUR FATHER   490

Roger L. Holliman

Andante (Dolce)

Our   Fa-

done on earth as it is in heav-

en. Give us this day our dai-ly bread; and for-

give us our tres-pass-es as we for-give those who

tres-pass a-gainst us; and

lead us not in - to temp - ta - tion, but de - liv - er
us from e - vil, for the
king-dom, and pow-er, and glo - ry are yours, now and for
ev - er. A - men.

LAMB OF GOD

Timothy Gibson

Lamb of God, you take a - way the sins of the world, Lamb of

God, you take a - way the sins of the world, Lamb of

last time

God, you take a-way the sins of the world, have

mer-cy on us. Grant us your peace.

LAMB OF GOD

Tillis Butler

Lamb of God, you take a-way the sins of the world: have mer-cy on us.

Lamb of God, you take a-way the sins

of the world: have mer-cy on us.

Lamb of God, you take a-way

the sins of the world: grant us

peace, grant us peace.

LAMB OF GOD

493

Alexander Wilamowski III

494   LAMB OF GOD

Robert Ray

ry.
now.

Gsus

Fmaj^7/G   G^7($\flat$9)

ad lib. freely   *rit.*   *a tempo*

12

L.H.   R.H.   L.H.   R.H.

rit.   *a tempo*

p *ten.*

Lamb   of God you   take   a - way   the   sins   of   the

C(add^9)   Gsus/B   Am^9

p

p

for rehearsal only

Instruments optional to end

495   LAMB OF GOD

David Clark Isele

Cantor: All:

*Lamb of God: You take a - way the sins of the world, have mer - cy on us. grant us peace.

*Other invocations, e.g. "Bread of Life," "Prince of Peace," may be used.

© 1979, GIA Publications, Inc.

496   LAMB OF GOD

"New Plainsong"
David Hurd

Lamb of God, you take a - way the sins of the world:

have mer-cy on us. Lamb of God, you take a-way the

sins of the world: have mer-cy on us. Lamb of God,

you take a-way the sins of the world: grant us peace.

497 **LAMB OF GOD**

"Mass No. 1 in G"
Avon Gillespie

Lamb of God, you take a-way our sins: have mer-cy up-on us, up-on us.

Lamb of God, you take a-way our sins: grant us peace, peace, grant us peace.

© 1987, GIA Publications, Inc.

LAMB OF GOD

498

"Mass No. 2 in E♭"
Avon Gillespie

Lamb of God, you take a-way the sins of the world: have

mer - cy up - on us, up - on us.

Lamb of God, you take a - way the sins of the world:

grant us peace, peace, grant us peace.

499   Psalm for Advent

Howard Hughes, SM

To you I lift up my soul, O Lord; in you, O my God, I trust.

Psalm tone 12

OR

500   Psalm for Advent

Rawn Harbor

To you, O Lord, I lift up my

soul, to on-ly you, O Lord;

rit.

I wait for your re - turn.

rit.

© 1987. Rawn Harbor

Psalm tone 12

Psalm 24(25), 4-5.8-9.10.14.

Your ways, O Lord, make known to me;
teach me your paths,
Guide me in your truth and teach me,
for you are God my savior.

Good and upright is the Lord;
thus he shows sinners the way.
He guides the humble to justice,
he teaches the humble his way.

All the Lord's paths are kindness and constancy
toward those who keep his covenant and his decrees.
The Lord's friendhsip is with those who fear him,
and his covenant, for their instructions.

501 Psalm for Advent

Rawn Harbor

O Lord, let us see your kind - ness. O Lord, let us see your truth. O Lord, let us see your kind - ness.

to repeat　　　*fine*

We place our trust in you. you.

Psalm tone 5, 7, or 10

OR

502

Marty Haugen

Lord, let us see your kind - ness;

mf

Lord, let us see your kind - ness.

Psalm tone 10

Psalm 84(85), 9-10.11-12.13-14

I will hear what the Lord God has to say,
a voice that speaks of peace,
peace for his people and his friends.
His help is near for those who fear him
and his glory will dwell in our land.

Mercy and faithfulness have met;
justice and peace have embraced.
Faithfulness shall spring from the earth
and justice look down from heaven.

The Lord will make us prosper
and our earth shall yield its fruit.
Justice shall march before him
and peace shall follow his steps.

503 Psalm for Advent

Paschal Jordan, OSB

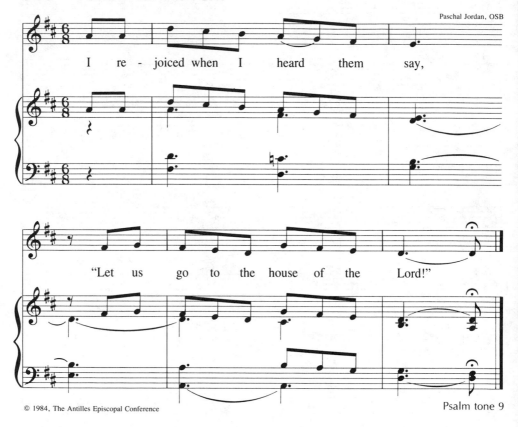

I re - joiced when I heard them say,

"Let us go to the house of the Lord!"

Psalm tone 9

Psalm 121(122), 1-2.3-4.4-5.6-7.8-9.

I rejoiced when I heard them say:
"Let us go to God's house."
And now our feet are standing
within your gates, O Jerusalem.

Jerusalem is built as a city
strongly compact.
It is there that the tribes go up,
the tribes of the Lord.

For Israel's law it is,
there to praise the Lord's name.
There were set the thrones of judgment
of the house of David.

For the peace of Jerusalem pray:
"Peace be to your homes!
May peace reign in your walls,
in your palaces, peace!"

For love of my brethren and friends
I say: "Peace upon you!"
For love of the house of the Lord
I will ask for your good.

Psalm for Christmas 504

Rawn Harbor

All the ends of the earth have seen the sav - ing pow'r of God!

© 1987, Rawn Harbor

Psalm tone 13

OR

505

Paschal Jordan, OSB

All the ends of the earth have seen the sal - va - tion of our God.

© 1984, The Antilles Episcopal Conference

Psalm tone 2 or 6

Sing a new song to the Lord
for he has worked wonders.
His right hand and his holy arm
have brought salvation.

The Lord has made known his salvation;
has shown his justice to the nations.
He has remembered his truth and love
for the house of Israel.

All the ends of the earth have seen
the salvation of our God.
Shout to the Lord all the earth,
ring out your joy.

Sing psalms to the Lord with the harp
with the sound of music.
With trumpets and the sound of the horn
acclaim the King, the Lord.

506 Psalm for Epiphany

Rawn Harbor

Lord, ev-'ry na-tion on earth will a-dore you, ev-'ry na-tion on earth will bow down and say you are the one, you are the one, you are the one, you are the one, you are

the one, you are the one, you are

the one Lord.

Psalm tone 13

Ps. 71(72), 1-2.7-8.10-11.12-13

O God, give your judgment to the king,
to a king's son your justice,
that he may judge your people in justice
and your poor in right judgment.

In his days justice shall flourish
and peace till the moon fails.
He shall rule from sea to sea,
from the Great River to earth's bounds.

The kings of Tarshish and the sea coasts
shall pay him tribute.
The kings of Sheba and Seba
shall bring him gifts.
Before him all kings shall fall prostrate,
all nations shall serve him.

For he shall save the poor when they cry
and the needy who are helpless.
He will have pity on the weak
and save the lives of the poor.

507 Psalm for Lent

Rawn Harbor

Be mer-ci-ful, O Lord, for we have sinned.

Psalm tone 14

OR

508

Paschal Jordan, OSB

Have mer-cy on us, O Lord, for we have sinned.

Psalm tone 7 or 8

Ps. 50(51), 3-4.5-6.12-13.14.17.

Have mercy on me, God, in your kindness.
In your compassion blot out my offense.
O wash me more and more from my guilt
and cleanse me from my sin.

My offenses truly I know them;
my sin is always before me.
Against you, you alone, have I sinned;
what is evil in your sight I have done.

A pure heart create for me, O God,
put a steadfast spirit within me.
Do not cast me away from your presence,
nor deprive me of your holy spirit.

Give me again the joy of your help;
with a spirit of fervor sustain me,
O Lord, open my lips
and my mouth shall declare your praise.

Psalm for Lent 509

Leon C. Roberts

Be with me, Lord, when I am in trou - ble

Be with me, Lord, when I am in trou - ble.

Psalm tone 6

OR

510

Marty Haugen

Be with me, Lord, when I am in trou-ble, be with me, Lord, I pray.

Psalm tone 10

Ps. 90(91), 1-2.10-11.12-13.14.16.

He who dwells in the shelter of the Most High
and abides in the shade of the Almighty
says to the Lord: 'My refuge,
my stronghold, my God in whom I trust!'

Upon you no evil shall fall,
no plague approach where you dwell.
For you has he commanded his angels,
to keep you in all your ways.

They shall bear you upon their hands
lest you strike your foot against a stone.
On the lion and the viper you will tread
and trample the young lion and the dragon.

Since he clings to me in love, I will free him,
protect him for he knows my name.
With length of life I will content him;
I shall let him see my saving power.

Psalm for Lent 511

Leon C. Roberts

With the Lord there is mer - cy and full - ness of re - demp - tion.

Psalm tone 13

OR

512

Paschal Jordan, OSB

With the Lord there is mer - cy and full-ness of re - demp-tion.

Psalm tone 2, 3, or 8

Psalm 129(130), 1-2.3-4.4-6.7-8.

Out of the depths I cry to you, O Lord,
Lord, hear my voice!
O let your ears be attentive
to the voice of my pleading.

If you, O Lord, should mark our guilt,
Lord, who would survive?
But with you is found forgiveness:
for this we revere you.

My soul is waiting for the Lord,
I count on his word.
My soul is longing for the Lord
more than watchman for daybreak.
(Let the watchman count on daybreak
and Israel on the Lord.)

Because with the Lord there is mercy
and fullness of redemption,
Israel indeed he will redeem
from all its iniquity.

513   Psalm for Holy Week

Rawn Harbor

My God, my God, why have you a-ban - doned me?

Psalm tone 10

OR

David Clark Isele

My God, my God, why have you a-

ban - doned me, a - ban - doned me?

Psalm tone 2

Psalm 21(22), 8-9.17-18.19-20.23-24.

All who see me deride me.
They curl their lips, they toss their heads.
"He trusted in the Lord, let him save him;
let him release him if this is his friend."

Many dogs have surrounded me,
a band of the wicked beset me.
They tear holes in my hands and my feet.
I can count every one of my bones.

They divide my clothing among them.
They cast lots for my robe.
O Lord, do not leave me alone,
my strength, make haste to help me!

I will tell of your name to my brethren
and praise you where they are assembled.
"You who fear the Lord give him praise;
all sons of Jacob, give him glory."

515 Psalm for Holy Week

Marty Haugen

Fa - ther, I put my life in your hands.

Psalm tone 13

Psalm 30(31), 2.6.12-13.15-16.17.25.

In you, O Lord, I take refuge.
Let me never be put to shame.
In your justice, set me free,
Into your hands I commend my spirit.
It is you who will redeem me, Lord.

In the face of all my foes I am a reproach,
an object of scorn to my neighbors
and of fear to my friends.
Those who see me in the street
run far away from me.
I am like a dead man, forgotten,
like a thing thrown away.

But as for me, I trust in you, Lord;
I say: "You are my God."
My life is in your hands, deliver me
from the hands of those who hate me.

Let your face shine on your servant.
Save me in your love.
Be strong, let your heart take courage,
all who hope in the Lord.

516 Psalm for Holy Thursday

Garfield Rochard

The bless-ing - cup which we bless

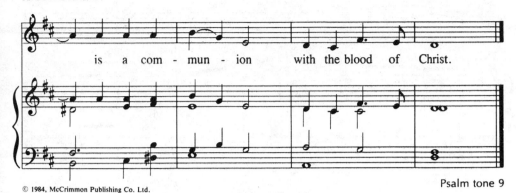

is a com - mun - ion with the blood of Christ.

Psalm tone 9

Psalm 115(116), 12-13.15-16.17-18.

How can I repay the Lord
for his goodness to me?
The cup of salvation I will raise;
I will call on the Lord's name.

O precious in the eyes of the Lord
is the death of his faithful.
Your servant, Lord, your servant am I;
you have loosened my bonds.

A thanksgiving sacrifice I make;
I will call on the Lord's name.
My vows to the Lord I will fulfill
before all his people.

Psalm for Easter Vigil   517

Leon C. Roberts

His   love,   his   love,   his

love   is   ev - er - last - ing.

Psalm tone 7 or 10

Psalm 135(136), 1-3.4-6.7-9.24-26

O give thanks to the Lord for he is good,
for his love endures for ever.
Give thanks to the God of gods,
for his love endures for ever.
Give thanks to the Lord of lords,
for his love endures for ever.

Who alone has wrought marvelous works,
for his love endures for ever;
whose wisdom it was made the skies,
for his love endures for ever;
who fixed the earth firmly on the seas,
for his love endures for ever.

It was he who made the great lights,
for his love endures for ever;
the sun to rule in the day,
for his love endures for ever,
the moon and stars in the night,
for his love endures for ever.

And he snatched us away from our foes,
for his love endures for ever.
He gives food to all living things,
for his love endures for ever.
To the God of heaven give thanks,
for his love endures for ever.

518   Psalm for Easter

Leon C. Roberts

Let all the earth   cry out to God   with joy,

joy!   with joy!

Psalm tone 3 or 8

OR

Psalm for Easter   519

David Clark Isele

Let all the earth cry out to God with joy!

Psalm 65(66), 1-3.4-5.6-7.16.20   Psalm tone 15

Cry out with joy to God all the earth,
O sing to the glory of his name.
O render him glorious praise.
Say to God: "How tremendous your deeds!

Before you all the earth shall bow,
shall sing to you, sing to your name!"
Come and see the works of God,
tremendous his deeds among men.

He turned the sea into dry land,
they passed through the river dry-shod.
Let our joy then be in him;
he rules for ever by his might

Come and hear, all who fear God.
I will tell what he did for my soul;
Blessed be God who did not reject my praye
nor withhold his love from me.

Psalm for Easter   520

David Clark Isele

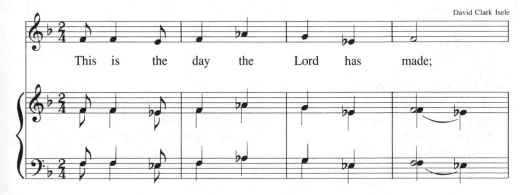

This is the day the Lord has made;

let us re - joice, re - joice and be glad.

© 1979, GIA Publications, Inc.

Psalm tone 6 or 13

OR

521

Leon C. Roberts

This is the day the Lord has made;

let us re - joice and be glad.

© 1987, Leon C. Roberts

Psalm tone 2 or 6

Psalm 117(118), 1-2.16-17.22-23

Give thanks to the Lord for he is good,
for his love endures for ever.
Let the sons of Israel say:
"His love endures for ever."

The Lord's right hand has triumphed;
his right hand raised me.
The Lord's right hand has triumphed;
I shall not die, I shall live
and recount his deeds.

The stone which the builders rejected
has become the cornerstone.
This is the work of the Lord,
a marvel in our eyes.

Psalm for Ascension 522

Leon C. Roberts

God mounts his throne with shouts of joy, with shouts of joy!

Psalm tone 2

Psalm 46(47), 2-3.6-7.8-9

All peoples, clap your hands,
cry to God with shouts of joy!
For the Lord, the Most High, we must fear,
great king over all the earth.

God goes up with shouts of joy;
the Lord goes up with trumpet blast.
Sing praise for God, sing praise,
sing praise to our king, sing praise.

God is king of all the earth,
Sing praise with all your skill.
God is king over the nations;
God reigns on his holy throne.

Psalm for Pentecost 523

Rawn Harbor

Lord, send out your spir - it!

Lord, send out your spir-it!

Lord, send out your spir-it! and re-new the face of the

earth.

Psalm tone 4 or 9

OR

524

David Haas

Lord, send out your spir-it, and re-new the face of the earth; Lord, send out your spir-it, and re-new the face of the (earth.) earth.

last time only

rit.

Psalm tone 12

Psalm 103(104), 1.24.29-30.31.34

Bless the Lord, my soul!
Lord God, how great you are,
How many are your works, O Lord!
The earth is full of your riches.

You take back your spirit, they die,
returning to the dust from which they came.
You send forth your spirit, they are created;
and you renew the face of the earth.

May the glory of the Lord last for ever!
May the Lord rejoice in his works!
May my thoughts be pleasing to him.
I find my joy in the Lord.

525 Psalm for Ordinary Time

David Haas

Lord, you have the words of ev-er-last-ing life.

after final refrain

Psalm tone 9, 10, or 12

OR

526

Leon C. Roberts

Lord, you have the words of ev-er-

last - ing life, of ev-

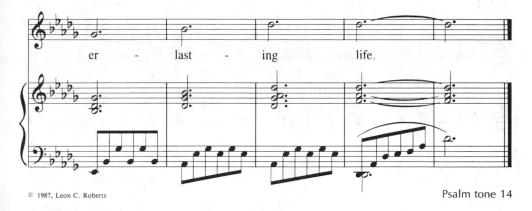

Psalm tone 14

Psalm 18(19), 8.9.10.11

The law of the Lord is perfect,
it revives the soul.
The rule of the Lord is to be trusted,
it gives wisdom to the simple.

The precepts of the Lord are right,
they gladden the heart.
The command of the Lord is clear,
it gives light to the eyes.

The fear of the Lord is holy,
abiding for ever.
The decrees of the Lord are truth
and all of them just.

They are more to be desired than gold,
than the purest of gold
and sweeter are they than honey,
than honey from the comb.

Psalm for Ordinary Time   527

Leon C. Roberts

The Lord is my light and my sal - va - tion.

Psalm tone 12

OR

528

Anthony E. Jackson

The Lord is my light and my sal - va - tion.

Psalm tone 11

529

OR

David Haas

The Lord is my light and my sal - va - tion, of whom should I

be a - fraid, of whom should I be a - fraid?

last time rit. and [⌢]

Psalm tone 1, 2, or 6

Psalm 26(27), 1.4.13-14

The Lord is my light and my help;
whom shall I fear?
The Lord is the stronghold of my life;
before whom shall I shrink?

There is one thing I ask of the Lord,
for this I long,
to live in the house of the Lord,

all the days of my life,
to savor the sweetness of the Lord,
to behold his temple.

I am sure I shall see the Lord's goodness
in the land of the living.
Hope in him, hold firm and take heart.
Hope in the Lord!

Psalm for Ordinary Time 530

Marty Haugen

O God, I seek you, my soul thirsts for you, your love is fin-er than life.

Psalm tone 16

OR 531

Leon C. Roberts

My soul is thirst-ing for you, O Lord, my God, O Lord, my God!

Psalm tone 15

Psalm 62(63), 2.3-4.5-6.8-9

O God, you are my God, for you I long;
for you my soul is thirsting.
My body pines for you
like a dry, weary land without water.

So I gaze on you in the sanctuary
to see your strength and your glory.
For your love is better than life,
my lips will speak your praise.

So I will bless you all my life,
in your name I will lift up my hands.
My soul shall be filled as with a banquet,
my mouth shall praise you with joy.

For you have been my help;
in the shadow of your wings I rejoice.
My soul clings to you;
your right hand holds me fast.

532 Psalm for Ordinary Time

Rawn Harbor

If to - day you hear his voice, don't you
turn a deaf ear; give the Lord your heart.

Psalm tone 3, 5, or 8

OR

533

David Clark Isele

If to-day you hear his voice, hard-en not your hearts.

If to-day you hear his voice, hard-en not your hearts.

Psalm tone 1

Psalm 94(95), 1-2.6-7.8-9

Come, ring out our joy to the Lord;
hail the rock who saves us.
Let us come before him, giving thanks,
with songs let us hail the Lord.

Come in; let us bow and bend low;
let us kneel before the God who made us
for he is our God and we
the people who belong to his pasture,
the flock that is led by his hand.

O that today you would listen to his voice!
"Harden not your hearts as at Meribah,
as on that day at Massah in the desert
when your fathers put me to the test."

534 Psalm for Ordinary Time

Leon C. Roberts

The Lord is kind and mer - ci - ful, ful.

Psalm tone 17

OR

535

Marty Haugen

The Lord is kind and mer-ci - ful, the

Lord is kind and mer-ci - ful.

Psalm tone 18

Psalm 102(103), 1-2.3-4.8.10.12-13

My soul, give thanks to the Lord,
all my being, bless his holy name.
My soul, give thanks to the Lord
and never forget all his blessings.

It is he who forgives all your guilt,
who heals every one of your ills,
who redeems your life from the grave,
who crowns you with love and compassion.

The Lord is compassion and love,
slow to anger and rich in mercy.
He does not treat us according to our sins
nor repay us according to our faults.

As far as the east is from the west
so far does he remove our sins.
As a father has compassion on his sons,
the Lord has pity on those who fear him.

Psalm for Ordinary Time   536

Rawn Harbor

We are God's peo-ple, the sheep of his flock.

© 1987, Rawn Harbor

Psalm tone 2, 6, or 13

OR

537

Paschal Jordan, OSB

We are his peo - ple, the sheep of his flock.

© 1984, The Antilles Episcopal Conference

Psalm tone 5, 7, 10 or 12

Psalm 99(100), 2.3.5

Cry out with joy to the Lord, all the earth.
Serve the Lord with gladness.
Come before him, singing for joy.

Know that he, the Lord, is God.
He made us, we belong to him,
we are his people, the sheep of his flock.

Indeed, how good is the Lord,
eternal his merciful love.
He is faithful from age to age.

538 Psalm for Ordinary Time

Paschal Jordan, OSB

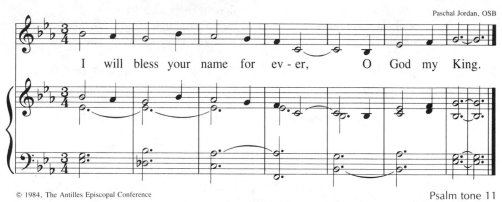

I will bless your name for ev-er, O God my King.

Psalm tone 11

539

OR

Leon C. Roberts

I will praise your name for ev-

er, my King and my God.

Psalm tone 6

Psalm 144(145), 1-2.8-9.10-11.13-14.

I will give you glory, O God my King,
I will bless your name for ever.
I will bless you day after day
and praise your name for ever.

The Lord is kind and full of compassion,
slow to anger, abounding in love.
How good is the Lord to all,
compassionate to all his creatures.

All your creatures shall thank you, O Lord,
and your friends shall repeat their blessing.
They shall speak of the glory of your reign
and declare your might, O God.

The Lord is faithful in all his words
and loving in all his deeds.
The Lord supports all who fall
and raises all who are bowed down.

Psalm for Ordinary Time 540

Rawn Harbor

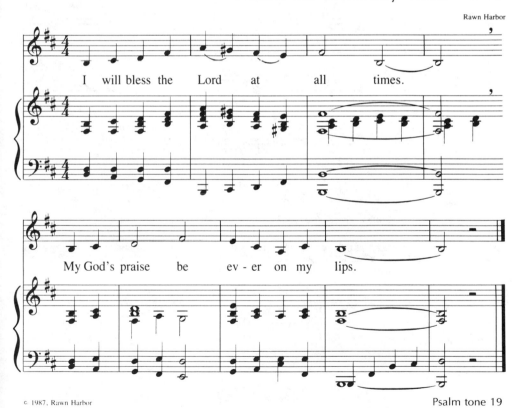

I will bless the Lord at all times.
My God's praise be ev - er on my lips.

Psalm tone 19

Psalm 33(34), 2-3.4-5.6-7.8-9

I will bless the Lord at all times,
his praise always on my lips;
in the Lord my soul shall make its boast.
The humble shall hear and be glad.

Glorify the Lord with me.
Together let us praise his name.
I sought the Lord and he answered me;
from all my terrors he set me free.

Look towards him and be radiant;
let your faces not be abashed.
This poor man called; the Lord heard him
and rescued him from all his distress.

The angel of the Lord is encamped
around those who revere him, to rescue them.
Taste and see that the Lord is good.
He is happy who seeks refuge in him.

541 Psalm for Ordinary Time

David Clark Isele

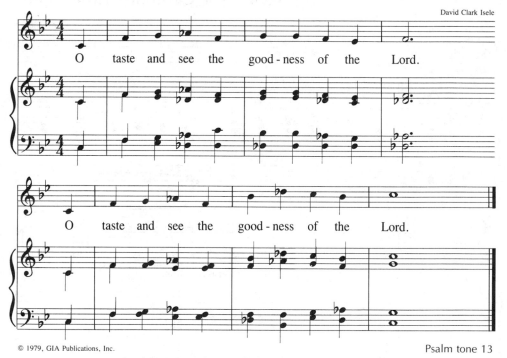

O taste and see the good-ness of the Lord.

O taste and see the good-ness of the Lord.

Psalm tone 13

Psalm 33(34), 2-3.4-5.6-7.

I will bless the Lord at all times,
his praise always on my lips;
in the Lord my soul shall make its boast.
The humble shall hear and be glad.

Glorify the Lord with me.
Together let us praise his name.
I sought the Lord and he answered me;
from all my terrors he set me free.

Look towards him and be radiant;
let your faces not be abashed.
This poor man called; the Lord heard him
and rescued him from all his distress.

The angel of the Lord is encamped
around those who revere him, to rescue them.
Taste and see that the Lord is good.
He is happy who seeks refuge in him.

Psalm for the Last Weeks   542

Rawn Harbor

OR

Psalm tone 14

543

Leon Roberts

© 1981, GIA Publications, Inc.

Psalm tone 20

Psalm 121(122), 1-2.3-4.4-5.6-7.8-9

I rejoiced when I heard them say:
"Let us go to God's house."
And now our feet are standing
within your gates, O Jerusalem.

Jerusalem is built as a city
strongly compact.
It is there that the tribes go up,
the tribes of the Lord.

For Israel's law it is,
there to praise the Lord's name.
There were set the thrones of judgment
of the house of David.

For the peace of Jerusalem pray:
"Peace be to your homes!
May peace reign in your walls,
in your palaces, peace!"

For love of my brethren and friends
I say: "Peace upon you!"
For love of the house of the Lord
I will ask for your good.

Additional Psalms 544

Leon C. Roberts

The Lord is my shep - herd;
there is noth - ing I shall want.

Psalm tone 2 or 6

Psalm 22(23), 1-3.3-4.5.6

The Lord is my shepherd;
there is nothing I shall want.
Fresh and green are the pastures
where he gives me repose.
Near restful waters he leads me,
To revive my drooping spirit.

He guides me along the right path;
he is true to his name.
If I should walk in the valley of darkness
no evil would I fear.
You are there with your crook and your staff;
with these you give me comfort.

You have prepared a banquet for me
in the sight of my foes.
My head you have anointed with oil;
my cup is overflowing.

Surely goodness and kindness shall follow me
all the days of my life.
In the Lord's own house shall I dwell
for ever and ever.

545 Evensong

Norah Duncan, IV

My prayer shall rise like in-cense,

my hands like an eve-ning ob-la-tion.

© 1987, GIA Publications, Inc.

Psalm tone 13

Psalm 140(141), 1-2.3-4.4-5.6-7.8-9.10

I have called to you, Lord; hasten
  to help me!
Hear my voice when I cry to you.
Let my prayer arise before you like
  incense,
the raising of my hands like an
  evening oblation.

Set, O Lord, a guard over my mouth;
keep watch, O Lord, at the door of
  my lips!
Do not turn my heart to things that
  are wrong,
to evil deeds with men who are sinners.

Never allow me to share in their feasting.
If a good man strikes or reproves me it
  is kindness;
but let the oil of the wicked not anoint
  my head.
Let my prayer be ever against their malice.

Their princes were thrown down by the
  side of the rock;
then they understood that my words were
  kind.
As a millstone is shattered to pieces on
  the ground,
so their bones were strewn at the mouth
  of the grave.

To you, Lord God, my eyes are turned;
in you I take refuge; spare my soul!
From the trap they have laid for me keep
  me safe;
keep me from the snares of those who
  do evil.

Let the wicked fall into the traps they
  have set
whilst I pursue my way unharmed.

Psalm Tones 546

Chrysogonus Waddell, OCSO

Psalm Tone 1

547

Chant tone 8-g
Acc. Richard Proulx

Psalm Tone 2

548

Rawn Harbor

Psalm Tone 3

Psalm Tone 4

549

Joseph B. Smith

550
Psalm Tone 5

Rawn Harbor

551
Psalm Tone 6

Paschal Jordan, OSB

552
Psalm Tone 7

Paschal Jordan, OSB

553
Psalm Tone 8

Laurence Bevenot, OSB

Psalm Tone 9

554

Garfield Rochard

Psalm Tone 10

555

Stanbrook Abbey

Psalm Tone 11

556

Cyril Baker

Psalm Tone 12

557

Joseph B. Smith

558
Psalm Tone 13

Rawn Harbor

559
Psalm Tone 14

Joseph B. Smith

560
Psalm Tone 15

Laurence Bevenot, OSB

561
Psalm Tone 16

Laurence Bevenot, OSB

Psalm Tone 17

562

Chant tone 8-g
Acc. by Richard Proulx

Psalm Tone 18

563

Chant tone 8-g
Acc. by Richard Proulx

Psalm Tone 19

564

Laurence Bevenot, OSB

Psalm Tone 20

565

Stanbrook Abbey

566　Liturgical Index

Liturgical Index/*continued*

PASSION SUNDAY (also Lent and Holy Week, Christ the King)

EASTER TRIDUUM (Holy Thursday, Good Friday, Easter Vigil) (also Easter Season, Christian Initiation of Adults, Eucharist; Topical Index: Cross)

Liturgical Index/*continued*

Liturgical Index/*continued*

Liturgical Index/*continued*

Liturgical Index/*continued*

CONFIRMATION *(also: Pentecost, Christian Initiation of Adults; Topical Index: Commitment, Discipleship, Ministry, Mission)*

Liturgical Index/*continued*

Liturgical Index/*continued*

Liturgical Index/*continued*

Liturgical Index/*continued*

Liturgical Index/*continued*

ORDINATION (*also Topical Index: Challenge of the Gospel, Commissioning, Commitment,*

Liturgical Index/*continued*

Liturgical Index/*continued*

Liturgical Index/*continued*

567 Topical Index

Topical Index/*continued*

123 Be Not Afraid
114 Close to Thee
120 I Can Hear My Savior Calling
248 I Come to the Garden Alone
248 In the Garden
112 I've Decided to Make Jesus My Choice
286 Only What You Do for Christ Will Last
264 Ride On, Jesus, Ride
111 Sign Me Up
112 Some Folk Would Rather Have Houses and Land
114 Thou My Everlasting Portion
286 You May Build Great Cathedrals
123 You Shall Cross the Barren Desert
120 Where He Leads Me

CHILDREN'S HYMNS* *(also: Baptism of Children, Christmas, Easter)*
30 All Glory, Laud and Honor
121 Certainly, Lord
218 Come by Here
287 Come to Jesus
130 Eat This Bread
14 Gloria III
22 Go Tell It on the Mountain
188 God Is So Good
125 God Sends Us His Spirit
282 Good News
121 Have You Got Good Religion
86 He Is King of Kings
87 His Name Is Wonderful
133 I Am the Bread of Life
252 I've Got a Feeling
299 I've Got Peace Like a River
247 I've Got the Joy, Joy, Joy
33 Jesu, Jesu, Fill Us with Your Love
131 Jesus
131 Jesus, in the Morning
266 Jesus Is All the World to Me
106 Jesus Loves Me
109 Jesus Loves the Little Children
48 Jesus, Remember Me
300 Let There Be Peace on Earth
201 Let's Just Praise the Lord
222 Lord, Make Me More Holy
3 O Come, O Come, Emmanuel
310 O I Woke Up This Morning
34 Somebody's Knockin' at Your Door
34 Somebody's Knockin'
206 Thank You, Lord
190 This Little Light of Mine
127 Veni Sancte Spiritus
282 When Jesus Worked Here on Earth
184 Yahweh, I Know You Are Near
104 Ye Watchers and Ye Holy Ones
284 Yes, Lord

284 Yes, Yes, Yes
184 You Are Near
*i.e., particularly suitable for children

CHRISTIAN LIFE *(also: Discipleship, Ministry, Mission)*
117 A Follower of Christ
121 Certainly, Lord
114 Close to Thee
241 God Is Love
282 Good News
121 Have You Got Good Religion
120 I Can Hear My Savior Calling
118 I Have Decided to Follow Jesus
276 I Shall Not Be Moved
117 I Want to Be a Follower of Christ
113 I'll Be Somewhere, Listening for My Name
119 Lord, I Want to Be a Christian
278 Make Me a Blessing
128 Mold Me, Lord
278 Out in the Highways and Byways of Life
318 Plenty Good Room
264 Ride On, Jesus, Ride
111 Sign Me Up
74 Spirit of God, Descend upon My Heart
50 Take Up Thy Cross
318 There's Plenty Good Room
115 The Way Is Jesus
114 Thou My Everlasting Portion
115 To Go to Heaven
107 Wade in the Water
117 What Do I Have to Do
113 When He Calls Me I Will Answer
282 When Jesus Worked Here on Earth
120 Where He Leads Me
50 Wherever He Leads, I'll Go

CHURCH *(also: Discipleship, Ministry, Mission, Social Concern)*
134 At That First Eucharist
105 For All the Saints
276 I Shall Not Be Moved
301 In Christ There Is No East or West
92 To Jesus Christ, Our Sovereign King
307 We Gather Together

CITY OF GOD *(also: Eternal Life/Heaven, Lamb)*
316 Come, We That Love the Lord
150 Deep River
144 He Understands, He'll Say "Well Done"
145 I Have Heard of a Land

Topical Index/*continued*

COMMISSIONING (see Liturgical Index: Commissioning of Ministers/Institution of Ministries)

COMMITMENT (also: Discipleship, Mission)

COMMUNION (see Unity; Liturgical/Index: Eucharist)

COMMUNION OF SAINTS (also: Church, Saints)

COMPASSION (also: Comfort/Assurance)

Topical Index/*continued*

Topical Index/*continued*

Topical Index/*continued*

Topical Index/*continued*

Topical Index/*continued*

EVANGELIZATION (also: *Christian Life, Discipleship; Liturgical Index: Christian Initiation of Adults*)

EVENING (*See: Liturgical Index: Evening Prayer*)

EXILE (also: *Struggle, Suffering*)

FAITH (also: *Trust*)

Topical Index/*continued*

Topical Index/*continued*

Topical Index/*continued*

Topical Index/*continued*

Topical Index/*continued*

Topical Index/*continued*

Topical Index/*continued*

Topical Index/*continued*

Topical Index/continued

Topical Index/*continued*

Topical Index/*continued*

Topical Index/*continued*

Topical Index/*continued*

Topical Index/*continued*

Topical Index/*continued*

Topical Index/*continued*

Topical Index/*continued*

Topical Index/*continued*

Topical Index/*continued*

Topical Index/*continued*

Topical Index/*continued*

Topical Index/*continued*

Topical Index/*continued*

Topical Index/*continued*

Index of Service Music 568

569 Index of Psalm Refrains

Index of First Lines and Common Titles   570

Index of First Lines and Common Titles/*continued*

Index of First Lines and Common Titles/*continued*

Index of First Lines and Common Titles/*continued*

Index of First Lines and Common Titles/*continued*